ROADSIDE GEOLOGY

of Minnesota

ROADSIDE GEOLOGY
of Minnesota

RICHARD W. OJAKANGAS

2009
Mountain Press Publishing Company
Missoula, Montana

Cover image modified from the
Minnesota Geological Survey state geology map

Back cover photographs: ©2009 by Richard W. Ojakangas
Top: Ripple marks in sandstone on the North Shore.

Middle: Folded iron-formation near the Soudan Mine.

Bottom: Minneopa Falls, west of Mankato, cascades
over resistant layers in the Jordan Sandstone.

Photos © 2009 by Richard W. Ojakangas unless otherwise credited

Library of Congress Cataloging-in-Publication Data

Ojakangas, Richard W.
  Roadside geology of Minnesota / Richard W. Ojakangas.
    p. cm.
  Includes bibliographical references and index.
  ISBN 978-0-87842-562-4 (pbk. : alk. paper)
  1. Geology—Minnesota—Guidebooks. 2. Minnesota—Guidebooks. I. Title.
QE127.O34 2009
557.76—dc22

2009026140

PRINTED IN HONG KONG

P.O. Box 2399 • Missoula, MT 59806 • 406-728-1900
800-234-5308 • info@mtnpress.com
www.mountain-press.com

I dedicate this book to my loving and patient food-writer wife, Peaches, who put up with piles of references in my disorderly portion of our home office for so many years. We differ in our philosophy of writing. She says that deadlines are made to be met, whereas I say that deadlines are made to be broken. Therefore this book has taken many years to complete!

I also dedicate this book to Robert L. Heller (1919–1993), a good friend and my first geology professor, who inspired me as an undergraduate at the University of Minnesota Duluth to switch my major from business administration to geology, and who in 1964 hired me to become a fellow staff member of that same department of geology.

NORTHWESTERN AND CENTRAL

CANADA *Lake of the Woods*

11
Karlstad Baudette International Falls 11 NORTHEASTERN

75
59
72
71 Orr 53 23 116 12

Effie Tower 169 Ely
East Grand Forks Erskine Blackduck 38 135 1 61 Grand Marais
2 Bemidji 169 Eveleth 11 Illgen City
169 Eveleth Silver Bay
Grand Rapids 2 53 4
Moorhead Detroit Lakes 10 169 Two Harbors
NORTH DAKOTA 71 210 Duluth
Fergus Falls Brainerd Fond du Lac
Breckenridge 210 23
94 371 Hinckley
9 Little Falls 23
Browns Valley St. Cloud 10 35 WISCONSIN
75 Sauk Centre 169
28 Morris 23 10 Taylors Falls
Ortonville 9 New London 10 Twin Cities metropolitan area
12 Willmar 12 95 Stillwater
75 Granite Falls 15 Red Wing
SOUTH DAKOTA Morton 169 SOUTHEASTERN
Marshall New Ulm 35 52 61
14 Mankato Owatonna Rochester Winona
23 Jeffers 14 52 90 La Crosse, Wisc.
Pipestone Blue Earth 16 La Crescent
Jasper 71 Dexter Preston
Worthington 90 90 Albert Lea
Luverne Jackson Fairmont
SOUTHWESTERN IOWA

Roads and sections of **Roadside Geology of Minnesota.**

CONTENTS

PREFACE

This book was written for people who are not geologists but who are curious about Minnesota's rocks and geologic history. Terminology has been held to a minimum, but geology students and professional geologists should also find it a helpful source of general geologic information. What we know about Minnesota's geology today is a composite of work by hundreds of geologists since the late 1880s. To them we all owe a debt of gratitude. And although all of those geologists hammered on the rocks, I ask that if you must hammer, do so with care, so as to not deface good exposures. Studies of Minnesota's rocks are never complete, and most exposures will be looked at again and again by generations of future geologists.

Minnesota's landscape is geologically young, the result of the last few tens of thousands of years of glacial advances and of erosion during the 10,000 or so years since the glaciers melted. However, Minnesota has a much longer legacy, with rocks dating back to 3,500 million years ago (3.5 billion!), a figure quite incomprehensible even to a geologist who deals with the large numbers that delineate the history of this state. Major geologic events that formed Minnesota's rocks occurred approximately 3,500 million years ago (Minnesota River Valley), 2,700 million years ago (northern Minnesota), 1,850 million years ago (east-central Minnesota), 1,700 million years ago (southwestern Minnesota), 1,100 million years ago (the Lake Superior region), 500 to 300 million years ago (southeastern Minnesota), and 100 million years ago over the western half of the state. Fortunately, the thick blanket of glacial sediment deposited over most of the bedrock could not keep it hidden forever. Erosion by running water exposed the underlying rock for our study and enjoyment.

These exposed rocks contain clues to Minnesota's geologic story, an epic that includes lofty mountains with violent volcanoes, faulting, folding, and earthquakes; a sea in which valuable iron-formation was precipitated; the abortive splitting of the North American continent with magma rising to the surface along great cracks; and warm tropical to subtropical seas with abundant life.

For purposes of this book, I divided Minnesota into four regions. Before embarking on any road trip, you will find it useful to read the general introduction and the relevant regional introduction. The northeastern region, Minnesota's "arrowhead," has an abundance of rock exposures—igneous, metamorphic, and sedimentary—that range in age from 2,700 million to 1,100 million years. In the large northwestern and central region, "lake and moraine terrain," you can traverse landscapes formed during and after the great ice age. In the southwestern region, you will find the state's oldest rocks—3,500-million-year-old gneisses—as well as the much younger 1,700-million-year-old hard quartzites. The southeastern region is the place to see marine rocks—sandstones, limestones, and dolostones—that were deposited during part of Paleozoic time—between about 504 and 374 million years ago.

Many places in Minnesota have Native American names—both Dakota and Ojibwe—that have survived the settlement by European immigrants. For example, *Minnesota* comes from a Dakota word that means "water that reflects the sky." If you are interested in the origins of the name of any lake, stream, or place in Minnesota, go to the Web site of the Minnesota Historical Society.

You can see much of Minnesota's geology at the state's seventy-four state parks and recreation areas, more than 150 scientific and natural areas, Voyageurs National Park, Grand Portage National Monument, and Pipestone National Monument. You can also see geologic features along Minnesota's twenty-two scenic byways; six of these, including 562 miles of the Great River Road along the Mississippi River, are also national scenic byways.

Just as Minnesota has had a lengthy geologic history, this book also has had a long incubation period. Charles Matsch, my good friend and colleague at the University of Minnesota Duluth (UMD), and I finished writing *Minnesota's Geology* back in 1982, after four years of fairly intensive effort. In 1988, David Alt and Donald Hyndman, then part owners of Mountain Press, asked us to write *Roadside Geology of Minnesota*. Charlie declined, and I said I would not do it alone. In 1992, my youngest daughter, Susanna, graduated from UMD in geology and composition. She wanted to be a science writer and knew computer drafting as well. So, in 1993 the two of us decided to do this book together. However, I was still involved in teaching and research at UMD, and the book was relegated to a low priority. I retired in 2002, and in 2003 I said to Susanna, "Okay! Let's get going on the book!" The answer was "Dad! I now have a full-time job and two children." My procrastination meant I had to go it alone after all.

Meanwhile, Mountain Press editor Jennifer Carey was asked to ascertain whether I was really serious about writing this book or whether she should find a different author. To our mutual surprise, I had already written more words and taken more photographs than required. Because computer drafting of maps and illustrations was a major obstacle for me, Mountain Press agreed to handle that aspect. Slowly but surely, the book neared completion despite its share of unexpected problems, including the discovery that I inadvertently took half of my digital photographs at too low a resolution for printing in the book. You, the reader, are the beneficiary of my mistake, though, because my last-minute road trips to all four corners of the state to retake photos produced some up-to-date adjustments in the manuscript.

I sincerely hope *Roadside Geology of Minnesota* meets your expectations and that it will give you the satisfaction of learning more about the geology of our great state! Thanks for waiting.

Acknowledgments

Many people played a part in *Roadside Geology of Minnesota*. My patient editor, Jennifer Carey, urged me to finish and was probably surprised to find that I had written too much. This gave her the onerous task of deleting various items, especially paragraphs about Minnesota Finns. Jenn and other staff at Mountain Press also did much of the drafting of maps and illustrations.

Harvey Thorleifson, director of the Minnesota Geological Survey (MGS), was eager to see this volume reach fruition and offered the survey's full cooperation and support. Barb Lusardi of the MGS was a willing supplier of publications and maps. Val Chandler was a most helpful source on geophysical aspects. Because most of Minnesota's rocks are covered by glacial drift, I used the survey's *Geologic Map of Minnesota's Quaternary Geology*, by Howard C. Hobbs and Joseph E. Goebel (1982), as my general guide. However, I generalized the glacial geology, eliminating many small areas of glacial outwash, and I had several conversations with Howard Hobbs about new mapping developments. Numerous county atlases published by the MGS were sources of additional information. Finally, several MGS geologists served as reviewers of the manuscript and offered numerous, valuable suggestions: Terry Boerboom, Howard Hobbs, Carrie Jennings, Mark Jirsa, Gary Meyer, John Mossler, Tony Runkel, and Dale Setterholm.

Matthew Starry made the shaded relief maps and patiently incorporated my various additions and deletions of roads and other items. His online data sources included the Minnesota Department of Natural Resources, Minnesota Department of Transportation, U.S. Geological Survey, National Atlas, and Environmental Systems Research Institute.

My geological colleagues at the University of Minnesota Duluth, especially Charlie Matsch, John C. Green, and Howard Mooers, were always ready to answer questions and offer encouragement. G. B. Morey, retired from the Minnesota Geological Survey and a fountain of geological knowledge about Minnesota, received many phone calls from me.

On different road trips, I was accompanied by Charlie Matsch; my wife, Peaches; our daughter Susanna Ojakangas Elliott; and our grandson Frans Elliott.

The University of Minnesota Press kindly allowed the use and modification of numerous illustrations from *Minnesota's Geology*, by Richard W. Ojakangas and Charles L. Matsch.

It is impossible to list everyone else who assisted in one way or another. My heartfelt thanks to each and every one of you!

Age	Period	mya	Rocks in Minnesota	Geologic Events in Minnesota
CENOZOIC	Holocene Epoch	.01	peat	glacial lakes recede; plants colonize
CENOZOIC	Pleistocene Epoch / Quaternary		moraines, drumlins, kames, outwash, glacial lake sediments	Glacial Lake Duluth forms 11,000 years ago; drainage erodes St. Croix River Valley
CENOZOIC				Glacial Lake Agassiz forms 11,700 years ago; outlet channel carves Minnesota River Valley
CENOZOIC				Wisconsin glaciation between 75,000 and 10,000 years ago; Illinoian and pre-Illinoian glaciations earlier
CENOZOIC	Tertiary	1.8 / 65	NO RECORD	
MESOZOIC	Cretaceous		chalk, dark shale, clay, sandstone, conglomerate	sea enters Minnesota from west
MESOZOIC	Jurassic	145	red sandstone, shale, gypsum	highland cut by west-flowing streams in northwestern Minnesota
MESOZOIC	Triassic	208 / 251	NO RECORD	
PALEOZOIC	Permian	286	NO RECORD	
PALEOZOIC	Pennsylvanian	320		
PALEOZOIC	Mississippian	360		
PALEOZOIC	Devonian	417	limestone, dolomite	sea enters Minnesota from south
PALEOZOIC	Silurian	443	NO RECORD	
PALEOZOIC	Ordovician		limestone, dolomite, some sandstone and shale	sea covers Minnesota at intervals, depositing sediments
PALEOZOIC	Cambrian	495 / 542	sandstone, shale, glauconitic sandstone, some dolomite	sea enters Minnesota from south and west, depositing sediments
PRECAMBRIAN	Proterozoic Eon		lava flows, gabbro, sandstone, iron-formation, volcanic rocks, graywacke, granite	sediments, including Fond du Lac Formation and Hinckley Sandstone, deposited in rift basin
PRECAMBRIAN				Midcontinent Rift System forms 1,100 million years ago; lavas of North Shore Volcanic Group and Chengwatana Volcanic Group; Duluth Complex intrudes
PRECAMBRIAN				sediments from eroding mountains deposited in Animikie Basin to the north; Sioux Quartzite deposited to the south
PRECAMBRIAN				Penokean mountain building between 1,875 and 1,835 million years ago
PRECAMBRIAN		2,500		Pokegama Quartzite and iron-formation deposited 1,900 million years ago during a period of erosion
PRECAMBRIAN	Archean Eon		granites, volcanic rocks, gneisses	Algoman mountain building event 2,700 million years ago
PRECAMBRIAN				Giants Range, Saganaga, and Vermilion Batholiths intrude
PRECAMBRIAN				Volcanic arcs of Superior Province form on southern edge of Canadian Shield as ocean plates subduct
PRECAMBRIAN		4,500		3,500-million-year-old gneisses in southeastern Minnesota

mya=millions of years ago

Geologic time scale, major geologic events, and rocks in Minnesota. —After Morey and Dahlberg, 1995

INTRODUCTION

Minnesota's rocks record some 3,500 million years of history. The state is located on the southern edge of the Canadian Shield, the fairly well-exposed portion of the North American craton (the old nucleus of the North American continent), which is composed of Precambrian rocks. They lie deep beneath younger rocks in much of the United States. Since the end of Precambrian time (542 million years ago), other microcontinents and volcanic island arcs have been added to the craton's edges, forming the modern North American continent.

Minnesota's rock record is not complete. Long portions of geologic time—hundreds of millions of years in fact—are missing. Nevertheless, it is still an excellent rock column that has recorded numerous important events from vast swaths of time: Archean, Early Proterozoic (Paleoproterozoic), Middle

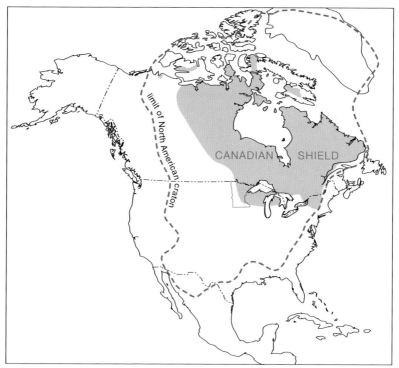

Generalized map of North America showing the Canadian Shield, the exposed portion of the ancient North American craton, much of which is overlain by younger rocks.

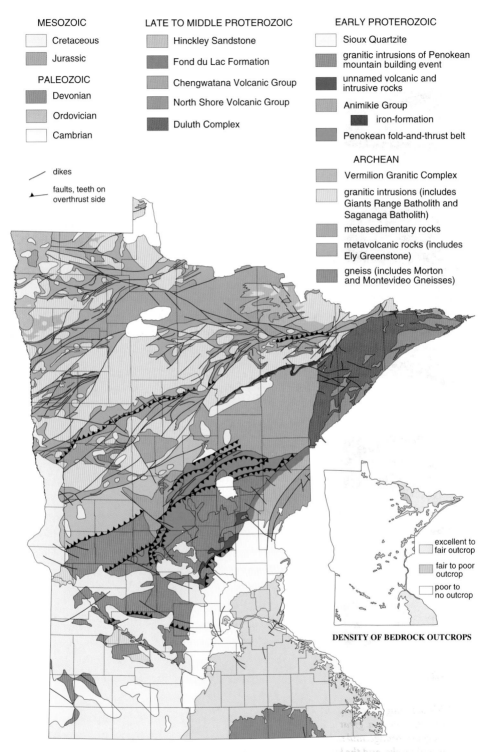

MESOZOIC

Cretaceous

Jurassic

PALEOZOIC

Devonian

Ordovician

Cambrian

dikes

faults, teeth on
overthrust side

LATE TO MIDDLE PROTEROZOIC

Hinckley Sandstone

Fond du Lac Formation

Chengwatana Volcanic Group

North Shore Volcanic Group

Duluth Complex

EARLY PROTEROZOIC

Sioux Quartzite

granitic intrusions of Penokean
mountain building event

unnamed volcanic and
intrusive rocks

Animikie Group

iron-formation

Penokean fold-and-thrust belt

ARCHEAN

Vermilion Granitic Complex

granitic intrusions (includes
Giants Range Batholith and
Saganaga Batholith)

metasedimentary rocks

metavolcanic rocks (includes
Ely Greenstone)

gneiss (includes Morton
and Montevideo Gneisses)

excellent to
fair outcrop

fair to poor
outcrop

poor to
no outcrop

DENSITY OF BEDROCK OUTCROPS

*Bedrock geology of Minnesota. The inset map shows the density of bedrock outcrops.
Areas in yellow were mapped primarily from drill cores and aeromagnetic data.*
—Modified from Morey, 1993

nanoTesla

-556.7 -361.3 -293.0 -260.3 -232.0 -206.1 -178.8 -153.1 -126.7 -100.0 -71.3 -41.6 -8.7 8.9 28.8 51.5 75.4 102.1 171.4 271.0 437.4 790.6

This aeromagnetic map of Minnesota indicates the rock types buried beneath glacial deposits and is a great aid in the making of bedrock geologic maps. The hot colors (magenta, orange, and red) depict rocks with a greater magnetic intensity, such as basaltic volcanic rocks, and the blues indicate rocks of lower magnetism. —From Chandler, 2007

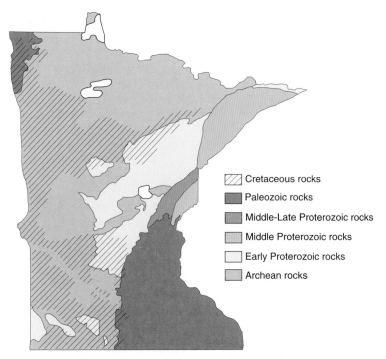

Generalized bedrock geology of Minnesota, showing rocks of various ages.

Cretaceous rocks
Paleozoic rocks
Middle-Late Proterozoic rocks
Middle Proterozoic rocks
Early Proterozoic rocks
Archean rocks

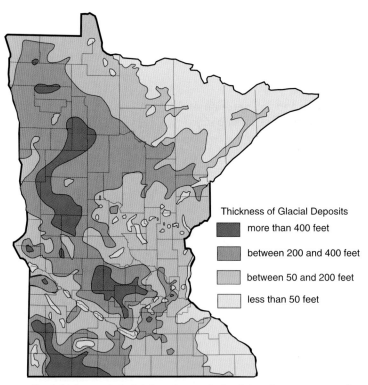

Thickness of Glacial Deposits

more than 400 feet

between 200 and 400 feet

between 50 and 200 feet

less than 50 feet

The generalized thickness of glacial deposits over bedrock in Minnesota ranges from less than 50 feet to more than 400 feet. Some small areas have glacial deposits up to 800 feet thick. The areas with less than 50 feet of glacial cover are the main areas of rock outcrops.
—From Ojakangas and Matsch, 1982

Proterozoic (Mesoproterozoic), Late Proterozoic (Neoproterozoic), Paleozoic, Mesozoic, and Cenozoic. Sediments deposited during the Pleistocene ice ages cover much of the state, obscuring most of the underlying rocks, but geophysical techniques, especially reading how magnetic Earth's crust is from an airplane and measuring how dense Earth's crust is, allow geologists to see through this glacial cover.

UNDERSTANDING THE EARTH

The three major rock types—igneous, metamorphic, and sedimentary—are well represented in Minnesota. Igneous rocks solidify from molten rock called magma. If magma cools slowly at depth, it crystallizes into intrusive igneous rocks, such as granite and gabbro. If molten lava explodes from a volcano or oozes onto Earth's surface, it solidifies quickly into extrusive igneous rocks such as basalt or rhyolite. The term *mafic*, a mnemonic word derived from *magne*-sium and *ferric*, refers to dark-colored igneous rocks containing minerals rich in magnesium and iron. Its counterpart *felsic*, from *fel*dspar and *si*lica, refers to light-colored igneous rocks rich in the minerals feldspar and quartz.

Sediments deposited by wind, water, and ice harden into sedimentary rock, such as conglomerate, sandstone, graywacke, siltstone, and mudstone. Limestone, which is precipitated from water, is also a sedimentary rock. When heat and pressure change the minerals and textures of an existing igneous or sedimentary rock, the result is a metamorphic rock, such as schist, gneiss, and marble. Geologists sometimes add the prefix *meta* to a rock name to show it's been metamorphosed. Metagraywacke, metasiltstone, and metavolcanic rocks all occur in Minnesota.

Plate Tectonics

In Precambrian time, the portion of the North American craton that is now Minnesota underwent two mountain building events and then almost broke in two. To understand these events, we must review modern plate tectonic theory. Earth's internal forces cause movement and deformation, and plate tectonic theory explains how this motion generates volcanoes, earthquakes, mountains, and ocean basins.

According to plate tectonic theory, Earth's surface is comprised of seven major and several smaller lithospheric plates, mostly remnants of larger plates, all moving relative to each other across the top of the asthenosphere. The lithosphere is the outer layer of Earth and behaves as a brittle solid. The thicker asthenosphere is the underlying zone of hot rock that can flow, albeit very slowly.

In plate tectonics, each continent is a passive passenger on a much larger plate of ocean-floor rocks. Each rigid plate can be as thick as 100 miles, with the oceanic lithosphere thinner than continental lithosphere. Plates move only a few inches per year, about the same rate as your fingernails grow. The lithospheric plates are being transported along the top of the asthenosphere, which is moving because of heat transfer by convection cells that emanate from deep within Earth near the hot boundary of the core and the mantle. Hot rock in the mantle rises and moves laterally in the asthenosphere below the cold and rigid lithospheric plates.

The plates move relative to each other in three ways: (1) Some plates are moving away from each other. New volcanic crust is formed at such spreading, or divergent, boundaries. A prime example is the Mid-Atlantic Ridge, with new crust most obvious in volcanic Iceland, which straddles the ridge. (2) Other plates move toward each other and are converging, or colliding. In this case

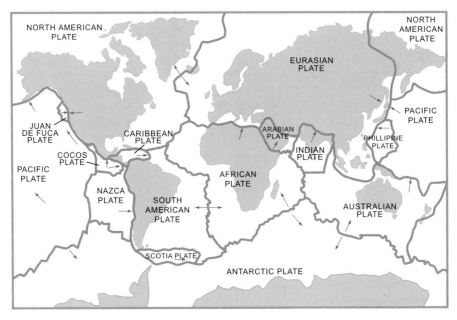

→   direction of plate movement

Plates of the world. Arrows show the direction of relative motion of each plate. Some small plates in the southwestern Pacific are not shown.

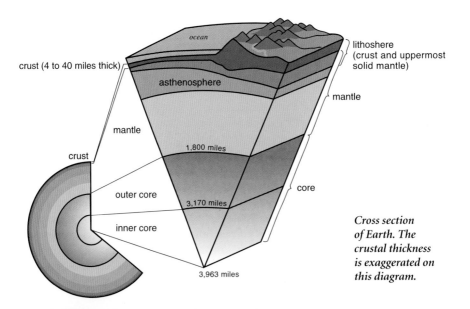

Cross section of Earth. The crustal thickness is exaggerated on this diagram.

one plate is commonly carried downward, or subducted. The subducted plate is partially or completely melted by the tremendous heat and pressures under Earth's surface. The collision zone is thus a zone of active volcanism and mountain building. Modern examples surround the Pacific Ocean. For example, the Nazca plate portion of the floor of the Pacific is being subducted beneath the South American plate. The Andes are still being formed along that convergent plate boundary. Other examples are the island arcs of the Pacific Ocean—the Aleutians, the Kurils, Japan, and the Philippines. (3) Some plates are moving sideways—horizontally—past each other. A well-known example is the San Andreas Fault in California, where the Pacific plate is moving northwestward relative to the North American plate. Minnesota has experienced divergent, convergent, and some horizontal movements in its 3,500-million-year history.

The seven major plates are made of terranes, fault-bounded pieces of crust and uppermost mantle that were welded to each other during collisions. As an

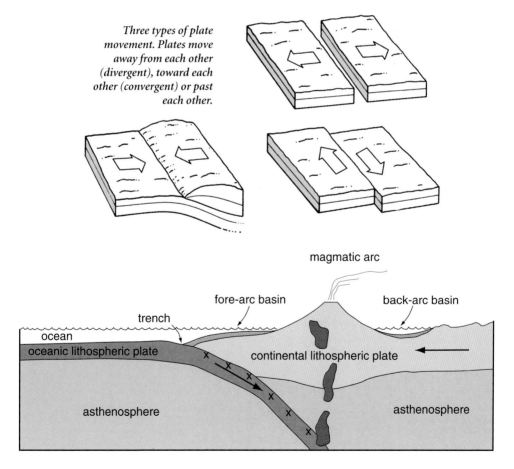

Three types of plate movement. Plates move away from each other (divergent), toward each other (convergent) or past each other.

Cross section illustrating the subduction of an oceanic plate beneath a continental plate. The X's denote the locations of earthquakes. Three sites of sediment accumulation are named—trench, fore-arc basin, and back-arc basin. Note the granitic plutons (dark brown) in the magmatic arc.

oceanic plate collides with a continental plate, more buoyant parts of the crust such as island arcs, ocean-floor plateaus, or microcontinents may be scraped off the oceanic plate and added to the continent rather than being subducted along with the ocean floor. Thus, the continents grow in size by accretion. North America, including Minnesota, grew by accretion.

ARCHEAN TIME
4,500 to 2,500 million years ago

The Minnesota River Valley of south-central Minnesota is home to gneisses, banded rocks produced from preexisting rocks by high temperatures and pressures. Some gneisses formed at depths of 15 miles or more inside Earth's crust. Because these rocks are now exposed on the surface, a great amount of uplift and erosion has occurred since they were formed. The gneisses in the Minnesota River Valley are some of the oldest on Earth.

The process of radiometric dating was first developed in the 1950s, and some of the cutting-edge work was done at the University of Minnesota. Gneisses in southwestern Minnesota were dated at 3,500 million years, and these were the oldest known rocks in the world for awhile. In the following decades, geologists found 3,800-million-year-old rocks in Greenland and Labrador. And these lost the record to 3,960-million-year-old rocks in northern Canada and Montana, which in 2008 lost it to a metavolcanic rock on the east shore of Hudson Bay in Quebec, which may be 4,280 million years old. The oldest dated minerals—not rocks—are microscopic zircon grains from a metamorphosed quartz sandstone in western Australia. They are 4,400 million years old—nearly as old as the estimated age of Earth, about 4,500 to 4,600 million years.

Minnesota has no record of rocks formed between 3,500 and about 2,700 million years ago, but that is not surprising. The 3,500-million-year-old gneisses of the Minnesota River Valley were part of a microcontinent that collided with rocks of the Canadian Shield, which made up the North American craton about 2,700 million years ago. Deep seismic-wave studies show that the gneisses were partially subducted northward beneath the craton, under a terrane of greenstone and granite. There are old gneisses of similar age in the Upper Peninsula of Michigan, so the microcontinent was not exactly small. The fault zone, or suture, along which the old gneisses are joined to the greenstone and granite terrane is called the Great Lakes Tectonic Zone. It extends from south-central Minnesota to eastern Ontario and is evidence for the growth of North America by accretion of smaller landmasses.

Prior to the collision of the microcontinent with the ancient craton, the ocean floor north of the microcontinent was subducted northward beneath

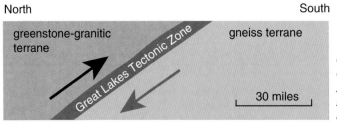

North   South

greenstone-granitic terrane   gneiss terrane

Great Lakes Tectonic Zone

30 miles

Cross section of the Great Lakes Tectonic Zone, a major suture, in east-central Minnesota.

the larger plate that constituted the North American craton of that time. The subducted rocks melted and formed magma, much of which reached Earth's surface as lava, forming volcanic rocks. Magma high in iron and magnesium, called mafic magma, poured out on the ocean floor and cooled underwater, forming the pillowed basalts found in northeastern Minnesota. These have been dated at 2,700 million years. Magmas richer in silica, which do not flow as readily as the mafic magmas, trapped gas, forming explosive volcanoes that rose from the seafloor as islands. These volcanoes were similar to the big volcanoes of the Aleutians, which are forming above a modern subduction zone off the coast of Alaska. Rocks above sea level are always eroding, so sedimentary rocks derived from the volcanoes are also common in island arcs.

As subsequent subduction zones shifted to the south, new volcanic arcs formed. The entire sequence of northeast-trending volcanic arc rocks and granitic plutons, which extends from Minnesota into Ontario and Michigan, is known as the Superior Province. The rock remnants of colliding volcanic arcs of northwestern Ontario are about 300 million years older than those in Minnesota because successive arcs became younger southward. Major fault and shear zones bound the arcs, attesting to their collisional origins. The north-trending Wawa and Wabigoon Subprovinces, which extend southwestward into Minnesota, are regions of island arcs and granites. These two subprovinces are separated by the Quetico Subprovince, a sequence of metasedimentary rocks originally composed of sediments eroded from volcanic arcs. The sediments were deeply buried, metamorphosed, and intruded by granitic magma, some of which solidified several miles below the surface into batholiths of granitic rocks. There are several batholiths in northern Minnesota.

The volcanic and sedimentary rocks were deformed and metamorphosed about 2,700 million years ago in the Algoman mountain building event. The same

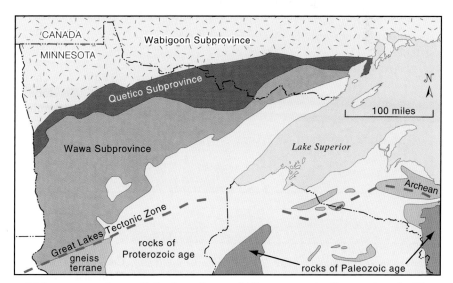

Major terranes, here called subprovinces, of Minnesota and adjacent Canada. The Precambrian geology of Wisconsin and Michigan is highly generalized as either Archean or Proterozoic. —Modified from Ojakangas, 1994

mountain building event is called the Kenoran in Ontario. The temperatures and pressures caused green minerals—chlorite, epidote, and actinolite—to form from the original minerals, so the generally low-grade metamorphic rocks are called greenstone belts. Greenstone belts around the world contain major mineral deposits of gold, copper, zinc, and lead, which combine with sulfur to form ore minerals. These minerals precipitated out of waters heated by the high temperatures associated with the volcanism, metamorphism, and collisions.

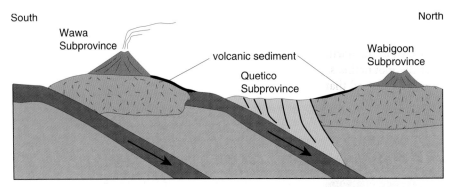

Simplified cross section of northern Minnesota and adjacent Ontario during Archean time about 2,700 million years ago depicting the accretion of successive island arcs and sedimentary terranes onto North America. The gray zones with arrows depict subducted oceanic crust.

EARLY PROTEROZOIC TIME
2,500 to 1,600 million years ago

The Algoman Mountains, which stretched across northern Minnesota, were eroded between 2,700 and 2,000 million years ago. Their weight had pushed the crust into the mantle, so as rock eroded from them, the crust rebounded, seeking an equilibrium with the mantle and adjacent blocks of crust. The granitic batholiths that had solidified several miles deep thereby reached the surface in northern Minnesota and Ontario.

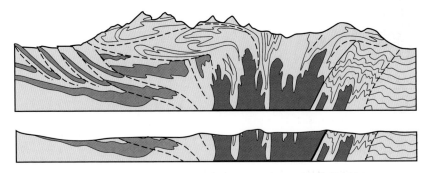

Cross sections of mountains before erosion and after uplift and erosion. The Algoman Mountains of northern Minnesota may have once looked like the Alps or Himalayas as depicted in the upper diagram, but today are completely eroded as in the lower diagram. The dark brown areas represent granites that formed deep within the mountains but are now exposed at the surface. —After Dott and Prothero, 1994

During this 700-million-year-long period, water, wind, and ice eroded a flat surface on the old granites and greenstones. As much as 300 feet of quartz sand and silt was deposited upon this eroded surface. The thick pile of sediment is the Pokegama Quartzite. Such a long period of erosion and weathering indicates a time of stability, without major tectonic events.

The tectonic stability was interrupted from about 1,980 to 1,770 million years ago when new volcanic arcs collided with the continent along its southern edge. Sheets of thrust-faulted rocks were stacked, one upon the other, forming the Penokean Mountains of east-central Minnesota, northern Wisconsin, and the Upper Peninsula of Michigan. The 50-mile-wide marine Animikie Basin formed to the north of the mountains. Some geologists argue the crust north of the mountains sagged under their weight, forming a foreland basin. Others have argued that the Animikie Basin may have been a back-arc basin that developed north of the volcanic arcs, on the back or continental side of the accreting arc.

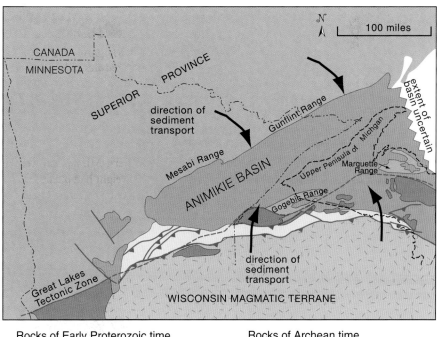

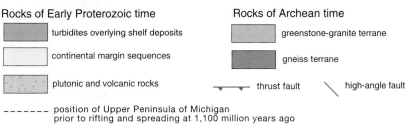

The fold-and-thrust belt of the Penokean Mountains lay south of the Animikie Basin. The lines with sawteeth are thrust faults, with the teeth on the side that moved up and onto the other side. The big arrows indicate sediment entering the basin. —After Ojakangas, 1994

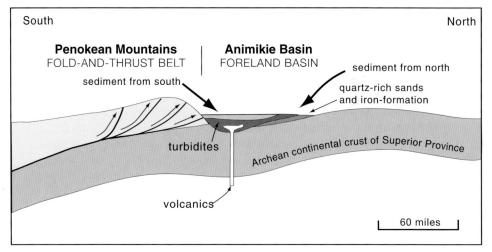

Cross section of the Penokean fold-and-thrust belt and the Animikie Basin. —After Ojakangas, 1994

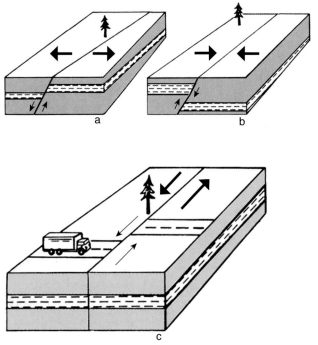

Cross sections of (a) a normal fault, formed during crustal extension; (b) a reverse fault, formed during crustal compression; and (c) a strike-slip fault, formed when one piece of crust slides horizontally past another. Small arrows indicate directions of movement on faults and large arrows indicate directions of forces that caused the faults. Very low angle reverse faults are called thrust faults.

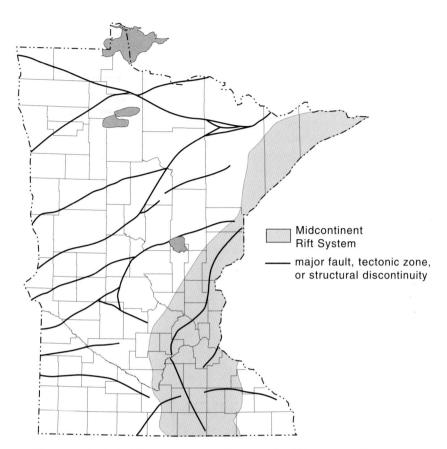

The major faults in Minnesota are mostly the result of Algoman (Archean) and Penokean (Early Proterozoic) mountain building events. Some are related to the Midcontinent Rift System. Thousands of small faults are not shown for obvious reasons of scale and clutter. —Modified from Minnesota Geological Survey, unpublished data

Iron-Formations

An iron-formation is a thinly bedded sedimentary rock that contains more than 15 percent iron. The Lake Superior iron-formations were precipitated upon the Animikie Basin's northern flank, a shallow-water marine shelf. Hundreds of mines have exploited the iron in the past century or so. The largest iron-formation is the gently dipping, 100-mile-long, 600-foot-thick Biwabik Iron Formation on the Mesabi Iron Range of northern Minnesota. An iron range is a linear feature, not a topographic feature. The Gunflint Iron Range of north-easternmost Minnesota and southern Ontario was once continuous with the Mesabi but the intrusion of the much younger Duluth Complex eliminated the connection. The highly folded and faulted iron-formations of the Cuyuna Iron Range in east-central Minnesota have a more complicated history because of their proximity to the Penokean mountain building event. The iron-formation of the Gogebic Iron Range in northern Wisconsin and Michigan was probably deposited in the same basin as the Biwabik and the Gunflint, but earlier, before the basin migrated north. The iron-formations in Michigan near Marquette and Iron Mountain were deposited in small basins formed along normal faults. All these ranges were deposited on quartz sand that formed during the long interval of erosion after the Algoman mountain building event. For discussion on the formation of the iron and iron mining, see the introduction to the chapter on northeastern Minnesota.

Most of the Animikie Basin was filled with sand, silt, and mud eroded from the Penokean Mountains on the south and the Archean rocks to the north. Graywacke sandstones were formed from muddy sands deposited by turbidity currents that flowed underwater toward the center of the basin. Fine clay and volcanic ash settled out of the water into layers that became mudstone. The sediments in the basin are more than 10,000 feet thick.

As with the Algoman Mountains, the granites that crystallized in the bowels of the Penokean Mountains became exposed as erosion removed the overlying rock and the crust rebounded. The granites of the St. Cloud area of central Minnesota are prime examples. The most stable, common mineral in granite is quartz, and as granite erodes over millions of years, quartz sand piles

Major iron ranges of the Lake Superior region. At the time of this writing in 2009, only the Mesabi and Marquette Iron Ranges had active mines. —Modified from Ojakangas and Matsch, 1982

up. The main products of the erosion of the Penokean Mountain granites are the Sioux Quartzite of southwestern Minnesota and southern South Dakota, the Barron Quartzite of northern Wisconsin, and the Baraboo Quartzite of south-central Wisconsin. These formed about 1,700 million years ago.

MIDDLE TO LATE PROTEROZOIC TIME
1,600 to 542 million years ago

Minnesota lacks rocks formed between about 1,700 and 1,100 million years ago. The region was probably above sea level and undergoing continued weathering and erosion. The sediments were probably carried into a sea and deposited far from Minnesota. Either nothing happened to the North American craton during those 600 million years, or something happened and evidence of it was removed by erosion.

Midcontinent Rift System

About 1,100 million years ago, North America began to split along a rift that now extends from Kansas to Lake Superior and then curves south through Michigan and Ohio. Perhaps a large magmatic plume and hot spot beneath what is now the Lake Superior region caused an upward bulging and splitting. Mafic magma from the mantle spilled out of long fissures at the surface along the rift, mostly as basaltic lava flows. The rift may have opened into an ocean at its eastern end. Only the lowest (oldest) flow cooled beneath water, as evidenced by pillow basalts. All the other exposed flows were deposited on dry land.

Beneath Lake Superior and the sediments deposited on top of the lava flows, there are more than 60,000 feet of lava flows. A portion of this volcanic pile is exposed along the North Shore of Lake Superior and is known as the North Shore Volcanic Group. The upper portion of the stack of flows exhibits normal magnetic polarity; that is, the flows were extruded when Earth's magnetic field was generally like today's. The lower portion of the flows has reversed polarity, indicating that when the lava surfaced the magnetic pole was the south pole. Flows are also exposed along the south shore of Lake Superior in Michigan and Wisconsin. The Chengwatana Volcanic Group is exposed along the St. Croix River on the Minnesota-Wisconsin border. An estimated 480,000 cubic miles of volcanic rock lie along the rift.

The lava flooded large areas along the rift, forming broad lava plateaus similar to much younger basalts seen today in the Pacific Northwest. The basaltic lava with its low silica content was very fluid, enabling it to flow quite a distance before cooling. One thick flow extends from Isle Royale to the Keweenaw Peninsula of northern Michigan, a distance of about 50 miles.

Some of the magma crystallized at depth beneath the lava flows, forming the Duluth Complex, nearly 2,000 square miles of gabbro and other coarse-grained igneous rock types in northeastern Minnesota. The magma mostly intruded between the Archean basement rocks and the North Shore Volcanic Group, but some intruded into the volcanic group, so we know the Duluth Complex is slightly younger than the lava flows. The Duluth Complex extends in a broad arc from Duluth northeastward to Ely and then nearly to the northeastern tip

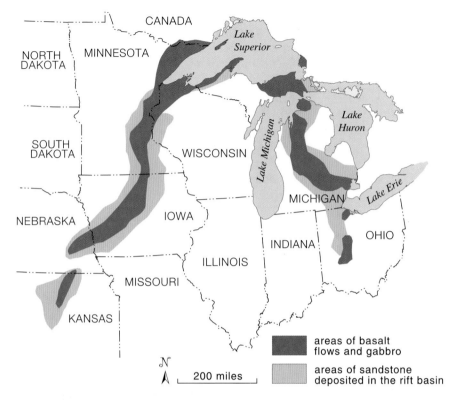

The Midcontinent Rift System formed 1,100 million years ago. The dark brown areas show lava flows and gabbros, which are covered with sediment in places. The light brown areas are sediments deposited at the edge of the rift basin over much older rocks. —Modified from Green, 1996

of Minnesota. It holds vast reserves of low-grade copper and nickel. At the beginning of this century, exploration also began in the complex for gold, silver, and rare platinum group elements: platinum, palladium, and polonium.

The extensional forces that formed the Midcontinent Rift System also created major normal faults along both sides. The land between the faults dropped down, forming an elongate basin. Rivers flowed into this topographic low, depositing sediment in streambeds, alluvial fans, and lakes. The sediments hardened into conglomerate, sandstone, siltstone, and shale. We know these sediments were not deposited in a deep sea because their red and brown color indicates they were exposed to oxygen, which oxidized the iron-bearing minerals to red and brown iron oxides. The sedimentary rocks that overlie the thick pile of volcanic rock are 30,000 feet thick beneath Lake Superior.

The spreading stopped about 1,100 million years ago when the rift reached a maximum width of about 50 miles. Changes in the convection cells deep in Earth's mantle may have played a part. Around the same time, a large tectonic plate collided with the east coast of North America. This may have "put the squeeze" on the entire Midcontinent Rift System. Normal faults formed during extensional rifting became reverse faults as a result of that compression.

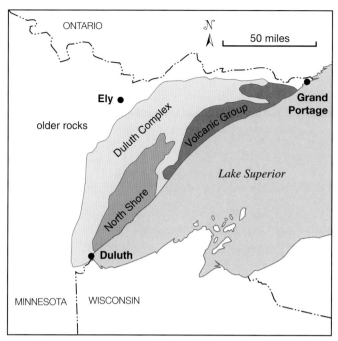

The Duluth Complex and North Shore Volcanic Group. —After Green, 1996

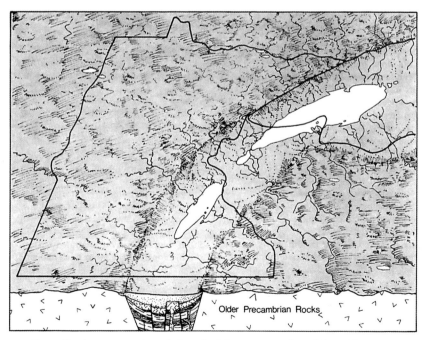

Generalized reconstruction of what the Minnesota portion of the Midcontinent Rift System may have looked like after cessation of volcanism about 1,100 million years ago. Note the streams entering the rift from the adjacent highlands and the presence of lakes (white). —From Ojakangas and Matsch, 1982

The spreading that created the Midcontinent Rift System 1,100 million years ago was similar to the spreading that split supercontinent Pangea about 220 million years ago, the event that formed the Atlantic Ocean, which grows about 2 inches wider every year. Had the spreading of the Midcontinent Rift System continued, Duluth, Sandstone, Minneapolis, St. Paul, and many other Minnesota towns might be situated on the coast of an ocean today. And if the plate had moved into equatorial latitudes, there may have even been coral reefs offshore. Alas, that was not to be. Instead, we live with the cold climate of the continental interior.

Paleozoic Time
542 to 251 million years ago

From late Precambrian time, perhaps 900 million years ago, until about 504 million years ago in Cambrian time, the Canadian Shield, including Minnesota, was above sea level. That 400 million years of erosion further leveled an already flat, low-lying continent. Sediments were carried out to sea, and no rocks exist in Minnesota from that time. In late Cambrian time, the ocean rose onto the low landmass, and the shoreline moved north and south in Minnesota as sea level fluctuated. Seafloors are great environments for the deposition of sediments, which made Minnesota a nice repository for rocks from early Paleozoic time.

Cambrian rocks are found throughout southeastern Minnesota, with some recorded as far north as the Twin Cities and Taylors Falls. They were once more extensive but were eroded from the more northerly parts of the state, which were above sea level from time to time. Most of the Cambrian rocks in southeastern Minnesota are quartz-rich sandstones eroded from the Precambrian rock surface of the Canadian Shield. Cambrian rocks total more than 600 feet in thickness in some drill cores in Minnesota.

The late Cambrian seas withdrew, but by early Ordovician time the seas returned, covering most of the continent with a warm, shallow sea. The equator ran through Minnesota, and life was abundant in the warm water. Limestone, shale, and a world-famous pure quartz sandstone, the St. Peter, were deposited. Some of the limestone was altered to dolostone by the addition of magnesium from the seawater. The eleven Ordovician formations in southeastern Minnesota are about 900 feet thick. Rocks of this age have also been found in a few deep wells in northwesternmost Minnesota.

There are no Silurian rocks in Minnesota, although they are present in Iowa. Either the Silurian seas never reached Minnesota or the Silurian rocks were eroded. Devonian dolomitic rocks, the youngest Paleozoic rocks in Minnesota, are about 150 feet thick in southernmost Minnesota. They rest on Ordovician rocks.

There are also no Mississippian, Pennsylvanian, or Permian rocks in Minnesota. It is likely that Minnesota was above sea level and undergoing erosion rather than deposition at this time. However, it is possible that some sediment could have been deposited during these younger Paleozoic periods but was removed by erosion.

Paleozoic seas advanced onto and withdrew from southeastern Minnesota and the upper Midwest several times, leaving horizontal sedimentary rocks. When a sea receded, sediments were left above sea level and erosion began. These eroded surfaces, now buried below other rocks, are called unconformities. They represent a period of time for which there is no rock record.

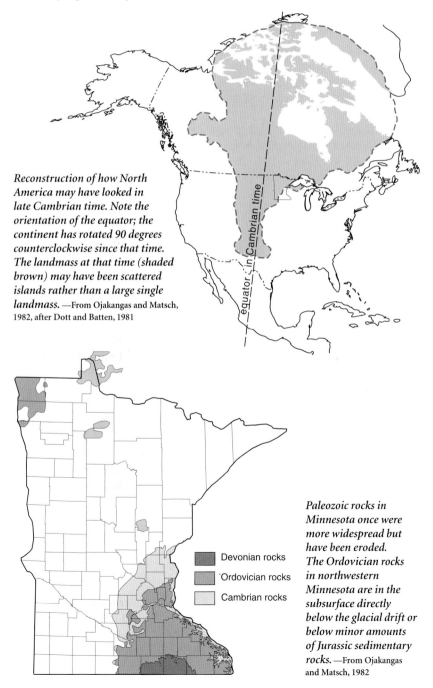

Reconstruction of how North America may have looked in late Cambrian time. Note the orientation of the equator; the continent has rotated 90 degrees counterclockwise since that time. The landmass at that time (shaded brown) may have been scattered islands rather than a large single landmass. —From Ojakangas and Matsch, 1982, after Dott and Batten, 1981

equator in Cambrian time

Devonian rocks

Ordovician rocks

Cambrian rocks

Paleozoic rocks in Minnesota once were more widespread but have been eroded. The Ordovician rocks in northwestern Minnesota are in the subsurface directly below the glacial drift or below minor amounts of Jurassic sedimentary rocks. —From Ojakangas and Matsch, 1982

MESOZOIC TIME
251 to 65 million years ago

During Mesozoic time, from 251 to 65 million years ago, much of Minnesota was above sea level and undergoing weathering and erosion. There is no evidence of rocks from Triassic time in Minnesota. Some Jurassic rocks have been penetrated in drill holes in the northwestern corner of the state, for a sea existed to the northwest at that time. During Cretaceous time, however, seas advanced from the west and covered western Minnesota, reaching as far east as the Mesabi Iron Range. Miners have found Cretaceous sedimentary rocks beneath Pleistocene glacial deposits and above Precambrian iron ore in many places along the range. Minnesota's Cretaceous rock record ranges only from about 100 to 80 million years ago.

Several clues suggest that the Cretaceous sediments were deposited in a warm, shallow sea: Fossils have been found of shark teeth; ammonites; a marine crocodile skull; a few teeth from mosasaurs (swimming reptiles); clams and snails indicative of brackish, slightly salty nearshore waters; and about sixty species and varieties of invertebrates, including many oysters. Thin beds of low-grade coal—lignite—have also been found, indicating swampy conditions. In the Minnesota River Valley, clay deposits formed by deep weathering

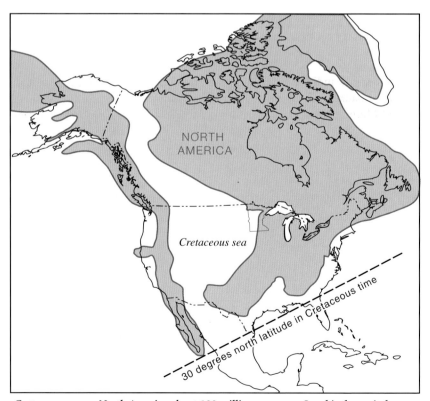

Cretaceous sea on North America about 100 million years ago. Land is shown in brown.
—From Ojakangas and Matsch, 1982, after Dott and Batten, 1981

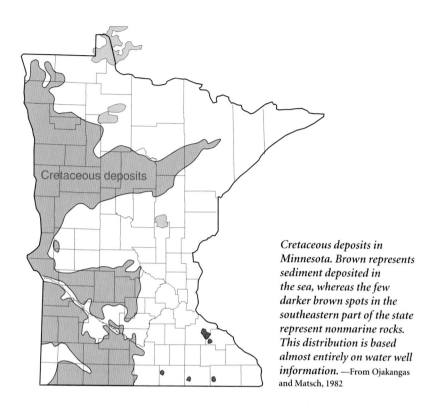

Cretaceous deposits in Minnesota. Brown represents sediment deposited in the sea, whereas the few darker brown spots in the southeastern part of the state represent nonmarine rocks. This distribution is based almost entirely on water well information. —From Ojakangas and Matsch, 1982

of the bedrock indicate that the Cretaceous climate was warm. Minor occurrences of bauxite minerals—the ore minerals of aluminum—in the southern half of Minnesota also indicate a humid subtropical to tropical climate during late Cretaceous time.

Why haven't dinosaur bones been found in Minnesota? First and foremost, Pleistocene glacial deposits obscure the nonmarine Cretaceous deposits that one might expect to host dinosaur fossils. Second, for fossils to exist, hard parts such as bones, teeth, and shells must be buried immediately after death. If dinosaurs existed in Minnesota (and they very probably did), they lived on a low landmass with no mountain ranges nearby, leaving less of a chance for their bones to be buried by sediment. Even if one died in a Cretaceous swamp and was quickly buried, the swamp was still above sea level and subject to erosion for many years to come. Some dead dinosaurs could also have been buried on sandbars during floods. The chances of finding dinosaur bones in Minnesota are very, very slim, but there have been unpublished reports of some findings.

TERTIARY TIME (PALEOGENE-NEOGENE)
65 to 1.8 million years ago

Throughout Tertiary time, from 65 to 1.8 million years ago, all of North America, including Minnesota, was above sea level and eroding. It is likely that small and large mammals were abundant. However, as during Mesozoic time, conditions for immediate burial in Minnesota were not the best. If you want to see mammal fossils, go to the Badlands of South Dakota, where sediment from the young Rocky Mountains covered the bones of mammals and other animals in Tertiary time.

PLEISTOCENE TIME
1.8 million to 10,000 years ago

Sometime about 1.8 million years ago, the climate cooled and glaciers probably moved into Minnesota and the northern United States from Canada. The ice may have been 2 miles thick near Hudson Bay but much thinner at its margins, as in Minnesota. It used to be thought that there were four major glaciations during Pleistocene time—Nebraskan, Kansan, Illinoian, and Wisconsin. However, the study of marine sediment cores suggests there were at least ten and perhaps even as many as forty advances of glacial ice. How many reached Minnesota is a good question. Drill hole data indicate many more than four. The resulting exposed deposits, collectively called glacial drift, are generally referred to in Minnesota as pre-Illinoian (formerly called Nebraskan and Kansan), Illinoian, and Wisconsin, arranged here from oldest to youngest. Glacial sediments of Wisconsin age cover the older deposits over almost all of Minnesota, and the modern topography is related to only the Wisconsin glaciation. The older glacial sediments are visible only in the southwestern and southeastern corners of the state where Wisconsin-age drift may have never existed or where it has been eliminated by erosion. The southeastern corner of the state is part of the so-called Driftless Area, which covers a wide swath in adjacent Wisconsin, part of which may have escaped glaciation during the Wisconsin glacial advance.

Glacial sediments of Wisconsin age are less than 75,000 years old, and most of them exposed on the surface in Minnesota are less than 20,000 years old. There were a number of minor advances and retreats of glacial lobes or ice tongues during the major Wisconsin advance. Glacial ice behaves somewhat like water and seeks the easiest route, so lobes or tongues of ice flowed along topographically low areas. A good example of this behavior is that of the Des Moines lobe. It moved southward down what is now the Red River Valley, then down a broad lowland through which the Minnesota River now flows. Then part of this glacial tongue, the Grantsburg sublobe, turned northeastward, through the Minneapolis lowland.

The deposits of the different Wisconsin-age lobes are distinguished from each other in several ways. First, their compositions vary. Superior lobe deposits are red to reddish brown and contain fragments of basalt, rhyolite, and red sedimentary rocks from the Lake Superior portion of the Midcontinent Rift System, as well as red clay. Its deposits are noncalcareous. The brownish Rainy lobe deposits are sandier and contain granites and greenstones from the Archean terranes of Minnesota and Ontario, gabbroic rocks and iron-formation from northeastern Minnesota, and even sedimentary rocks from the Hudson Bay area. The gray deposits of the Des Moines lobe contain fragments of white or tan Paleozoic carbonates from Manitoba and Cretaceous gray shale fragments from the Dakotas. The Wadena lobe is a gray calcareous drift without shale fragments. Another way to distinguish between various deposits is the

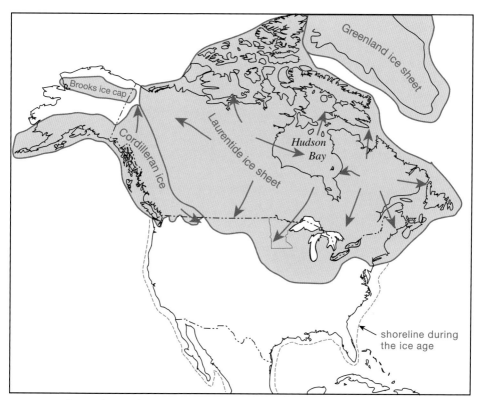

At several times during Pleistocene time, a continental ice sheet covered part of North America. Arrows indicate generalized ice movement. The dashed line is the approximate coastline during maximum glacial development, when sea level was as much as 250 feet lower than today. —After Matsch, 1976

variation in the proportions of sand, silt, and clay, but this requires laboratory analysis. Also, the topographic expressions of the deposits commonly indicate the different directions of ice movement. However, we must always bear in mind that a glacier can erode and then deposit previously deposited glacial drift, so the composition of a given deposit can be complicated.

Geologists do not always agree on the glacial history of Minnesota. For example, the carbonate-bearing Wadena lobe has long been interpreted as having come from Manitoba and then turning southwestward due to the topography of earlier glacial deposits or the presence of other contemporaneous ice lobes. However, newer evidence indicates that the Wadena lobe deposits contain carbonates from the Hudson Bay area, along with some very distinctive meta-graywacke erratics. The latter, called omars, are identified by the presence of holes from which concretions have been removed by chemical weathering. The omars were eroded from the Early Proterozoic Omarolluk Formation of the southern Hudson Bay area.

An omar, a distinctive rock from the Omarolluk Formation in the southern Hudson Bay area, was carried to Minnesota by ice. The holes formed when concretions weathered out of the rock.

The Des Moines lobe, the last *major* glaciation of Wisconsin age, reached as far south as—you guessed it—Des Moines, Iowa, by about 14,000 years ago. However, the lobe was really named for the Des Moines River, which has its headwaters in southwestern Minnesota, flows through the city of Des Moines, and joins the Mississippi at the southeastern corner of Iowa. It is becoming increasingly apparent that drift of the Des Moines lobe was deposited by cycles of rapid flow followed by stagnation that were not directly controlled by climate. Indeed, the climate had been warming for several thousand years before the Des Moines lobe first advanced to the Bemis moraine in southern Minnesota.

The very last glacial advances in Minnesota were those of the Superior lobe; the most recent was about 10,000 years ago. All of the other glacial lobes in Minnesota had melted back or stagnated in place by about 10,000 years ago. The ages are from carbon-14 dates on organic material, usually wood, buried in the glacial sediment. There are no reliable carbon-14 dates from Minnesota's glacial deposits between about 26,000 and 16,000 years ago because Minnesota was covered with glacial ice during that time and no trees were growing. Will glaciers visit Minnesota again? Probably. Since they left only 10,000 years ago and the major interglacial intervals average about 100,000 years, we are probably still in the ice age.

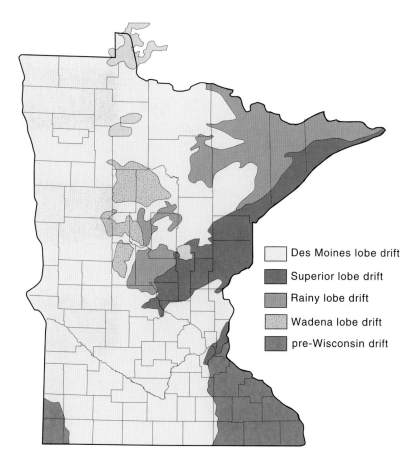

Glacial geology of Minnesota showing glacial deposits of the different ice lobes of Wisconsin age and the areas of pre-Wisconsin drift. In the legend they are arranged in order of age, youngest at the top, although some advances were simultaneous. Drift includes outwash, lake sediment, and till, so on this generalized map, it does not necessarily indicate the extent of the ice. —From Ojakangas and Matsch, 1982, after Wright, 1972a; Hobbs and Goebel, 1982

Glacial Deposits

Almost the entire surface of Minnesota has been glaciated, with the possible exception of the southeastern corner. In northeastern Minnesota, the glaciers scoured the loose material away and polished and scratched the exposed bedrock. However, over the rest of the state the glaciers were depositing rather than eroding. Virtually every grassed-over, sloping roadcut in the state is in glacial deposits of one type or another. As the ice reached warmer latitudes, it melted at its base and edges, dropping sediment embedded in the ice. Some material was deposited as ground moraine, beneath moving ice. Prominent hilly end moraines were formed where ice within a glacial lobe continued to move forward—pushing, thrusting, and slumping at its terminus—but melting as

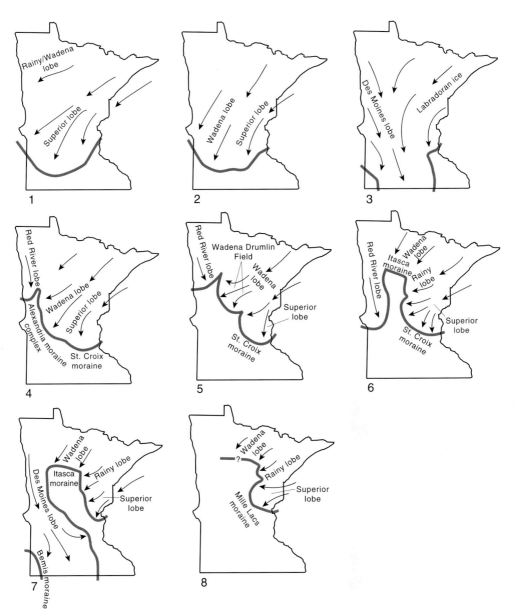

Generalized maps showing the succession of Wisconsin-age glacial lobes in Minnesota. The first advance shown was between 35,000 and 20,000 years ago and the last from about 14,000 to 10,000 years ago. Pleistocene geologists call them phases, a time subdivision equated with mappable rock units (formations). In northeastern Minnesota, thirteen phases have been named. Note that many phases were simultaneous. Most phases are separated by retreat of the lobes. —From Morey and Dahlberg, 1999, after Lehr and Hobbs, 1992

fast as it moved, thus depositing its load in the same area. Other lobes just stopped moving, stagnated, and melted in place, depositing stagnation moraine. In such cases, the debris was dropped over the entire area covered by the motionless ice. Meltwaters flowing over the stagnant ice carried sediment into various openings, depositing mounds of sediment that now stand as conical hills known as kames. Blocks of ice buried by the debris eventually melted, thus forming depressions that later filled with water and became kettle lakes. The resulting glacial landscape is known as knob-and-kettle topography.

Glacial ice does not sort sediment, and so it deposits a mixed sediment of different sizes, including clay, silt, sand, pebbles, and boulders. This mixed sediment is called glacial till and comprises ground moraine deposited beneath a glacier, end moraine deposited at the end of a melting glacier, and stagnation moraine deposited by a glacier that has stopped moving and is melting in place. In contrast, the meltwater rivers that carry sediment away from a melting glacier sort the debris and deposits layers of uniform sediment size, either silt, sand, or pebbles. These sorted layers are called outwash and make up outwash plains in front of melting glaciers. Blocks of ice are buried beneath the outwash sediment, and when they melt the depressions become kettles, the pits in a pitted outwash plain.

Clay-sized sediment remains in suspension and is carried by flowing meltwater to glacial lakes where it settles slowly. Lakebed deposits often contain thin annual couplets called *varves*. A darker (organic-containing) fine clay layer is

Meltwater deposited sorted layers of glacial outwash.

deposited in winter when ice covers the lake, and a coarser-grained silt layer is deposited in summer when the sediment-laden ice melts.

Several features form beneath glaciers. Snakelike ridges called eskers are deposited by streams flowing in tunnels in the base of the ice. Tunnel valleys are cut in glacial till by meltwater flowing beneath glaciers. These valleys are up to 0.5 mile wide, 200 feet deep, and 100 miles long. Some have eskers in them. Teardrop-shaped hills called drumlins are made of till sculpted by the moving

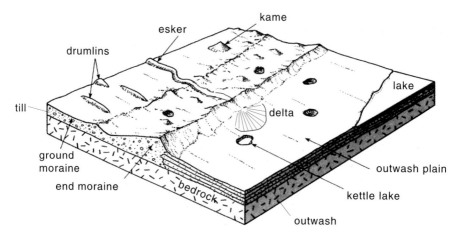

Glacial depositional features form beneath, at the front edge of, and in front of a glacier. —After Ojakangas, 1991

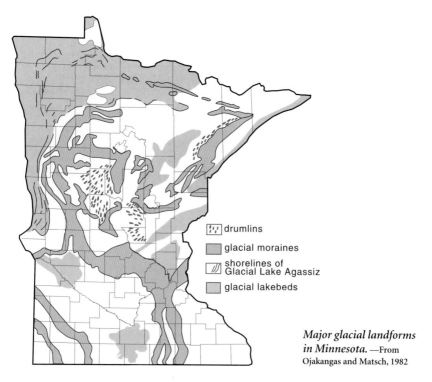

drumlins
glacial moraines
shorelines of Glacial Lake Agassiz
glacial lakebeds

Major glacial landforms in Minnesota. —From Ojakangas and Matsch, 1982

ice. Their steep ends are in the up-ice direction and their sloping ends point in the direction toward which the ice is moving.

In this book, the term *glacial drift* is used for glacial sediments in general, including both till and outwash. The term is especially useful in this volume because the scale of the maps prohibits till and outwash from being shown separately. The term came into usage long before continental glaciation was understood. In the eighteenth and nineteenth centuries, scientists found boulders far from their bedrock sources, and they wondered how these erratic boulders and associated sediments got there. In 1819, William Buckland of England said they were transported by the strong currents in the waters of Noah's Flood. In 1830, Charles Lyell of England proposed that polar glaciers spawned icebergs during warmer times when sea level was higher. According to Lyell, these icebergs drifted far and wide over the submerged continents and dropped the rock debris that they contained when they melted. These deposits became known as drift, and that is why glacial deposits even today are collectively called glacial drift and why the area in southeastern Minnesota and southwestern Wisconsin that may have escaped glaciation is called the Driftless Area.

Glacial Lakes and Glacial Rivers

As the continental ice sheet melted at the end of the last Wisconsin advance, meltwater must have been everywhere. It flowed toward lower areas and ponded into lakes if there was no outlet to escape through. Often the glacial lake backed up against the melting ice, escaping only when it overflowed the lowest point along its shore. Glacial ice carries a lot of sediment, so when it melts, the fine sediment settles to the lake bottom. Geologists can figure out where the lakes were by mapping the essentially flat lakebed deposits. There were eight major glacial lakes in Minnesota, but they did not all exist at the same time.

Glacial Lake Agassiz, which may have been the largest lake that ever existed in North America, began forming about 11,700 years ago when the Des Moines lobe in Minnesota and the James lobe in the Dakotas melted. Meltwater was trapped between the receding ice and topographically prominent glacial moraines. Warren Upham, a glacial geologist with the Minnesota Geological Survey, named the lake in 1880 after Louis Agassiz of Switzerland, who in the mid-1800s was the first major proponent of a great ice age with continental-scale ice sheets.

The overflow channel for Glacial Lake Agassiz was through the Big Stone moraine at its south end near Browns Valley on the Minnesota–South Dakota border. The lake level rose until it overtopped the moraine and began eroding through it. This huge overflow, known as Glacial River Warren, eroded a valley up to 5 miles wide and 300 feet deep. The river cut down through the unconsolidated Pleistocene glacial drift and the underlying soft Cretaceous deposits, exposing 3,500-million-year-old gneisses in the Minnesota River Valley. The lake disappeared completely from Minnesota two times, the first about 10,700 years ago when a lower outlet was exposed in Canada. But ice readvanced about 10,000 years ago, blocking the northern outlets and the meltwater ponded again. The reincarnation of the lake drained for the final time sometime after about 9,600 years ago. The history is complex, with other outlets to the northwest and hence to the Arctic Ocean and to the east via Lake Nipigon and Lake

Superior, and hence to the Atlantic. Dating of these outlets is in a state of flux, just as the lake levels were.

The relatively small Minnesota River now flows in the wide channel of Glacial River Warren. This glacial river is named after General G. K. Warren of the U.S. Army Corps of Engineers, who surveyed the Minnesota River Valley in the 1860s. He concluded that the wide valley must have been eroded by the catastrophic discharge of a large lake that once existed in the Red River Valley of the North. He was right!

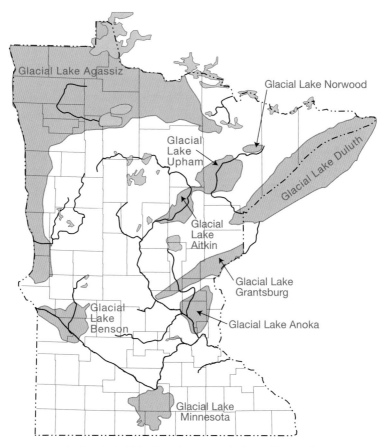

Major glacial lakes in Minnesota. The lakes did not all exist at the same time. —In part after Schwartz and Thiel, 1963

HOLOCENE TIME
10,000 years to present

Paleo-Indians likely lived in the region shortly after the glaciers left. Which Native Americans lived in what is now Minnesota during the last ten millennia is largely unknown. We do know that in historical times the Ojibwe moved in from the east and displaced the Dakota.

Land of 10,000 Lakes

"Land of 10,000 Lakes" makes a good slogan for tourism and has been in use since 1916, but the actual number of lakes greater than 10 acres in size is 12,034. These lakes, along with our rivers, give Minnesota more shoreline than Hawaii, California, and Florida combined—90,000 miles.

You may have read that Minnesota's ten thousand lakes are the hoofprints of Paul Bunyan's big blue ox, Babe, back when Paul was logging off the state's white pine forests. Don't you believe it! The lakes all have a glacial origin and are of two main types. Those of northeastern Minnesota, including those in the Boundary Waters Canoe Area Wilderness and Voyageurs National Park, are scoured lakes, formed on glacially eroded bedrock. Lakes elsewhere in Minnesota formed in depressions on glacial deposits, many of which are kettles created where blocks of buried ice melted.

Peatlands

Peat is water-saturated soil composed of dead plants that have not completely decayed because of lack of oxygen. When oxygen is absent, so too are the bacteria that cause decomposition. Peatlands are classified as either bogs or fens. Bogs are raised peatlands that are not receiving runoff water from mineral-bearing soils and are thus low in nutrients. Fens are wetter than bogs and have an inflow of water from mineral-bearing soils. Therefore fens have more nutrients for a greater variety of plants. The term *peat bogs* has become a general catchall term for all of us nonspecialists.

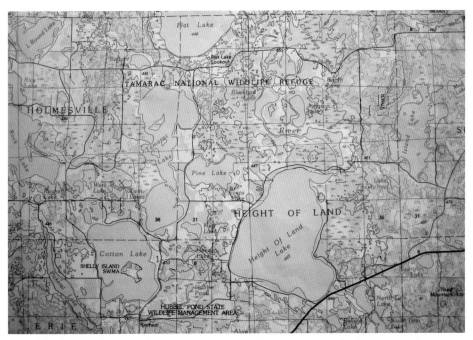

These lakes northeast of the town of Detroit Lakes in west-central Minnesota are just a few of Minnesota's many lakes. —U.S. Geological Survey topographic map of the Wilmar Quadrangle (scale 1:100,000)

Peat bogs have formed on the sites of numerous small, shallow lakes gradually eliminated by encroaching vegetation. Have you ever walked across one of these bogs, especially near remnants of a lake? The ground surface jiggles as you walk on it because it is on top of water. If you were to fall through that surface layer, you might never be found. Quite likely, that is why many extinct bison, *Bison occidentalis*, have been found in peat bogs during Minnesota highway construction projects.

Minnesota has the "peat bog title" for the Lower 48 states, with 6 million acres, or about 9,375 square miles, of such wetlands. One reason for this is that parts of the lakebed of Glacial Lake Agassiz did not completely drain and are now peatlands. One remnant of this lake is the Red Lake Peatland, also known

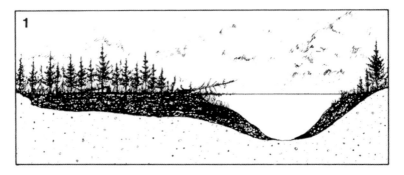

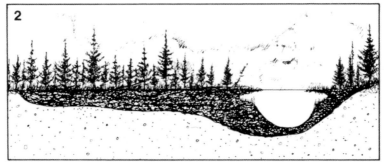

Encroaching bog vegetation eliminated a lake. Not shown in this figure is lake sediment made of algae. When it dies and falls to the lake floor, it forms a layer of soft jellylike sediment known to field geologists as "loonshit." —From Ojakangas and Matsch, 1982

as Big Bog, north and west of Upper Red Lake. It is 50 miles long in an east-west direction and 9 miles wide. Peat can be as thick as 20 to 30 feet, although it is commonly less than 5 feet thick according to the Minnesota Peat Inventory Project. The many plant types growing in Minnesota's peatlands include sphagnum mosses and sedges. Tamarack and black spruce forests may grow on the peat where the water table is not as close to the surface.

In 1850, Minnesota had 18.6 million acres of wetlands. In 2003, the number was 9.3 million acres. Drainage of wetlands to create farmland is responsible for most of that loss. Today, a state program encourages the development of more wetlands.

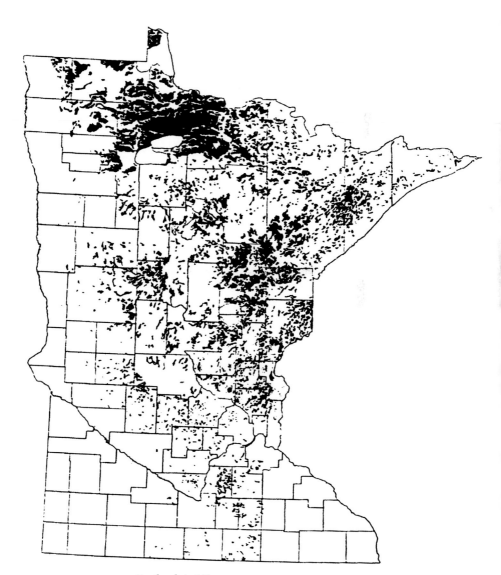

Peatlands in Minnesota. —From Wright and Glaser, 1983

A close-up of peat.

A vanishing lake.

Vegetation Changes

As the climate warmed and the glaciers left, plants colonized the barren land. Pollen studies of cores taken from lakes and bogs document the step-by-step changes in the plant succession. In general, the succession was tundra to forest to prairie. After the Des Moines lobe disappeared, spruce was the dominant tree in southern Minnesota, and as the climate warmed it was succeeded by birch and alder. With further warming, the birches were succeeded by elm and oak.

Finally, prairie vegetation took over in the south and west. In the north, pines became dominant. Three major biomes—prairie, deciduous forest, and coniferous forest—are found in Minnesota today.

The word *prairie* comes from the French word, *praierie*, meaning "meadow." The French explorers of the late 1600s must have been astonished to see those treeless meadows—seas of grass—covered with grasses and flowers several feet tall! Almost all of the 20 million acres of original tallgrass prairie in Minnesota, which covered about one-third of the state, has been plowed under for agriculture. However, there are now more than fifty prairie preserves between the northwestern and southeastern corners of the state with the goal of preserving and reestablishing the original prairie biota. Five main species of grass and another nine hundred plant species have been catalogued from the remaining prairie.

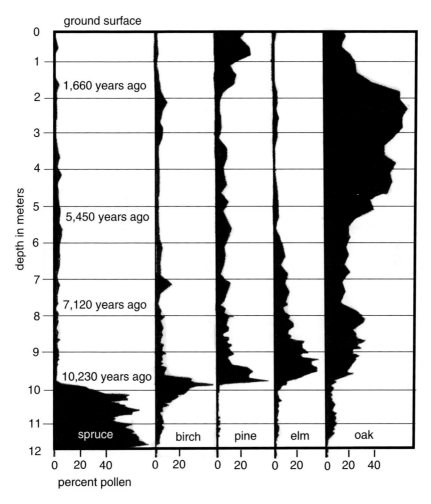

This pollen diagram from a bog near St. Paul shows that spruce dominated the landscape immediately after the glaciers melted but were soon succeeded by other trees. —From Ojakangas and Matsch, 1982, after Winter, 1961

The prominent red and white pine forests of northeastern Minnesota are largely gone, consumed by America's great demand for lumber. The late 1800s and early 1900s saw the height of the logging of the white pines, the last uncut stands in the United States. Minnesota's peak year for the lumber industry was 1905. Aspen and birch have colonized the logged areas. Only about 40 square miles of old-growth pine forests have survived, largely in the Boundary Waters Canoe Area Wilderness.

With global warming, the boundaries between vegetation types will move northward. Some scientists predict that northern Minnesota will be taken over in less than a century by the oaks and maples so prominent in east-central Minnesota. The last remaining pines in northern Minnesota may also vanish.

Continental Divides, Rivers, and Drainage Basins

You might not expect to find a continental divide in Minnesota, but there are several. Of the eight major drainage basins in Minnesota, two drain north to Hudson Bay, one drains east to Lake Superior and then via the St. Lawrence River to the Atlantic Ocean, and five ultimately drain into the Mississippi River and to the Gulf of Mexico. The Laurentian Divide separates northward-flowing waters that end up in Hudson Bay via the Rainy River or the Red River of the North from southward-flowing waters that end up in the Gulf of Mexico via the Mississippi River. The eastern part of this divide separates northward flow to Hudson Bay from southward flow into the Lake Superior Basin.

The Mississippi River is Minnesota's largest river, the largest river in North America, and the seventh largest in the world. It is 2,552 miles long, of which

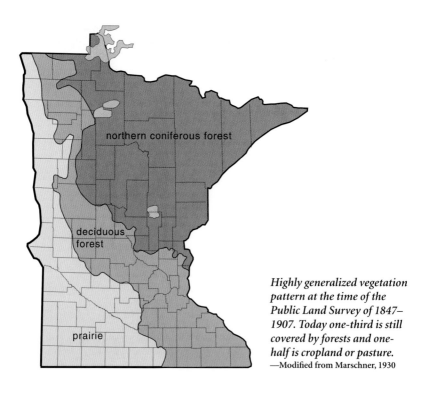

Highly generalized vegetation pattern at the time of the Public Land Survey of 1847–1907. Today one-third is still covered by forests and one-half is cropland or pasture.
—Modified from Marschner, 1930

696 miles, from its source at Lake Itasca to the Iowa border, are in Minnesota. It was a major "highway" for Native Americans and early European explorers. The name of this great river comes from the Ojibwe and Algonquin, who knew it as the Missi-zibe or the Gichiziibi, the "great river." Today it is a commercial highway; below the Twin Cities, the channel is dredged 14 feet deep and 400 feet wide so that barges and large boats can navigate it. Ten locks and associated dams have been built between the Twin Cities and the Iowa border.

The Minnesota River, a tributary of the Mississippi, was first called St. Peter's River, commemorating its early exploration by Pierre Charles LeSueur of France. In 1852 the territorial legislature said the Dakota name *Minnesota*, meaning "clear river," should be used.

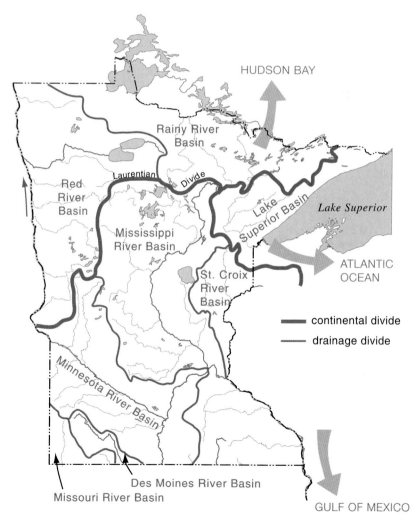

Minnesota's drainage basins. The darkest lines show the locations of the major continental divides separating flow toward Hudson Bay, the Atlantic Ocean, and the Gulf of Mexico.
—After Schwartz and Thiel, 1963

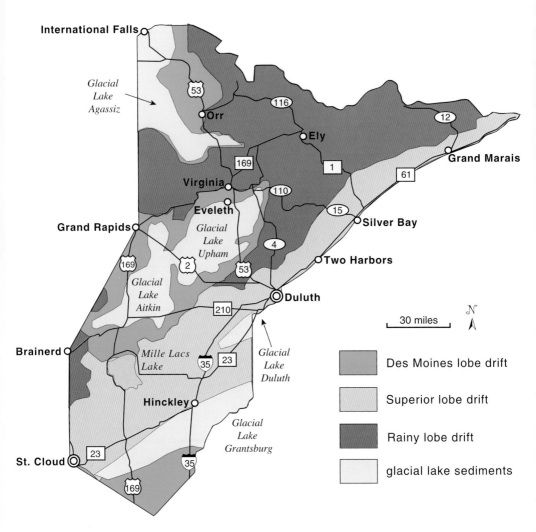

International Falls

Glacial Lake Agassiz

53

116

Orr

12

Ely

Grand Marais

169

1

Virginia

110

61

Eveleth

Glacial Lake Upham

15

Grand Rapids

Silver Bay

169

2

53

4

Two Harbors

Glacial Lake Aitkin

Duluth

Brainerd

210

30 miles

N

Mille Lacs Lake

35

23

Glacial Lake Duluth

Hinckley

Glacial Lake Grantsburg

St. Cloud

23

35

169

	Des Moines lobe drift
	Superior lobe drift
	Rainy lobe drift
	glacial lake sediments

Generalized Quaternary geology map of northeastern Minnesota.
Ice advances of the different lobes sometimes moved simultaneously.
—Modified from Hobbs and Goebel, 1982

NORTHEASTERN MINNESOTA
The Arrowhead of Exposed Bedrock

Northeastern Minnesota is where the rocks are! This arrowhead-shaped region contains more exposed bedrock than the rest of the state because the glacial drift is generally thin to nonexistent. The glaciers were actively eroding here rather than depositing. Glacial striations on the bedrock are abundant, and polished surfaces are not uncommon. The bedrock is Precambrian in age, with the only exception being minor Cretaceous rocks temporarily exposed by mining on the Mesabi Iron Range.

Most of the lakes in northeastern Minnesota, especially in the Boundary Waters Canoe Area Wilderness, are in bedrock basins. During the long several-billion-year interval of weathering prior to the Pleistocene ice ages, a layer of decomposed rock probably existed on the parts of the land surface that escaped erosion by running water. The glaciers removed this layer, which varied in thickness, exposing the uneven bedrock surface we see today. Fault zones and softer rocks were more easily weathered, so many of the lakes are long and narrow, following structural trends and bedding layers.

GLACIAL GEOLOGY

Three lobes of glacial ice left their mark on northeastern Minnesota. The Superior lobe repeatedly moved toward the southwest down the Lake Superior Basin, depositing prominent moraines with each advance. Meltwater filled the basin as each advance melted back to the northeast, with Glacial Lake Duluth filling it after the last major advance. The Rainy lobe, located north of Lake Superior, also moved southwest and deposited moraines. In addition, it left a cluster of 1,400 drumlins, the Toimi Drumlin Field. The third lobe, the St. Louis sublobe of the Des Moines lobe, entered this region from the west and moved eastward, even northeastward in some spots.

Glacial Lakes Aitkin and Upham existed in the region covered by the St. Louis sublobe. Early phases of the lakes formed before the advance of the sublobe, about 13,000 years ago, dammed by moraines of the Superior lobe. They formed again as the St. Louis sublobe stagnated. At their higher levels, the two lakes were connected. Glacial Lake Upham eventually emptied into Glacial Lake Duluth via the St. Louis River and its main tributary, the Cloquet River, between 9,800 and 9,300 years ago. Glacial Lake Aitkin emptied through the Mississippi River about 7,400 years ago. Glacial Lake Grantsburg formed about 14,000 years ago and lasted only about 100 years before it emptied toward the south. The lakes drained as the land in the region rose more than 200 feet after the great weight of the glacial ice was removed.

Bedrock Geology

Vermilion District

Archean rocks about 2,700 million years old can be observed in the Vermilion District, a greenstone belt of volcanic and related sedimentary rocks. Greenstone belts are present in the Precambrian shields of all the continents. There are more than thirty such belts in the Superior Province of Canada. Increased temperature and pressure metamorphosed the original mafic volcanic rocks, forming the green minerals chlorite, epidote, and actinolite—hence the name *greenstone.* The district is flanked by three large Archean granitic batholiths— the Giants Range Batholith to the south, the Vermilion Batholith to the north, and the Saganaga Batholith to the east.

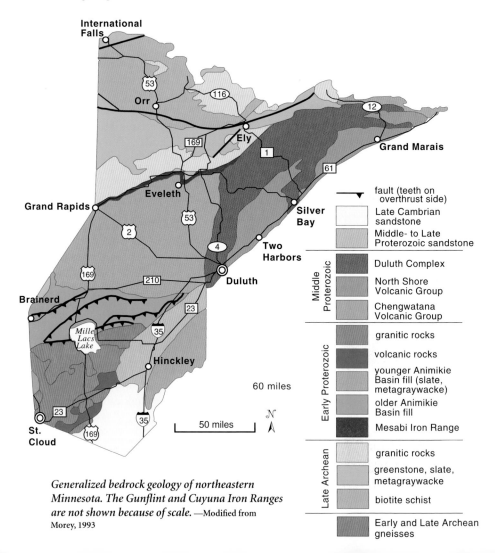

Generalized bedrock geology of northeastern Minnesota. The Gunflint and Cuyuna Iron Ranges are not shown because of scale. —Modified from Morey, 1993

Animikie Basin and Iron-Formation

Early Proterozoic rocks, including quartzite, iron-formation, and thick gray-wacke sandstone and mudstone sequences, all between about 2,000 and 1,730 million years old, were deposited in the Animikie Basin. There are two main ideas as to how the basin formed. It may have been a foreland basin that developed north of the Penokean fold-and-thrust belt situated to the south of present-day Lake Superior. It could have also been a back-arc basin that formed north of the volcanic arcs of the Wisconsin magmatic terrane. Geologists have not reached a consensus on the matter. The basin formations in Minnesota include the Pokegama Quartzite, Biwabik Iron Formation, Gunflint Iron Formation, Virginia Formation, Thomson Formation, and Rove Formation.

The Biwabik Iron Formation was named for the Biwabik Mine and the town of that name in the eastern part of the Mesabi Iron Range. *Biwabik* is the Ojibwe word for "iron," and *Mesabi* is an Ojibwe word for a legendary Indian giant who hunted by hurling big boulders. The taconite found in the formation was deposited layer by layer on a shallow, nearshore, tidally influenced portion of a sea about 1,900 million years ago. It is composed of about 70 to 80 percent silica (present as fine-grained chert) and only 20 to 30 percent iron.

What is the evidence for deposition in a tidal environment? Sedimentary structures, especially cross-bedding that indicates current flow in opposite directions, is one main clue. Another is the presence of stromatolite mounds, which form when sticky filamentous algae trap sediments layer by layer. Similar mounds are found in modern environments where the water is too saline for algae-eating invertebrates to live, and thus the structures are preserved.

Stromatolite mounds in Biwabik Iron Formation of the eastern Mesabi Iron Range. Unfortunately, this particular site has since been eliminated by mining, but others still exist.

Close-up of the top of a stromatolite mound showing vertical "fingers" of algae that grew through sediment toward the sun.

Modern stromatolite mounds in hypersaline Shark Bay on the west coast of Australia.

Natural processes increased the iron content of the low-grade iron-formation to more than 50 percent in some places. Water flowed along faults, dissolving and removing much of the silica. Therefore, many high-grade ore bodies are long and narrow, following faults. Oxygen in the water converted the iron carbonates, iron silicates, and magnetite to iron oxides—red hematite and brown goethite. The high-grade deposits have long been referred to as "raisins in the Biwabik Iron Formation cake."

The high-grade ore of the Mesabi Iron Range, discovered in 1890, was largely depleted by 1980. At its peak, there were nearly four hundred high-grade iron ore mines on the Mesabi, and 2,300 million tons of iron ore were shipped from these mines. Nearly 600 million tons of slightly lower grade ores were also mined. The mining began in shallow underground mines, but with the advent of equipment capable of removing large quantities of overlying glacial drift, open pit mining became economical.

When it became apparent in the 1950s that the high-grade ore would soon be gone, a process that concentrated magnetite from low-grade ore was developed. Development of the taconite process was spurred on by the passage of Minnesota's "taconite amendment" in 1964, which guaranteed that taconite concentrates would be taxed no higher than other manufactured products. Taconite containing the magnetic iron oxide mineral magnetite is first crushed to a very fine grain size and then the magnetite is removed by strong magnets. A binding material, commonly Cretaceous-age bentonite clay from Montana or

High-grade ore immediately below glacial drift. The soft ore could be easily removed by large shovels.

Wyoming, is then used to turn the magnetite into marble-sized pellets of about 68 percent iron. The spherical shape of the pellets allows more oxygen to circulate around them in blast furnaces, increasing the speed of steel production. In 2008, about 46 million tons of taconite pellets were shipped from the mines in Minnesota to the steel mills in the lower Great Lake states.

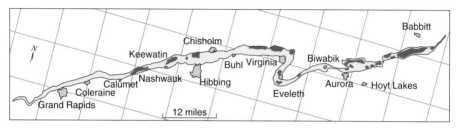

Map of the Mesabi Iron Range, showing cities and taconite pits. —From Morey, 2003

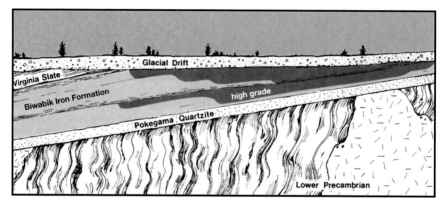

Generalized cross section of a high-grade iron ore body (dark gray) in the low-grade taconite of the Biwabik Iron Formation. —From Ojakangas and Matsch, 1982, after U.S. Steel

Duluth Complex and North Shore Volcanic Group

Several hundred lava flows of the 1,100-million-year-old North Shore Volcanic Group can be observed on the North Shore of Lake Superior. The given age of 1,100 million years ago is an easy one to remember, but radiometric ages range between 1,109 and 1,087 million years, with the major magmatic activity occurring within a time span of about 15 million years. The lava flows, mostly basalts, were extruded from large faults of the Midcontinent Rift System between Kansas and Michigan in Middle Proterozoic time. The rift is a 1,375-mile-long zone of normal faults along which magma rose from the mantle beneath Earth's crust. These are called fissure eruptions, and the magma that reached the surface as lava was mostly mafic. This basaltic lava had a low viscosity and flowed as flood basalts across the rift and some adjacent areas. Gas bubbles trapped in the quickly cooling lava left cavities, or vesicles, in the rock. When filled by minerals precipitated out of hot water moving through the flows on a submicroscopic scale, the vesicles become amygdules. Minnesota's state gemstone,

Sketch illustrating two lava flows. The tops of the flows have an abundance of vesicles formed by gas bubbles (mainly water vapor) in the lava, and the bases are more massive. Some elongated pipe vesicles may be present at the base of a flow, probably related to water present on top of the previous flow at the time of extrusion of the next hot flow. The water turns to steam, forming vescicles. —From Ojakangas, 1991

the Lake Superior agate, formed as amygdules and is found on beaches of Lake Superior and in gravel pits southwest of the lake.

Some of the mafic magma cooled at depth to form the Duluth Complex, one of the world's largest gabbroic rock bodies. It contains copper, nickel, gold, and platinum group elements. The Duluth Complex consists of multiple intrusions that cooled beneath the thick sequence of lava flows of the essentially contemporaneous North Shore Volcanic Group. The gabbro cuts across the oldest lava flows, so it is slightly younger than at least some flows. It was originally interpreted as a single large intrusion and called the Duluth Gabbro. However, detailed work by geologists of the Minnesota Geological Survey since the 1960s showed that the Duluth Complex is composed of a variety of igneous plutonic rocks, including gabbro, peridotite (an ultramafic rock), and even red granitic rocks.

Gabbro is the dark gray to black, coarse-grained equivalent of basalt, the black volcanic rock type that makes up 90 percent of the lava flows on the North Shore of Lake Superior. If the iron- and magnesium-rich magma had reached the surface and cooled quickly, the crystals would have been small and invisible to the naked eye, as in basalt. However, because the magma cooled slowly beneath the surface, perhaps under a cover of lava flows a few miles thick, the crystals had time to grow larger. The rock thus became gabbro comprised of visible crystals of calcium-rich plagioclase, pyroxene, and olivine. The gabbro is now at the surface because of uplift, tilting, and erosion of the overlying lava flows.

Along the complex's northern margin, mafic magmas engulfed parts of the Biwabik Iron Formation and the overlying Virginia Formation. Prior to this event, the Biwabik Iron Formation and the Gunflint Iron Formation to the east in Minnesota and adjacent Ontario had been continuous. Today they are separated by a 60-mile-long stretch of the Duluth Complex. The easternmost portion of the Biwabik Iron Formation was metamorphosed by the hot magmas, and some new iron-bearing minerals such as cummingtonite, an asbestos-like mineral, were formed. Reserve Mining Company processed the magnetite ore from the eastern Mesabi Iron Range and dumped waste rock tailings into Lake Superior at Silver Bay. Because asbestos is a known carcinogen, litigation throughout the 1970s convinced the company to begin disposing of the tailings on land.

A large basin formed along the rift, and sediments were deposited there long after the volcanism ended. They are best seen in Wisconsin and Michigan, but two formations are exposed in Minnesota. The Fond du Lac Formation can be seen southwest of Duluth in the village of Fond du Lac. The overlying Hinckley Sandstone is observable along the Kettle River in Banning State Park and the village of Sandstone. These two rocks, deposited during Late Proterozoic time, are thought to be the youngest Precambrian rocks in Minnesota. However, some geologists think that the Hinckley may even be early Cambrian in age, but as there are no fossils present, it is an open question.

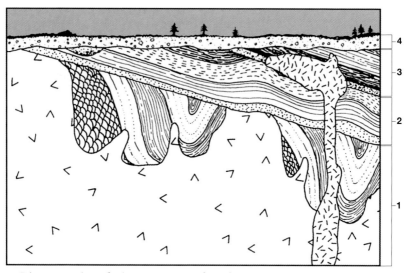

Diagrammatic geologic cross section of northeastern Minnesota. Rocks labeled 1 are Archean in age and include folded greenstone belt rocks (volcanics and metasediments) and granite. Rocks labeled 2 are Early Proterozoic in age, rest on eroded Archean rocks, and include the Pokegama Quartzite, the Biwabik Iron Formation, and the Virginia, Thomson, and Rove Formations. Rocks labeled 3 are Middle to Late Proterozoic in age and include a thin basal quartzite, the North Shore Volcanic Group, younger sedimentary rocks (the Fond du Lac Formation and Hinckley Sandstone), and the intrusive Duluth Complex. The glacial sediments of Pleistocene age are labeled 4. —From Ojakangas and Matsch, 1982

Road Guides in Northeastern Minnesota

Duluth

Duluth, about 21 miles long and 3 miles wide, is built on the southwestern end of a long, steep hillside that marks the northern edge of the Lake Superior Basin. The hillside is made up of lava flows and sills of the North Shore Volcanic Group and gabbroic rocks of the intrusive Duluth Complex, all about 1,100 million years old. The gabbro occurs westward from Mesaba Avenue in downtown Duluth, and lava flows and intruded sills are present eastward; the boundary passes through a topographic prominence of gabbro known as the Point of Rocks.

Look for the gabbro at the top of the hill in the vicinity of the shopping malls between mileposts 6 and 7 on US 53, where you can see it in roadcuts, natural outcrops, and embankments covered with quarried rock. See the first part of the road guide for **I-35: Duluth—Twin Cities** for additional information on the gabbro. You can also see this rock type along Skyline Parkway, as described elsewhere in this section.

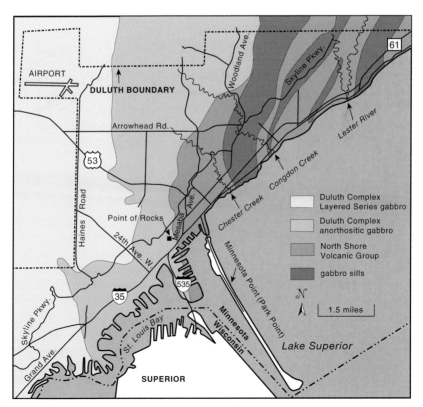

Highly generalized geologic map of Duluth. —From Ojakangas and Matsch, 1982

Coarse-grained gabbro of the Duluth Complex at Point of Rocks in Duluth.

Glaciation and Glacial Lake Duluth

Glacial striations, scratches from rocks embedded in the moving ice, can be found on virtually every rock exposure in Duluth, clear evidence of glaciation. The most abundant glacier-related sediments are the sand and gravel deposits left by meltwater streams where they flowed into Glacial Lake Duluth. However, just above the uppermost level of Glacial Lake Duluth at about Skyline Parkway (Skyline Drive), outwash and till deposits have been noted during various excavations. Till is also widespread below the Duluth level. Most of it is so clayey that it has been confused with glacial lake sediment.

Glacial Lake Duluth, the ancestor of Lake Superior, formed as the Superior lobe melted back about 11,000 years ago. The ice still present in the eastern part of the basin formed a natural dam, preventing the meltwater from draining eastward via the St. Lawrence River. In the vicinity of Duluth, the water level rose to an elevation of 1,050 feet, about 450 feet above the present surface of Lake Superior—602 feet above sea level. Old beaches mark the upper lake level. The detailed history of Glacial Lake Duluth is quite complicated, and it doesn't help that it is difficult to distinguish lake clays from red clayey till of the Marquette advance, the last ice advance into the Lake Superior Basin, 10,000 years ago.

Glacial Lake Duluth drained southward through an outlet into the Kettle River in Minnesota and the Brule River in northwesternmost Wisconsin. These flowed into the St. Croix River, a major tributary of the Mississippi River. When the Superior lobe ice finally melted out of the eastern part of the Lake Superior Basin, drainage was reestablished to the Atlantic Ocean via the St. Lawrence River. This may have happened about 9,500 years ago.

Red glacial till of the Superior lobe overlies coarse outwash gravel in a short-lived 2007 excavation just off Arlington Avenue at the top of the hill, below Miller Hill Mall. This bank has since been cut down to a gentler slope and covered with broken rock for stability.

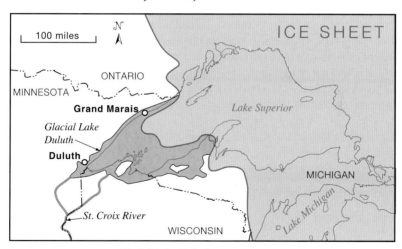

Glacial Lake Duluth. —After Green, 1978

Duluth-Superior Harbor

The harbor at Duluth-Superior, the most inland freshwater port in the world, is an international port visited by more than one thousand ships a year. Iron ore from the Mesabi Iron Range is shipped eastward to lower Great Lakes steel mills. Grain from the United States and Canada is shipped all over the world via the Great Lakes and the St. Lawrence Seaway, which together make up a 2,343-mile-long inland waterway connected to the Atlantic Ocean.

The drowned channel of the St. Louis River at the southwestern end of Lake Superior.

The Duluth-Superior Harbor, at the western tip of Lake Superior, has a rather unique geologic history. When glaciers of late Pleistocene time scoured and covered the Lake Superior Basin, the great weight of the thick ice sheet depressed Earth's crust. Ever since the ice melted away, the crust has been rising back to its preglacial elevation. Because the ice was thicker and persisted longer in the northeastern part of the lake basin, that part is experiencing a greater postglacial rebound than is the southwest end of the lake. The lake basin is thus being tilted southwestward, and rising water is gradually drowning Duluth and the St. Louis River channel. Imagine if you lifted one end of a filled bathtub—that is what's happening to the Lake Superior Basin. Having no outlet at Duluth, the water is rising there at nearly 1 foot per 100 years. Therefore, in about 500 years, the parking lot at Duluth's Entertainment and Convention Center on the edge of the harbor will be underwater.

Ancient beaches of Glacial Lake Duluth provide proof of this tilting. A beach formed on the shoreline of a lake should be at the same elevation everywhere because the water level is horizontal. However, an ancient beach that has an elevation of 1,050 at Duluth has an elevation of 1,350 feet at Grand Marais, 100 miles farther up the North Shore of Lake Superior. The beach was tilted after it formed. Older beaches are tilted more than younger beaches.

Minnesota Point and the Aerial Lift Bridge

The Duluth-Superior Harbor is situated on the west side of the long sandbar visible from the Blatnik interstate bridge between Duluth and Superior. This sandbar, one of the longest freshwater sandbars in the world, is divided into Minnesota Point (also known as Park Point) and Wisconsin Point by the St. Louis River as it flows into Lake Superior. Minnesota Point is 7 miles long and Wisconsin Point is 3 miles long; their average width is about 500 feet. Longshore drift currents supply sand for the sandbar from the Wisconsin shore, and the St. Louis and Nemadji Rivers also supply sand. There were two earlier versions of the sandbar west of the present bar, and there is a rudimentary sandbar to its east.

The Ojibwe commonly portaged across the sandbar of Minnesota Point at its narrowest part, now the site of the Duluth Ship Canal and the Aerial Lift Bridge. The native name for what was to become Duluth was *Onigamiinsing*, which means "at the little portage." The city's namesake, Daniel Greysolon, Sieur du Lhut, was the first European here, arriving in 1679.

The Aerial Lift Bridge in downtown Duluth spans a canal that has a bit of a complicated and even notorious history. The Lake Superior & Mississippi Railroad terminated in Duluth, and a dock and grain elevator were built on the lakeshore just north of the present canal. An 800-foot-long breakwater was added to protect this lakeside harbor from the fury of Lake Superior. Duluth city fathers feared that because the natural entrance to the harbor through the sandbar was near Wisconsin, Superior would grow and Duluth would not. A decision was made in 1871 to dig a canal through the sandbar at the Duluth end, thereby allowing ships easy access to Duluth. Superior city fathers got a federal injunction from Washington DC, ordering Duluth to stop the project because they thought the canal would change the course of the St. Louis River, and the Superior entry would silt up. When Duluthians heard on Friday evening, June 9, 1871, that the injunction was due to arrive by an Army officer on Monday's train, they mobilized a force of volunteers with shovels to quickly complete the digging of the canal. By Sunday night, water from the bay was flowing through their "ditch," and as the higher water of the bay flowed outward into the lake, it rapidly widened the channel to 30 feet. When the officer arrived, he was told by the canal supervisor, "You stop it if you can. I can't."

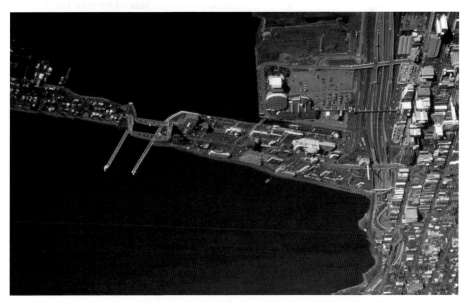

Aerial view of the Duluth Ship Canal and the Aerial Lift Bridge. The lower part of the bridge is lifted up when ships pass through.

The Department of War instructed Duluth to build a dike across the bay from Rice's Point (about a mile west of Minnesota Point) to Minnesota Point, presumably to guarantee the integrity of the natural water movement in the bay. Consequently, a heavy wood-piling dike 4,490 feet long and 10 feet wide was completed. In an 1872 State of Wisconsin versus Duluth court case, Wisconsin demanded that the canal be filled in and that the dike be removed, as it restricted the use of the entire harbor by citizens of Superior. In 1873, a federal appropriation of $100,000 was provided for the dike removal as well as for harbor dredging. Litigation lasted from 1871 until 1877, when the U.S. Supreme Court finally decided the case, stating that "the State of Wisconsin is not entitled to the relief asked by her bill and that it must therefore be dismissed with costs." Today relationships between Duluth and Superior are amicable. The dike is visible on a large 1872 Gilbert Munger painting that hangs in the Kitchi Gammi Club in Duluth.

At the far end of the point is the Park Point Recreation Area. Starting outside of the airport fence, you can take a 4-mile round trip hike to the natural Superior entrance to the harbor. You will see prominent sand dunes, the product of strong northeasterly winds. The Minnesota Point Pine Forest Scientific and Natural Area features an old-growth forest of tamarack, white pines, and red (Norway) pines, some of which are nearly 200 years old. A 50-foot-high lighthouse at the Superior entrance dates back to 1855. From here you can see the Burlington Northern ore docks, which receive ore from the Mesabi Iron Range for loading onto ore boats.

The Lake Superior Marine Museum and the Great Lakes Aquarium are located in the Canal Park area at the Duluth side of the Aerial Lift Bridge. The SS *William A. Irvin*, a large iron ore and coal carrier that was the flagship of U.S. Steel's Great Lakes Fleet, is now permanently anchored as a separate ore boat museum. The Union Depot Railway Museum is nearby.

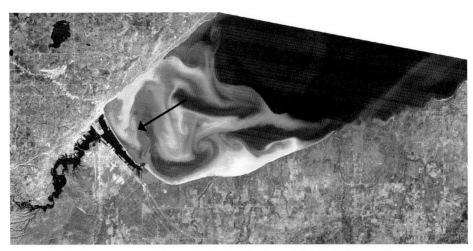

Satellite photo on October 10, 1995, after high winds dislodged sediment from the lake bottom. Note the submerged sandbar to the east of Minnesota Point (at tip of arrow).
—NASA image courtesy of UMD-NRRI and Tom Hollenhorst

Duluth Lakewalk

The Duluth Lakewalk, a 5-mile-long pathway along the shore of Lake Superior, starts in the Canal Park area and continues to Thirty-sixth Avenue East as of 2009. Plans are for it to reach the eastern edge of Duluth. You can observe lava flows and other geologic features at several points along the Duluth Lakewalk. Along the way, you can visit the Northland Vietnam Veterans and Korean War Memorials, Leif Erikson Park (see below), and the Rose Garden.

Leif Erikson Park

Leif Erikson Park, on Lake Superior off London Road, can also be accessed by the Lakewalk. Below the stone amphitheater that was built in the 1930s as a Works Progress Administration project is a long pebble beach with outcrops of a 1,100-million-year-old basaltic lava flow and a 100-foot-thick, cross-bedded sandstone deposited during a long lull in the volcanism. The large scale of the cross-beds indicates that the sand may have been deposited by wind. The polished surface of the lava flow has glacial striations and curved crescentic gouges indicating that the glacier was moving toward the southwest. At the eastern end of the pebble beach are four faults in the sandstone. One fault contains a nearly vertical basalt dike, and another separates the sandstone from a basalt flow.

The beach at Leif Erikson Park consists of a variety of pebble types. Most are volcanic rocks, either massive or with crystal-filled gas cavities, most of which contain white calcite or green epidote. You may also find Lake Superior agates on the beach. They were precipitated in gas cavities but later weathered free. Humans have contributed concrete, tile, brick, and small pieces of colored glass to the beach as well. The heavy surf—similar to that of an ocean—moves the beach pebbles into parallel rows.

Crescentic gouges on basalt in Leif Erikson Park were formed by glaciers flowing toward the southwest. The pen is parallel to the striations and pointing toward the southwest.

This cross-bedded sandstone in Leif Erikson Park was deposited during a pause in volcanism.

Skyline Parkway

Skyline Parkway, also called Skyline Drive, extends 25 miles through Duluth and is located 450 to 600 feet above the city, providing spectacular views. It has been called one of the world's most magnificent drives and is one of Minnesota's twenty-two scenic byways. In 1875 William K. Rogers came up with the idea for this parkway and a parallel walkway on the lakeshore, where the Lakewalk is today. Parks along stream valleys were to connect the two routes but were never completed. The elevation of Lake Superior is 602 feet, whereas much of Skyline Parkway is located on the old shoreline of Glacial Lake Duluth, at an elevation of about 1,050 feet. The lake level was that high when the glacier was melting and retreating to the northeast. Glacial ice continued to block drainage through the Great Lakes to the Atlantic Ocean, thus impounding the meltwaters.

The eastern portion of Skyline Parkway is the Seven Bridges Road. To get there, drive east on Superior Street to Glenwood Street, which is close to the Lester River, and then turn up Occidental Boulevard, the street adjacent to the river's west bank. The boulevard crosses the winding river seven times on stone bridges within a distance of 1.7 miles, and there is an eighth bridge a bit farther at the junction of Skyline Parkway and Maxwell Street. Each picturesque bridge with its arches is made of locally quarried blocks of basaltic lava flows or intrusive sills, and is capped by pink granite from St. Cloud, Minnesota. The original bridges were made of wood.

About 1.3 miles beyond the uppermost bridge you will come to Hawk Ridge Nature Reserve, a high clifflike area made of a resistant sill of gabbro. Raptors migrating southward in the fall fly along the north shore of Lake Superior because they don't like to cross the wide lake. A plaque on Hawk Ridge states that the lake basin was cut 600 million years ago by a glacier, but this is wrong! Glaciers that advanced southward down the lake basin during the last several tens of thousands of years scoured out the soft rock that had been deposited in the Lake Superior portion of the Midcontinent Rift System sometime between 1,000 million and 500 million years ago.

A unique house built of black gabbro is on the upper side of West Skyline Parkway at Seventh Avenue West.

Watch for a pullout from which to view Minnesota Point, the long sandbar at the western tip of Lake Superior. A geologic marker at the pullout describes the Duluth-Superior Harbor.

You will cross a bridge at Twin Lakes, where the bedrock is no longer basaltic lava flows and sills but is coarse-grained gabbro that crystallized at depth beneath the great thickness of lava flows. Turn left at the T by Twin Ponds and drive the short loop road to see good exposures of the massive gabbro. A plaque at a turnout describes Rice's Point, an industrial complex within the harbor situated on a broader, older version of the Minnesota Point sandbar. Note the flooded St. Louis River channel. Within this looped part of the road is the five-story-high, cylindrical Enger Memorial Tower constructed of gabbro in 1939. You can climb it for an even better view.

The next plaque, at a pullout about 2 miles farther west, describes the location of Oneota, home of the Merritt brothers, who discovered iron ore on the Mesabi Iron Range at Mountain Iron in 1890. The iron ore docks visible from this lookout, which resulted from the Merritt's discovery, are located in Oneota. The iron ore, now shipped as taconite pellets, originates from the Mesabi Iron Range 50 miles to the north.

The ore docks in the harbor at Duluth.

About 0.6 mile southwest of the intersection with Haines Road, a gabbro cliff above Skyline Parkway is barely visible behind the trees. This cliff is located at the elevation of the shoreline of Glacial Lake Duluth. Some geologists once suggested it may have formed by wave action, but most think the lake was not at this level long enough for waves to erode a cliff in hard rock. (This cliff is also visible from I-35 far below, above an old quarry in the gabbro at about Fifty-seventh Avenue West.) A roadcut a bit farther on features a large white inclusion of anorthosite, a rock made almost entirely of the mineral plagioclase feldspar, within the gabbro host rock. It has been painted gray to cover graffiti.

At the intersection of Skyline Parkway and US 2, look for faint layering in the roadcuts of gabbro. The layers are mineral segregations formed by differential settling of plagioclase, pyroxene, and olivine crystals as the magma solidified. Continue across the highway and turn into the Thompson Hill Rest Area for more outcrops of layered gabbro and a great view of Duluth and the drowned St. Louis River channel. See the road guide for **Interstate 35: Duluth—Twin Cities** for more on this location.

Lester River and Kitchi Gammi Park

At the mouth of the Lester River at the east end of Duluth, you can see a black basaltic lava flow below the parking area. The glaciers that moved down the Lake Superior Basin from northeast to southwest about 12,000 years ago left striations and crescentic scour marks on this rock. The metal plaque at this site erroneously states that glaciers carved the lake basin 600 million years ago. The glaciers that removed soft sedimentary rocks from the basin passed by here several times in the last few tens of thousands of years.

Kitchi Gammi Park is located on the shore of Lake Superior just northeast of the mouth of the Lester River. As you walk along this picnic area, you will see outcrops of basalt and the coarser-grained Lester River Sill protruding a few feet above the pebble beach. The sill formed when magma intruded between existing lava flows. Most of the pebbles on the beach are composed of basalt. They commonly contain amygdules, gas cavities (vesicles) filled with minerals that precipitated out of hot water when the lava flow was covered with the hot lava of successive flows. The common minerals in the cavities are white calcite, dark green chlorite, apple green epidote, white or pink or orange zeolite, and white to gray to red banded agates. The pebble types also include massive black basalt, basalt with some larger crystals in an otherwise fine-grained matrix, and reddish rhyolite. Also present are gray granite and pink granite transported by glaciers from rock exposures to the northeast in Minnesota and Canada.

INTERSTATE 35
Duluth—Twin Cities
148 miles
See map on page 61

The northernmost 2.5 miles of I-35 in the United States, from Twenty-sixth Avenue East to about Fifth Avenue West, are built on and even tunneled through the North Shore Volcanic Group. However, these rocks are not directly visible from I-35. Outcrops are present along the shore of Lake Superior and are easily reached along Duluth's Lakewalk, which parallels I-35 from Lake Avenue to Twenty-sixth Avenue East. These volcanic rocks, mostly basaltic lava flows, poured out along the elongate Midcontinent Rift System when North America started to split apart 1,100 million years ago.

Near the Twenty-seventh Avenue West exit, I-35 passes under a railroad at the docks where ore boats are loaded with taconite pellets for transportation to the steel mills on the lower Great Lakes. The pellets are made by crushing and grinding magnetic iron-formation to a very fine grain size, separating the magnetite, adding a binder, and roasting the ore in very hot rotating kilns. The ore trains wend their way down the gabbro hillside to the docks from three taconite plants in the central Mesabi Iron Range about 60 miles to the north. Near the ore docks are piles of loose material. The big dark pile is composed of small one-quarter- to one-half-inch-diameter taconite pellets. The white pile is limestone imported from Michigan for rail transport to the Mesabi Iron Range, where it is incorporated into the taconite pellets as a flux. A flux combines with the impurities during the steel-making process, making them easily separated from the metal.

One variety of gabbro of the Duluth Complex, the Layered Series, is exposed in roadcuts along I-35 between the bottom and the top of the Duluth hillside. There is a faint layering in the rock that might be missed from a moving car unless one looks carefully. For a closer look at the layered gabbro, and to get a scenic overlook of Duluth, take exit 250 at the top of the hill to the Thompson Hill Rest Area. You can see the gabbro in a rock cut at the rear of the parking lot. This coarse-grained rock has alternating light and dark bands, the result of

Gabbro of the Duluth Complex with layers of different crystals at the rear of the parking lot at the Thompson Hill Rest Area.

crystals slowly settling out from moving magma within the magma chamber at a depth of a few miles. Also note the big whitish inclusions of the slightly older anorthosite gabbro. The layers are even more obvious in a roadcut on the frontage road just below the information center. The plagioclase in the light layers has altered somewhat to whitish clay minerals, and the olivine in the dark layers has oxidized to a rusty brown.

From the information center at the Thompson Hill Rest Area, or from the viewpoint on the frontage road immediately below the information center, you can see the Duluth-Superior Harbor in the distance and the drowned St. Louis River Valley below. Both are products of postglacial rebound of the Lake Superior Basin after the last glaciers melted about 10,000 years ago. The thick glacial ice placed a heavy weight on Earth's crust, bending it downward. Once the ice was gone, the crust began to rise to its former elevation. The glacial ice was thickest and lasted longest at the northeastern end of the basin, so the rebound is greatest there. Thus, the Lake Superior Basin is being tilted toward the southwest, toward Duluth. The tilting has increased the water depth at Duluth, deepening the Duluth-Superior harbor behind the big sandbar that extends between Duluth and Superior, Wisconsin. The flooded valley of the St. Louis River constitutes part of this harbor.

On a clear day, you will be able to see far up the North Shore of Lake Superior. Here at the Thompson Hill Rest Area, you are on the highest shoreline of Glacial Lake Duluth, about 450 feet higher than the present level of Lake Superior. Glacial Lake Duluth, the 11,000- to 10,000-year-old ancestor of Lake Superior, formed as the Superior lobe retreated to the northeast but still blocked

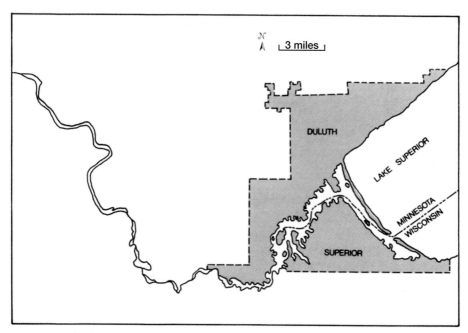

Sketch of the drowned St. Louis River Valley. —From Ojakangas and Matsch, 1982

drainage in that direction. A distant ridge on the skyline in Wisconsin, about 15 miles to the south, was the southern shoreline of the ancient lake. The old lakebed is covered with red clay that slowly settled out into the deep lake. Heavy rains erode this soft red clay and carry it into Lake Superior, where it forms bright red plumes in the normally clear water.

Near milepost 247 are roadcuts in the oldest basalt lava flows of the North Shore Volcanic Group. If you are heading north toward Duluth, these roadcuts appear as prominent rocky bluffs from about milepost 245. These flows are separated from the main body of the North Shore Volcanic Group by about 6 miles of the intrusive Duluth Complex.

We know these are the oldest lava flows because in a stacked sequence of layers of either sedimentary or volcanic rocks, the oldest are at the bottom and the youngest are at the top, assuming the stack has not been overturned. In this location, we know they haven't because each lava flow has an abundance of gas bubbles or vesicles at its top, formed as gases rose while the lava flow was cooling. These flows dip gently toward the axis of Lake Superior, as do those along the North Shore, and both are clearly part of the same sequence.

Cloquet Area

Between the roadcuts in lava flows at exit 247 and the St. Louis River near exit 239, you are driving on the clayey lakebed of Glacial Lake Duluth. Much of this easily eroded clay has been removed from the area by the St. Louis River, the largest river entering the western part of Lake Superior. Between exits 239 and 235, I-35 is built upon glacial outwash, with the higher hills just to the east of the highway composed of Nickerson end moraine.

Drive about 2 miles into downtown Cloquet via exit 237 to see the only gas station designed by Frank Lloyd Wright. It is at the corner of MN 33 and Avenue C, just south of the bridge over the St. Louis River. Just beneath the west side of the bridge are outcrops of the Thomson Formation.

Jay Cooke State Park and the Thomson Formation

Deep erosion by the St. Louis River as it was draining Glacial Lake Upham has cut through the glacial deposits and exposed the Thomson Formation of Early Proterozoic age in Jay Cooke State Park, which is a few miles east of I-35 on MN 210, via exit 235. For a detailed description of the park and the Thomson Formation, see the road guide for **MN 210: Fond du Lac—Brainerd**.

A Whale of a Tale

Between mileposts 232 and 233 is a big low outcrop between the two lanes of I-35, exposed during highway construction. This outcrop is the Early Proterozoic Thomson Formation, one of only two bedrock exposures on I-35 between the top of the hill above Duluth and the Twin Cities. Though this is a very interesting exposure, it is illegal to stop on interstate highways except for emergencies. However, even a quick "flyby" can be informative.

The Superior lobe streamlined this outcrop into two whalebacks, which are partially buried by glacial drift. A whaleback is so named because it resembles a whale's back protruding out of the water. The northeastern ends of the whalebacks gently taper toward the ground, and the southern ends have steep faces. As the ice moved southwest, sand and gravel in the ice tapered the rock. The southwest side is steep because if the ice becomes frozen to the bedrock during a lull in forward movement, when the ice moves again it will pluck out large pieces of the jointed rock on the side toward the direction of movement. I-35 trends northeast to southwest here. The whalebacks do not exactly parallel the highway—they trend about 20 degrees more to the west than does the highway.

Moraines of the Superior Lobe

Glacial ice of the Superior lobe moved southwestward out of the Lake Superior Basin four times, depositing a hilly ridge, or end moraine, each time it reached its southwesternmost position. However, most of the till is ground moraine, deposited beneath the glacial ice. A fifth advance did not move beyond the lake basin. The first and strongest advance reached the Twin Cities. In general, each successive advance was weaker than the former, so its morainal area is smaller than and partially bound by the former. Each advance has been given a name based on a natural or cultural feature located on deposits of that particular advance. The oldest, about 21,000 to 16,000 years ago, deposited the St. Croix drift. The Mille Lacs drift was deposited about 14,000 years ago. The Cloquet drift was deposited about 13,000 years ago. The Nickerson drift was deposited about 12,000 to 11,500 years ago. Drift of the Marquette advance, deposited about 10,000 years ago, has been found on the North Shore of Lake Superior. Few good radiocarbon dates exist, so these dates are estimates at best.

Geologists know that these were indeed separate advances, partly because of the composition of the glacial sediments. All are red because of the incorporation of red Late Proterozoic sedimentary rocks eroded out of the Lake Superior Basin, but the younger ones have more clay. Between advances, the Superior lobe retreated into the Lake Superior Basin and a lake formed in front of the ice. When the ice advanced again, it incorporated clayey lake sediment. Therefore, each successive advance deposited a more clayey till than the former.

Between mileposts 229 and 227, including the Mahtowa exit, the hilly area is a small, eroded remnant of the northeastern part of the Cloquet moraine. The remnant is surrounded by flat areas of glacial outwash deposited in a series of meltwater channels. Before ice melted back from the Lake Superior Basin, flow from Glacial Lakes Aitkin and Upham drained down the St. Louis River and then south to the St. Croix River.

Between mileposts 221 and 220, including the Barnum exit, and at mileposts 218 and 216, including the Moose Lake exit, the high hills are part of the Nickerson end moraine near its southwesternmost part. The lakes adjacent to I-35 near Barnum and Moose Lake occupy low spots on the irregular moraine. Just north of Barnum the highway crosses the drainage divide that separates waters flowing east to the Atlantic via Lake Superior and those flowing southward via the Mississippi drainage basin to the Gulf of Mexico.

The Moose Horn River, crossed twice between Moose Lake and Barnum, was one of the rivers that drained Glacial Lake Duluth. The meltwater-eroded valley is considerably wider than the present river.

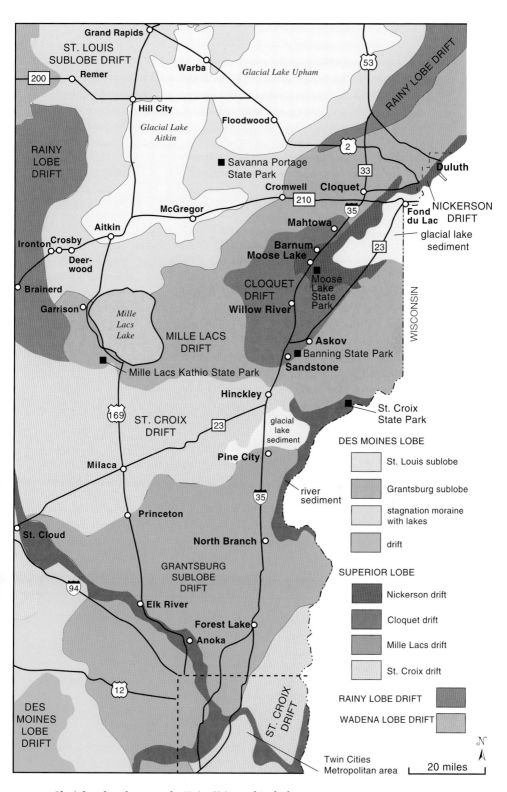

Grand Rapids

ST. LOUIS
SUBLOBE DRIFT

Remer

Warba

Glacial Lake Upham

200

RAINY LOBE DRIFT

53

Hill City

Floodwood

Glacial Lake Aitkin

Duluth

2

■ Savanna Portage
State Park

33

RAINY
LOBE
DRIFT

Cromwell   **Cloquet**

McGregor

210

NICKERSON
DRIFT

Aitkin

Fond
du Lac

glacial lake
sediment

Ironton **Crosby**

Mahtowa

35

**Deer-
wood**

Barnum
Moose Lake

Brainerd

CLOQUET
DRIFT

Moose
Lake
State
Park

23

Garrison

*Mille
Lacs
Lake*

Willow River

MILLE LACS
DRIFT

WISCONSIN

■

Askov

■ Banning State Park

Mille Lacs Kathio State Park

Sandstone

169

Hinckley

■ St. Croix
State Park

ST. CROIX
DRIFT

23

glacial
lake
sediment

DES MOINES LOBE

St. Louis sublobe

Milaca

Pine City

Grantsburg sublobe

35

stagnation moraine
with lakes

Princeton

river
sediment

drift

94

St. Cloud

North Branch

SUPERIOR LOBE

GRANTSBURG
SUBLOBE
DRIFT

Nickerson drift

Elk River

Cloquet drift

Mille Lacs drift

Forest Lake

Anoka

St. Croix drift

RAINY LOBE DRIFT

12

WADENA LOBE DRIFT

DES
MOINES
LOBE
DRIFT

ST. CROIX
DRIFT

N

Twin Cities
Metropolitan area

20 miles

Glacial geology between the Twin Cities and Duluth. —Modified from Hobbs and Goebel, 1982

Moose Lake State Park

Moose Lake State Park is located just 0.5 mile off I-35 at the Moose Lake exit. There are numerous geological exhibits in the Moose Lake Agate and Geological Interpretive Center ("Magic"). A large state map on the floor is inlaid with five of Minnesota's main rock types. The main emphasis of this park is the Lake Superior agate, Minnesota's gemstone, found in the glacial debris that was transported to this area from the Lake Superior Basin. The agates formed in gas cavities in the basaltic lava flows of the Midcontinent Rift System and are about 1,100 million years old. Echo Lake in the park is a kettle lake, formed when a buried ice block in the moraine melted. In Moose Lake there is also a museum devoted to the fires of 1918.

Outwash Plain between Moose Lake and Willow River

The flat topography between mileposts 214 and 200, especially prominent between mileposts 204 and 202, is a slightly dissected, nearly horizontal sandy glacial outwash plain deposited by meltwater from the Nickerson advance of the Superior lobe and from Glacial Lake Upham. A large sod farm is located on this plain at about milepost 204. The lakes between Moose Lake and Willow River, exits 214 and 205, are kettle lakes on the flat glacial outwash sand deposits. Sandy areas like this outwash plain generally support the growth of pines, which need good drainage. In fact, the presence of pine forests can be used as an indicator of underlying sandy material. You can see hilly moraine a few miles to the east and west of I-35. The higher terrain from about milepost 202 to milepost 199 is part of the Cloquet moraine.

Hinckley Sandstone Exposed along the Kettle River

Between mileposts 199 and 198, near the rest area in the northbound lane, I-35 crosses the Kettle River, the first Minnesota Wild and Scenic River. It gets its name from the Ojibwe word *Akikizibi*. *Akik* means "kettle" and *zibi* means "river." The name alludes to potholes in the rock, worn down by rocks swirled in high-velocity river water. These potholes can be seen at Hell's Gate Rapids in Banning State Park, which is along the river about 5 miles downstream from the I-35 bridge.

The highway drops considerably in elevation as it approaches the Kettle River, which has eroded the glacial sediment and cut down into the Hinckley Sandstone, deposited in the Midcontinent Rift in Late Proterozoic time. It contains no fossils or volcanic ashes with which a more precise age can be determined. Weathered roadcuts in the Hinckley Sandstone are present on the south side of the river along both the northbound and southbound lanes, about one-quarter to one-half mile from the bridge.

You can examine the Hinckley Sandstone up close in Banning State Park, in Sandstone, and along MN 23 where it crosses the Kettle River. To reach the latter location, take exit 195 (MN 23) toward Banning State Park and Askov. About 1 mile from I-35, a long roadcut is present on the east side of the MN 23 bridge over the river. If you have a hand lens, you will see that the buff sandstone is composed completely of rounded, clear quartz grains. The color is due to the presence of a very small amount of limonite (hydrated iron oxide) coating the grains.

The beds are horizontal, and some are cross-bedded. A close search will reveal ripple marks on the bottoms of a few beds. Regional measurements of the cross-bedding indicate that the currents that deposited this sandstone were generally moving from west to east. The rounding of the grains may have been accomplished by wind action, for there was as yet no land vegetation when the sands were deposited. Detailed studies have shown that some characteristics of modern sand dune fields are present in these rocks, although most of the sand was probably reworked by water and deposited in water, possibly in a lake in the rift basin.

Banning State Park and Sandstone

The Hinckley Sandstone is well exposed in Banning State Park. The entrance to the park is about one-half mile east of I-35 on MN 23 at exit 195. Trails will lead you past rock quarries that were active in various degrees from 1885 until 1938. The sandstone was shipped to Minneapolis, St. Paul, and Duluth on the St. Paul & Duluth Railroad. Although most of the building stone was used in the Midwest, some was shipped to the east and west coasts of the United States. A small town, Banning, once existed where the park is now. Foundations of some quarry buildings still exist, but the townsite is totally overgrown. The town of Sandstone, at the southern margin of the park, was the main town associated with the quarries.

Also visible in the park are deep gorges cut into the sandstone by the Kettle River. In places the cliffs are 40 feet high, but the total height from the river

The Hinckley Sandstone of Late Proterozoic age is exposed along the Kettle River at Banning State Park and Sandstone. This outcrop is on MN 23, 1 mile east of I-35. The hammer provides scale.

bottom to the top of the cliffs can be 100 feet. Hell's Gate is a fast rapids between the cliffs, and a favorite of canoeists and kayakers. Where did the Kettle River get the erosive power to cut so deeply into the sandstone? Great amounts of water flowed down the Kettle River from melting glaciers to the north and from Glacial Lake Duluth when it drained. On the tops of the cliffs, especially along the Hell's Gate Trail, are deep cylindrical depressions called potholes. These were formed when rocks were swirled around in place by the fast-moving floodwaters of the large meltwater river.

Sandstone, reached via exit 191, is known as the Quarry City. A large, accessible abandoned quarry is in Robinson Park, on the north side of County Road 30 adjacent to the Kettle River. There are also roadcuts on County Road 30 on the east side of the river. *Sandstone: The Quarry City*, a book researched by the Sandstone History Club and edited by Muriel Langseth, contains many old photographs of the quarrying operations and interesting tidbits, such as how outhouses were built to project out over the river, where running water was always available.

Geologists usually name a rock for a place where it is well exposed, but they chose not to call this rock the "Sandstone Sandstone" for obvious reasons. The first stone quarried here, in 1885, was hauled 10 miles by teams of oxen to the nearest railroad, which at that time was at Hinckley—hence the name. The name Kettle River Sandstone, as it was known commercially, would have been an ideal name because the exposures and quarries are all on the valley walls of the Kettle River. The Department of Geology and Geophysics at the University of Minnesota's Minneapolis campus is housed in Pillsbury Hall, which is built of Hinckley and Fond du Lac Sandstones. Paving blocks and crushed stone for concrete were other major uses.

Between about milepost 198 near the bridge over the Kettle River and a point about 2 miles south of Sandstone near milepost 189, I-35 is constructed upon Cloquet ground moraine. Ground moraine was deposited beneath a glacier, rather than at its end, and is flat to gently undulating.

Hinckley Area

Between milepost 189 and the Grindstone River just north of Hinckley, the underlying glacial sediment is the Mille Lacs ground moraine. The Grindstone River was named for an outcrop of Hinckley Sandstone where the river joins the Kettle River east of Hinckley. The outcrop was used by the Ojibwe and early fur traders for sharpening their iron and steel tools. The Grindstone River, and Grindstone Lake about 9 miles upstream from Hinckley, occupy a tunnel valley that was 0.5 mile broad and 200 feet deep but is now filled with glacial outwash.

About 5 miles east of Hinckley near the MN 48 bridge over the Kettle River, rocks of the Chengwatana Volcanic Group are exposed by the boat launch site. These basaltic rocks erupted in the Midcontinent Rift System and are the same age as those you can see on the North Shore of Lake Superior. They are also exposed along the St. Croix River. A forest fire in the Hinckley area in 1894 killed 418 people as it burned 400 square miles and six towns, all within a few hours.

St. Croix State Park

St. Croix State Park, one of Minnesota's largest, with an area of more than 50 square miles, is located on a bluff above the St. Croix River 15 miles east of I-35 and Hinckley on MN 48. The St. Croix River, a National Wild and Scenic Waterway, served as a water route for Native Americans and later for fur traders. There is evidence that Native Americans lived in this river valley as far back as 5,000 years ago. The logging industry floated white and Norway pine logs downstream during the late 1800s and early 1900s.

The St. Croix River is relatively small at this point, but it flows in a much broader 1.5-mile-wide valley that was a spillway for the great amounts of water that came from melting glaciers to the north in the last stages of glaciation 10,000 years ago. Glacial Lake Duluth, which filled the Lake Superior Basin and was about 450 feet deeper than the modern lake, drained through the Kettle River in Minnesota and the Brule River in Wisconsin, and then into the St. Croix. The Kettle River joins the St. Croix River along the southwestern boundary of the park. You can see bedrock of 1,100-million-year-old Chengwatana lava flows and interflow sediments in the park at Kettle River Highbanks along the Kettle River upstream from the confluence. You can also see glacial varves—annual couplets of clay and silt deposited in Glacial Lake Lind—behind the visitor center. The clay of this small glacial lake, which existed before the advance of the Grantsburg sublobe, is red because it was derived from the Superior lobe.

Glacial Lake Grantsburg

Between Hinckley and the Snake River at Pine City, the gently rolling topography is ground moraine of the Superior lobe, but the very flat area between exit 180 (MN 23) and exit 175 (Beroun) was the lakebed of Glacial Lake Grantsburg. The northeastward-moving (yes, northeast!) Grantsburg sublobe of the Des Moines lobe blocked southward drainage from melting glaciers in northern

Glacial Lake Grantsburg formed along the northern edge of the Grantsburg sublobe of the Des Moines lobe. —From Ojakangas and Matsch, 1982, after Cooper, 1935

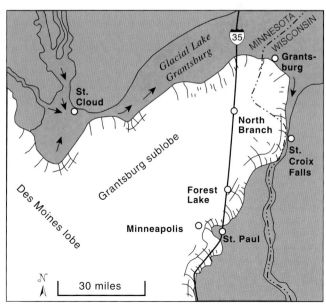

Minnesota, impounding the lake about 14,000 years ago. The lake may have been short-lived, lasting only an estimated 100 years. Most of the lake was in Wisconsin, but its long, narrow southwestern arm extended to the St. Cloud area. It covered an area previously occupied by Glacial Lake Lind, which may have existed for 1,000 years about 18,500 years ago.

Pine City to the Twin Cities

I-35 is on glacial sediments of the Grantsburg sublobe of the Des Moines lobe for the entire distance between Pine City and the southern edge of the Twin Cities. The Des Moines lobe was the last major glacial advance over Minnesota, about 14,000 years ago. And just 2,000 years later, it was gone. The Grantsburg sublobe moved northeastward across the older St. Croix ground moraine of the Superior lobe. This is clearly indicated by the presence of St. Croix end moraine to the south of the Des Moines lobe sediments in the Twin Cities area.

The Snake River was one of the rivers that drained Glacial Lake Aitkin, which was about 50 miles to the northwest. Snake River is the translation of the Ojibwe word *kanabec*, which means "snake." Pine City is a translation of *Chengwatana*, the name of an Ojibwe village at this site. Lava flows of the Chengwatana Volcanic Group along the river east of town were unsuccessfully explored for copper in the 1800s after copper deposits were found in flows of similar age in the Upper Peninsula of Michigan.

Between milepost 171 and milepost 167, I-35 crosses the hilly end moraine of the Grantsburg sublobe along its northern side. Between milepost 167 and exit 152, to Harris, you are driving on ground moraine of the Grantsburg sublobe. Between exit 152 and Forest Lake at exit 131, you are on sand of Glacial Lake Anoka, which formed when meltwater from the stagnated Des Moines lobe was dammed by an alluvial fan that formed south of the retreating Superior lobe. After this lake ceased to exist, the sand was reworked by wind into sand dunes of the Anoka Sand Plain.

US 2
Duluth—Grand Rapids
74 miles

Along US 2, you will see bedrock in the vicinity of Duluth, but the remainder of this route crosses glacial drift generally more than 200 feet thick. This highway crosses the St. Louis Bay between Superior, Wisconsin, and Duluth via the Richard I. Bong Bridge and coincides with I-35 for a few miles. Note the large roadcuts in black gabbro of the Duluth Complex as I-35/US 2 climbs the hill west of Duluth. Look for the layering of slightly lighter and slightly darker bands in this igneous rock, a function of crystals settling as the magma was cooling at depth about 1,100 million years ago. It is the chemical equivalent of the basalt flows of the North Shore Volcanic Group.

Where US 2 and I-35 diverge southwest of Duluth, take advantage of the view from the Thompson Hill Rest Area located above the interchange. From there you can see the drowned mouth of the St. Louis River and the big sandbar that protects the Duluth-Superior Harbor. If you want to get a really close look

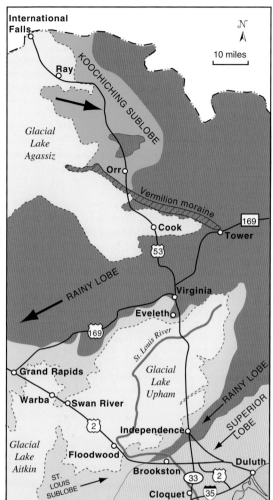

N

10 miles

International
Falls

Ray

KOOCHICHING SUBLOBE

*Glacial
Lake
Agassiz*

Orr

Vermilion moraine

Cook

Tower
169

*Glacial deposits
along US 2 and
US 53.* —Modified
from Hobbs and
Goebel, 1982

53

RAINY LOBE

Virginia

Eveleth

169

St. Louis River

*Glacial
Lake
Upham*

Grand Rapids

Warba

Swan River

2

Independence

RAINY LOBE

SUPERIOR
LOBE

*Glacial
Lake
Aitkin*

Floodwood

Brookston

Duluth

ST.
LOUIS
SUBLOBE

33

2

Cloquet

35

*Layered gabbro of the Duluth Complex along the
frontage road below the Thompson Hill Rest Area.*

at the layered gabbro, walk over to the rock exposure at the back of the parking lot. For an even better appreciation of this layering, which resembles sedimentary layering, stop along the frontage road just below the information center as you leave the parking area via the western exit.

You'll see the additional roadcuts in gabbro as US 2 climbs higher up the hill to Proctor, which is a major railroad yard for the CN Railroad, formerly the Duluth, Missabe & Iron Range Railroad. The railway's main cargo is iron ore hauled from the iron range to Lake Superior for shipment by ore boats to the steel mills on the lower Great Lakes. A few miles northwest of Proctor you will encounter the last rock exposures—more gabbro—along this stretch of US 2.

Between Duluth and the turnoff to Brookston, you are generally driving on Mille Lacs end moraine deposited by the Superior lobe about 14,000 years ago. The topography is quite hilly, and there are numerous roadcuts in the glacial till, now grassed over to prevent erosion. In 2003, the bridge over the St. Louis River just east of Brookston was widened. Photos taken before the cuts were grassed over show the unsorted nature of the glacial till and the striated boulders that it contains. Striations form when pebbles and boulders embedded in the ice are scratched against other boulders or against bedrock at the base of the ice.

The turnoff to Brookston is on top of a hill, the northwestern edge of the Mille Lacs end moraine of the Superior lobe. Watch for the abundant boulders in the

Till in a roadcut in 2003, now grassed over, just east of the US 2 bridge over the St. Louis River. There are three layers in the till here. The top layer is a wet clayey till, probably end moraine of the Mille Lacs till of the Superior lobe. The middle layer is a gray bouldery till, probably from the Rainy lobe. The bottom layer is a red sandy till, probably St. Croix till of the Superior lobe.

streambed of Stoney Brook at the base of the hill just east of the Brookston turnoff. The stream carries away the finer-grained sediment, and the bigger glacial boulders lag behind in the streambed.

Between Brookston and a point about 4 miles to the west, you are driving on ground moraine deposited by the Rainy lobe. Geologists can distinguish the Superior lobe till from the Rainy lobe till mainly by the color but also by the composition. The deposits of the Superior lobe are red and contain rocks derived from the Lake Superior Basin—basalt, rhyolite, and red sedimentary rocks. The Rainy lobe deposits are gray to tan and contain granites and greenstones from the older Archean rocks to the north, as well as gabbro and rhyolite pebbles, but no red sandstone. Of course, the roadcuts are grassed over, so these clues won't help you recognize till from the car.

Between 4 miles west of Brookston and the wide spot in the road called Gowan, you are driving on a low-relief end moraine of the northwestward-moving St. Louis sublobe of the Des Moines lobe. Yes, you read that correctly: northwestward moving! Glaciers flow like water, and although the Des Moines lobe moved from north to south, this sublobe flowed off to the side. Between mileposts 227 and 234, watch for boulders in the pastures and rock piles built by farmers over the decades as they picked the rocks out of their fields. About 4 miles east of Gowan, on the south side of US 2 there is a high hill and the remains of a large-scale gravel operation. This was a large esker of sorted gravels deposited under the St. Louis sublobe by a meltwater stream.

Between Gowan and Floodwood, you are driving on flatter terrain—a lakebed that is glacial till leveled off by currents and waves of Glacial Lake Upham, which existed from about 11,600 years ago until about 9,800 years ago, when it emptied to the south via the St. Louis River. The lake was named after Warren Upham, who mapped the glacial geology of much of Minnesota in the late 1800s and early decades of the 1900s. Glacial Lake Upham was connected to Glacial Lake Aitkin for most of its life, until its level got low enough to expose land between them.

Floodwood was an important spot in the late 1700s and early 1800s because of its location at the confluence of three rivers: the St. Louis, the Floodwood, and the East Savanna. To reach the Mississippi River from Lake Superior, Native Americans and fur traders canoed up the St. Louis from Lake Superior to Floodwood, and then up the East Savanna River to where it ends in open swampy grassland or savanna, which they portaged. See the road guide for **MN 210: Fond du Lac—Brainerd** for details about the Savanna Portage.

Between Floodwood and Swan River, the very flat countryside is more lakebed of Glacial Lake Upham. A layer of peat several feet thick formed many thousand years after the lake dried up and vegetation took over. Such old lakebeds now commonly support black spruce and tamarack forests; these can grow very slowly, and even small trees can be many decades old. Peat was mined for agricultural purposes for many years near Wawina. To the northeast of US 2, 7 miles northwest of Floodwood, is the Wawina Peatland, a Minnesota Scientific and Natural Area. It is the only major peatland in the Glacial Lakes Aitkin and Upham area, encompassing nearly 7 square miles.

Peat bog on the bed of Glacial Lake Upham between Floodwood and Wawina.

The town of Swan River is situated at the western edge of Glacial Lake Upham. The hilly terrain between Swan River and Warba is an arm of an irregular end moraine deposited on the northern edge of the St. Louis sublobe. The name of Warba, a little town on the Swan River, was derived from either the Ojibwe word *warbarsibi,* meaning "resting place," or the word *waiba,* meaning "white swan." Either one seems appropriate. Why does anyone care? The author of this book cares, for he grew up in this town of 125 people. At one time he planned to spend his life here operating a general store, hunting, fishing, and playing county league baseball until the age of sixty-five.

Warba and Blackberry are situated on flat ground that is glacial till modified by waves in the northern end of Glacial Lake Aitkin. The lake existed from about 11,600 years ago until perhaps about 7,400 years ago. Most of the lake drained with Glacial Lake Upham about 9,800 years ago, but a shrunken remnant remained behind, separated from the rest of the eastern drainage by a belt of higher ground. The soil is sandy, as indicated by the abundance of pines, because a giant subaqueous delta formed where the Prairie River channel entered Glacial Lake Aitkin. This channel drained Glacial Lake Koochiching, which later became the eastern arm of Glacial Lake Agassiz.

Grand Rapids, the westernmost city on the Mesabi Iron Range, is located on rather flat terrain that is glacial outwash associated with the melting St. Louis sublobe of the Des Moines lobe. There are former iron mines a few miles to the northeast and west. See **US 169/MN 169: Grand Rapids—Ely** for discussion of the Mesabi Iron Range.

US 53

Duluth—International Falls

150 miles
See maps on pages 67, 75, and 90

US 53 in Minnesota begins on the high bridge—the Blatnik Bridge—between Duluth and Superior, Wisconsin. The bridge spans St. Louis Bay where the St. Louis River enters the natural Duluth-Superior Harbor. Duluth is built on two 1,100-million-year-old rock units, the North Shore Volcanic Group and the Duluth Complex. The dividing line is at about Mesaba Avenue (north of US 53), with volcanics to the east and gabbros to the west. Thus, when you start climbing the hill at about Twenty-first Avenue West on US 53, any rock exposures you see on the hillside or at the top of the hill in the vicinity of the shopping malls by milepost 6 are gabbro.

For additional information about Duluth's geology, see the section on Duluth at the beginning of the road guides in this chapter.

Glacial Deposits between Duluth and Eveleth

Northwestward beyond the expanse of shopping malls, there are no rock exposures on US 53 for the next 50 miles. Three glacial lobes—the Superior lobe, the Rainy lobe, and the St. Louis sublobe of the Des Moines lobe—deposited glacial sediment that covered the bedrock. The flat area upon which the Duluth International Airport is located, near milepost 8, is glacial outwash. So are other flat areas between the airport and the village of Twig about 15 miles to the northwest. This sediment was deposited by meltwaters from the Superior lobe, whose northern edge flowed up and out of the Lake Superior Basin and headed northwestward toward the iron range. The hilly areas between the airport and a point a few miles northwest of Twig comprise its end moraine. The major movement of the Superior lobe, however, was toward the southwest along the Lake Superior Basin.

A water well driller reported a concentration of agates and wood in glacial sediment a few miles north of the airport at a depth of about 150 feet. The famous Lake Superior agates formed in gas cavities in the 1,100 million-year-old lava flows of the North Shore Volcanic Group. If you have searched gravel pits or the shore of Lake Superior for agates, you know they are not exactly abundant. So why this concentration? Agates are very resistant to weathering because they are made of fine-grained precipitated quartz. They may have become concentrated as weathering and erosion removed other rock. This could have happened millions of years prior to the advance of the first glaciers of the Pleistocene ice age, about 1.8 million years ago. The wood may be too old for dating by the carbon-14 method, which only goes back to a maximum age of 70,000 years and has a practical limit of about 45,000 years.

The first community north of Duluth and the suburb Hermantown, where the malls are located, is Twig, a town whose name Bob Hope poked fun at. In the vicinity of Twig, the bedrock changes from gabbro of the Duluth Complex to the metamorphosed sedimentary rocks of the older Thomson Formation. However, the contact lies beneath 50 to 100 feet of glacial deposits.

Glacial gravel and sand beds in a highway cut on the east side of MN 53 between mileposts 27 and 28, prior to grading and grassing over. The photo was taken in 1998.

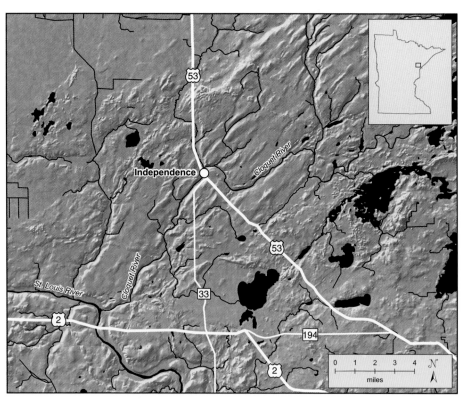

Landscape image showing drumlins of the Rainy lobe, part of the Toimi Drumlin Field, near Independence. The featureless lakebed of Glacial Lake Upham is in the upper left corner. The lakes at the lower right are in deposits of the Superior lobe.

The gently rolling topography near Independence at the junction of US 53 and MN 33 (where US 53 passes over the Cloquet River between mileposts 24 and 25) is ground moraine of the Rainy lobe. As you cross the bridge, notice the large boulders in the river channel, derived from the till of the moraine. The Rainy lobe moved southwestward, parallel to the Superior lobe. Some large teardrop-shaped drumlins, formed beneath the moving ice, are present in the area, but they are too wooded and too large to be easily distinguished as drumlins from the ground. The highway crosses these hills at nearly right angles between mileposts 21 and 29. The town Canyon is located on a north-south-oriented topographic high about a mile long and a half-mile wide, and 25 feet higher than the flatter surrounding area. It appears to be a buried drumlin originally formed beneath the Rainy lobe but modified by ice of the St. Louis sublobe and perhaps further modified by wave action in Glacial Lake Upham.

Between Independence and Eveleth, a distance of about 40 miles, the hilly areas comprise the end moraine of the St. Louis sublobe of the Des Moines lobe. Here the glacial ice on the eastern side of the main lobe flowed toward the northeast. Cobbles and boulders in a large gravel pit between mileposts 27 and 28 indicate that the pit is probably in Rainy lobe drumlins overlain by thin Des Moines lobe deposits that contain limestone pebbles and cobbles from Manitoba.

Glacial Lake Upham

The flat areas of open, grassy swamps and spruce or tamarack bogs are parts of the bed of Glacial Lake Upham, which existed between about 11,600 and 9,800 years ago. It occupied the drainage basin of the St. Louis River. Glacial Lake Upham, as well as Glacial Lake Aitkin to its west, formed as the St. Louis sublobe stagnated and melted. Glacial Lake Upham drained out through the St. Louis River after the ice was gone. These flat areas are underlain by a layer of peat that formed as the shallow lakes filled in with encroaching vegetation. If highway ditches have been recently cleaned of debris, look for the dark brown peat layer.

The Whiteface River, the Paleface River, and Hellwig Creek, as well as the St. Louis River, which empties into Lake Superior at Duluth, meander across this flat lakebed. Hellwig Creek and the St. Louis River were outlets of Glacial Lake Upham and emptied into Glacial Lake Duluth. Several shallow lakes such as Central Lakes, Murphy Lakes, Three Lakes, and Half Moon Lake are descendants of Glacial Lake Upham. The shallow lakes are scattered over an area of about 30 square miles. Many other small remnants of Glacial Lake Upham gradually dried up. Wave action in the glacial lake leveled previously deposited glacial till and formed sandy beaches in places. The junction of County Road 49 (Three Lakes Road) and US 53 at milepost 35 is on one of these low, sandy beach areas.

Three-Way Continental Divide

At the rest area at Anchor Lake, between mileposts 49 and 50, is an informational sign describing a three-way continental divide. Waters from this area flow northward to Hudson Bay, eastward to the Atlantic via the Great Lakes, and southward to the Gulf of Mexico via the Mississippi River. However, the divide, which you can think of as a geographic point, is actually about 25 miles to the northwest of this rest area. It is located on a hill of Pokegama Quartzite within the Hibbing Taconite Mine, an open pit. The hill is a sacred spot to Native Americans, and because of mining activities, it is inaccessible to the public. Anchor Lake is one of the closest official Minnesota rest areas at which to place a descriptive sign describing this important feature. Official highway maps of Minnesota show the continental divides and where they meet just north of Hibbing. The hill at the Anchor Lake roadside rest area was an island in Glacial Lake Upham.

St. Louis River

Between mileposts 53 and 54, US 53 crosses the St. Louis River, which is the largest Minnesota river that discharges into Lake Superior. It flows across glacial terrain until it reaches Cloquet. Between there and Duluth, it has cut down to bedrock, exposing the Early Proterozoic Thomson Formation and the Late Proterozoic Fond du Lac Formation.

In 1903 the author's Ojakangas grandparents homesteaded on the St. Louis River about 6 miles northeast of the US 53 bridge. Reportedly, Grandpa used to row a boat down the river to this point, and then walk 6 miles into Eveleth along a primitive predecessor to US 53. Then he would walk back with a 100-pound sack of flour and other necessities, and then row back upstream. The river meanders quite a bit, so he rowed about 11 miles each way!

Wellstone Memorial

Near the junction of US 53 and MN 37 are signs pointing to the Senator Paul Wellstone Memorial. The senator was killed in a plane crash near this site in 2002. The memorial, just a few miles east of US 53, is built of taconite from the nearby Mesabi Iron Range.

Mesabi Iron Range and Biwabik Iron Formation

As you approach the Mesabi Iron Range at Eveleth from the south, you'll see the higher terrain come into sight, held up by hard bedrock. The difference in elevation between Eveleth and the broad, flat area 5 to 6 miles south of town is about 350 feet.

In Eveleth at the junction of US 53 and MN 37 are the first bedrock exposures north of Duluth. Rusty-weathering roadcuts of Biwabik Iron Formation on both sides of US 53 clearly display the bedded nature of the dark gray iron-formation, known as taconite, which was deposited layer by layer in an ancient sea about 1,900 million years ago. On the iron range, the beds of iron-formation have a total thickness of about 600 feet.

The taconite rock is generally comprised of 70 to 80 percent silica (SiO_2) and 20 to 30 percent iron. The silica is present as chert, a fine-grained chemical precipitate. Geologists assume that both the iron minerals and the chert were precipitated from seawater when the oxygen content of the water reached high enough levels. This oxygen was produced by photosynthetic blue-green algae, now known as cyanobacteria.

If you look at the long roadcut on the west side of US 53, you can see that the beds or layers are dipping gently southward toward Lake Superior and Duluth, at about 10 degrees from the horizontal. The beds were originally horizontal but were tilted during regional deformation.

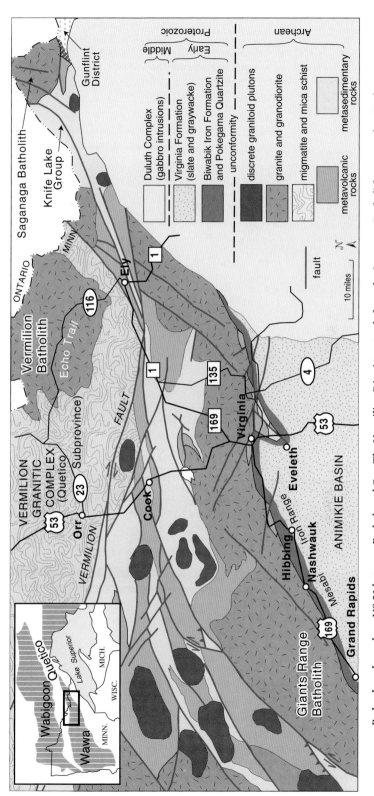

Bedrock geology along US 53 between Eveleth and Orr. The Vermilion District extends from the Saganaga Batholith westward to Cook.
—From Jirsa and Boerboom, 2003

If you look closely at the beds, especially in the shorter roadcut on the east side, you will see that some beds contain cross-beds deposited one inclined layer at a time by strong bottom currents. The direction toward which the cross-beds dip within the bed give the direction toward which the current was moving. Measurement of more than one hundred cross-bedding directions in the iron-formation in this area and in nearby taconite pits indicates that currents were

Biwabik Iron Formation exposed in a roadcut on the east side of US 53 just south of the junction with MN 37 at Eveleth. The beds are dipping at a low angle toward the right, which is to the south.

Iron-formation bed with cross-bedding in the eastern roadcut along US 53 just south of the junction with MN 37 at Eveleth.

moving in opposite directions at different times. The depositional environment of this cross-bedded iron-formation was probably in a shallow sea with active tides moving toward and away from the shore.

If you examine a piece of this iron-formation with a hand lens, you will see clear to reddish, sand-sized, rounded grains of chert and dark grains of magnetite or hematite. The magnetic mineral magnetite, the ore mineral of Minnesota's taconite industry, is attracted to a hand magnet. If you hold a compass close to the rock, you will see the needle deflected.

From 1892 until 1955, all the iron ore produced on the Mesabi Iron Range was high-grade natural ore. This ore was formed where water moved through broken taconite rock in fault zones and dissolved away much of the silica, increasing the iron content from the original 20 to 30 percent to about 55 percent. When it became apparent that the high-grade ore was approaching depletion, a process for extracting magnetite from low-grade taconite ore, known as the taconite process, was developed, especially by Edward W. Davis at the University of Minnesota.

The taconite process is used when the iron present in the taconite is in the magnetic mineral magnetite rather than nonmagnetic hematite. The taconite is crushed to a very fine grain size and then the magnetite is removed by magnets. The fine magnetite is then formed into marble-sized pellets of about 68 percent iron because pellets are easier to ship to the steel mills than powdered magnetite. Also, they are ideal for a blast furnace because the spherical shapes allow more space for oxygen between the pellets. Using this method, steel is produced twice as fast compared to when the mills used chunks of high-grade ore.

Pokegama Quartzite at Eveleth

The roadcut on the east side of US 53 just north of the overpass over MN 37 is an exposure of the Pokegama Quartzite, which underlies the Biwabik Iron Formation. The Pokegama was named for Pokegama Falls on the Mississippi River, a few miles west of Grand Rapids on the west end of the Mesabi Iron Range. It is present beneath the iron-formation over the length of the range but is exposed at only a few localities. The thick nearly horizontal beds in this roadcut are composed of a very hard quartzite, originally quartz sand that was later well cemented by silica. If you look at a piece of this quartzite with a hand lens, you can see the sand-sized grains of quartz. The Pokegama Quartzite was probably deposited near the edge of a sea in a tidal environment. The sand was likely carried to the sea by southward-flowing rivers draining the weathered older Archean bedrock to the north.

The 1,900-million-year-old Pokegama Quartzite in this area was deposited upon 2,700-million-year-old metamorphosed sedimentary rocks. However, this relationship is not clearly visible at any one place along US 53. On the east side of US 53 just north of the stoplight for Grant Avenue and Industrial Boule-vard are three small, low roadcuts of nearly vertical beds of the underlying older metamorphosed sedimentary rocks. A taconite plant is visible to the west of the highway at this point. Original knobs of Archean rock in this area, most of them now modified by human activity, were nearshore islands in the Pokegama sea about 1,900 million years ago.

Thick beds of the Pokegama Quartzite along US 53 in Eveleth just north of the MN 37 overpass.

These vertical beds of Archean metagraywacke and slate were deposited as horizontal beds of muddy sand and mud and then hardened, deformed, and metamorphosed during the Algoman mountain building event.

The nearly horizontal, lowest part of the Pokegama Quartzite is exposed in a long, low roadcut on the west side of US 53 opposite Midway, near milepost 62. Beyond the trees farther back from the highway, the overlying Biwabik Iron Formation is present in a cliff exposure. The sedimentary rock in this low roadcut was deposited in a muddy tidal environment. The few fine-grained sandy beds are now well cemented with silica to form quartzite. A few of these quartzite beds have been cut into slabs and studied in great detail. The sand is present as thin layers less than one-sixteenth of an inch thick, separated by even thinner, muddier layers. Digital processing of these layers accompanied by computer modeling suggests they are semidiurnal (twice daily) tidal layers. This type of data may eventually provide information about Earth-Moon relationships, such as the distance between them, about 1,900 million years ago.

Mineview in the Sky and the Virginia Horn

On the south side of Virginia is an excellent observation point—Mineview in the Sky—on top of an iron ore mine dump comprised of waste chunks of low-grade iron-formation. From here you can view the Virginia Horn, a term used by geologists to describe the broad Z-shaped bend in the otherwise straight, 110-mile-long Mesabi Iron Range. The origin of the Virginia Horn is subject to

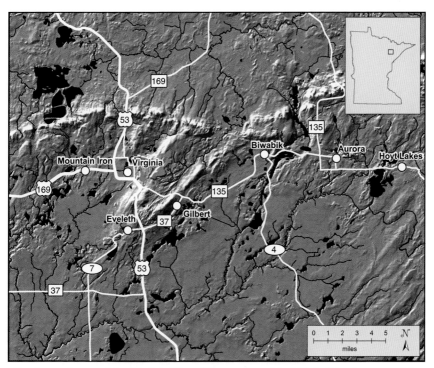

Landscape image of the Virginia Horn. The two large black "lakes" in the upper right corner are the tailings ponds of the large taconite plant at Mountain Iron. The broad flat area in the southern half of the image is the bed of Glacial Lake Upham; note how the rivers meander across this low-relief surface. At the lower right are drumlins of the Toimi Drumlin Field, deposited and shaped beneath the southwestward-moving Rainy lobe.

interpretation. Was it a topographic high in Archean time with the Early Proterozoic rocks simply deposited on it? Or was reactivation of the old Archean
faults during Early Proterozoic time an important factor, as indicated by the
concentration of faults along the axis of the horn? Some of these reactivated
faults also cut the iron-formation.

On the skyline to the north is the Giants Range, formed of granite. You can
also see the city of Virginia, taconite pits to the west, and a large taconite plant
on the skyline to the northwest. Plumes of steam may be visible to the north,
coming from another taconite processing plant. In 2008 a number of wind
turbines were added to the skyline. The total height of a tower with a blade
extended straight up is 420 feet. This wind farm, named Taconite Ridge, will
generate 25 megawatts of electricity per hour anytime the wind is blowing—
enough to power 8,000 homes.

From Mineview in the Sky, you overlook the Rouchleau high-grade iron mine,
which to the north merges with a dozen other mines. Ore was mined from this
composite pit from 1893 until 1997. More than 300 million tons of iron ore and
250 million tons of waste material were removed from this man-made canyon,

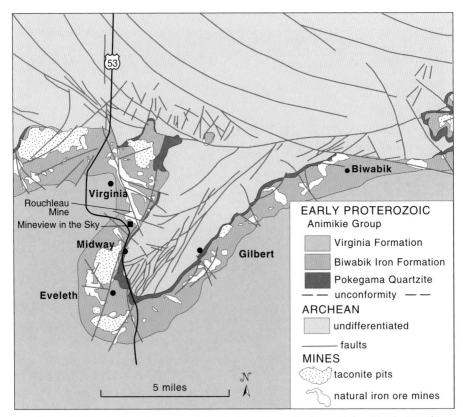

*Generalized bedrock geology map of the Virginia Horn, the dramatic bend in the Mesabi
Iron Range at Virginia and Eveleth. Note the relationship between the faults and the
high-grade (natural) ore mines, shown in white.* —Modified from Jirsa and Boerboom, 2003

The Rouchleau Mine from the Mineview in the Sky Overlook in 1974, when high-grade ore was still being mined. This mine was originally several mines; more than a dozen different properties merged as each was mined to its boundaries. Notice the long narrow pit in the distance. Compare this photo to the map of the Virginia Horn area to see the relationship between the faults and the high-grade mines.

which is as deep as 450 feet. The thick, light tan, sandy glacial deposits overlying the reddish oxidized iron-formation are clearly visible. They are thickest on the western and eastern edges of the mine and were deposited in an ice age river channel. The deep red, brown, and yellow colors in the pit are remnants of the high-grade oxidized iron ore. The red is from hematite (iron oxide), and the yellow and brown are from limonite (hydrated iron oxide). The original unoxidized iron-bearing taconite rock is dark gray, as seen in the taconite pits.

The Rouchleau Mine was once comprised of faulted and broken taconite rock from which groundwater removed much of the silica. Thus, natural processes increased the iron content from 20 to 30 percent to about 55 percent. This ore could be shipped directly to the steel mills without processing. Many of the former high-grade mines are long and narrow because the iron was concentrated along fault zones.

Side Trip to Pillowed Greenstone at Gilbert

Take either MN 135 from near Virginia or MN 37 from Eveleth to reach nearby Gilbert, where you can observe an excellent exposure of pillowed greenstone of Archean age, 2,700 million years old. This basement rock underlies the Pokegama Quartzite and the Biwabik Iron Formation. The exposure is at the north end of Wisconsin Avenue behind the Eveleth-Gilbert Junior High School athletic field. Wisconsin Avenue extends uphill from Gilbert's main street, Broadway.

The greenstone here is metamorphosed basaltic volcanic rock extruded underwater as lava in an ancient sea. Lava in water commonly forms rounded blobs called pillows. They accumulate as piles on the seafloor as lava emerges from holes and cracks and cools rapidly. The boundaries of individual pillows are distinguished by their finer-grained edges, which cooled very rapidly in the cold seawater and formed volcanic glass without crystals. They are not glassy now because glass is unstable, and metamorphism and deformation during mountain building caused it to recrystallize.

The original black basalt had a primary mineralogy of plagioclase, pyroxene, magnetite, and olivine. These were largely changed to green minerals such as chlorite, epidote, and actinolite during low-grade metamorphism at temperatures of several hundred degrees Fahrenheit and high pressures deep below Earth's surface. Because of the color imparted to the overall rock by the green minerals, the term *greenstone* is used.

The pillows are no longer in their original nearly horizontal positions; they have been tilted to vertical. They also were somewhat flattened during the Algoman mountain building event. Geologists use the shapes to tell the original top or up direction of the pillows at any given locality. Convex-upward rounded surfaces are the original tops, and points are the original bottoms. Not every pillow reveals this information, but close inspection of many pillows will provide the answer. The tops are to the northeast at this locality.

The pillows in this greenstone outcrop at Gilbert formed when lava extruded into water and cooled. Note the glacial striations where rocks embedded in glacial ice scratched the greenstone as the ice flowed toward the southwest. The curved pillow tops are to the upper right (northeast) on this outcrop.

Some of the greenstone at Gilbert is massive rather than pillowed. Basaltic magma probably intruded into the pillow pile and did not come into contact with water. Look for a small patch of red hematitic chert (jasper) on this outcrop, indicating that the Biwabik Iron Formation once covered the greenstone but has been eroded away. The contact between these two rock types represents a hiatus in deposition of about 800 million years.

Note also the well-developed glacial grooves and striations, or scratches, on the greenstone. Glaciers certainly removed some of the overlying iron-formation. However, nearly 2 billion years of running water had probably eroded away most of the iron-formation long before the glaciers of Pleistocene time arrived. The glacial grooves trend northeast-southwest and were made by the Rainy lobe, which moved toward the southwest.

Giants Range Batholith

Just to the north of Virginia is the Giants Range, here part of the Virginia Horn. It is most impressive when approached from the north. The name is based on the Ojibwe word *missabay*, which means "giant" or "big man hills." The Indian giant was a hero who hunted by throwing large boulders. Although it's not a mountain range, the Giants Range is a prominent topographic feature, rising about 300 to 500 feet above the surrounding terrain.

The Giants Range is composed largely of granite and is part of the Giants Range Batholith, a very large mass of intrusive rock 120 miles long by 5 to 20 miles wide. It is comprised of many distinct bodies of intrusive rock that cooled slowly from magma deep in the bowels of the mountains beneath a thick cover of older volcanic and sedimentary rocks. It formed about 2,700 million years ago during the Algoman mountain building event. Some radiometric dates from the mineral zircon in rocks of this batholith are 2,674 million years, and 2,685 million years. This mountain building was related to volcanic arcs that collided from the present-day south with what was then the nucleus of a much smaller North American continent.

Just a few miles north of Virginia on US 53/MN 169 is a Superior National Forest rest area that is an excellent geologic stop because of the large roadcuts. The rest area is also on the Laurentian Divide, from which waters flow both northward to Hudson Bay and southeastward to Lake Superior and hence to the Atlantic Ocean. You can see this continental divide marked on an official Minnesota highway map.

The roadcuts in the northbound and southbound lanes offer excellent exposures of pink and gray granites with some inclusions of a black amphibole-rich rock called amphibolite. This locality is likely somewhere near the southern edge of the Giants Range Batholith, at a place where the magma was penetrating and incorporating pieces of preexisting rock. Amphibolite is metamorphosed basalt, as is greenstone, but higher-grade metamorphism that occurred at temperatures of about 900 to 1,100 degrees Fahrenheit and pressures several thousand times the pressure at Earth's surface, probably at a depth of several miles. These conditions are more intense than the conditions that produce greenstones. However, some geologists think that the black rock, instead of being inclusions of basalt, may be igneous rock that crystallized from a mafic magma richer in iron and magnesium than the granitic magma. Thus there may have been two types of magma present at the same time in the magma chamber. It seems likely that both ideas are correct—some of the black rock was inclusions of amphibolite and some was a mafic magma. Geology students have affectionately named this spot Confusion Hill. To lessen your confusion, try to ignore the small black spots of tar splashed onto the rocks during highway resurfacing. A short distance north of Confusion Hill, the granite exposures are more homogeneous and light-colored, without inclusions of black rock.

At this locality, look for epidote, an apple green metamorphic mineral common on the flat surfaces of old joints or cracks in the granite. It formed during later stages of metamorphism when the temperature was lower.

Whereas the granite batholith extends northward for 5 to 20 miles, the topographic Giants Range itself is quite narrow. This southern portion of the batholith may have been better protected from erosion compared to the lower-lying terrain to the north. The overlying resistant Pokegama Quartzite and the hard siliceous Biwabik Iron Formation probably provided the protection. Most of these protective rocks have since been eroded off the granite, which in turn is now slowly but surely being weathered and eroded.

Granite of the Giants Range Batholith with dark inclusions at Confusion Hill, just north of Virginia along US 53.

From the MN 169 Intersection to Cook

For several miles north of the intersection with MN 169, US 53 traverses a pine-covered, sandy plain deposited in Glacial Lake Norwood, a small lake that formed to the north of the Giants Range from meltwaters of the retreating Rainy lobe. The lake eventually emptied via the Embarrass River into Glacial Lake Upham to the south of the Giants Range. An abundance of pine trees in a relatively flat area suggests abundant sand, which in turn suggests an outwash plain formed by meltwaters flowing away from the front or side of a melting glacier.

Look for a big gravel pit on the west side of US 53 about one-half mile north of Idington, between mileposts 86 and 87, about 15 miles north of the junction of US 53 and US 169. This pit is located in an end moraine complex of the Rainy lobe, which was moving toward the southwest.

Numerous roadcuts in bedrock along US 53 between the Giants Range and International Falls reveal pink to gray granites and dark gray to black metamorphic rocks in various proportions. The latter are mostly black biotite schists that originally were sedimentary rocks, probably derived from volcanic arcs. Unsorted glacial till is present above the bedrock in many roadcuts.

Have you noticed that several rock exposures in this stretch of road are somewhat rusty? The yellow and brown colors indicate that pyrite (iron sulfide) was originally present, which is easily oxidized to limonite (hydrated iron oxide) by exposure to oxygen and water. Pyrite may be associated with ore minerals such as sphalerite (the main ore mineral of zinc), chalcopyrite (the main ore mineral of copper), galena (the main ore mineral of lead), or native gold. Therefore, rusty rocks are of special interest to geologists who are exploring for economic mineral deposits.

The highway crosses the Little Fork River in Cook. This river flows north to the Rainy River on the Minnesota-Ontario border. Thus, some of the water eventually reaches Hudson Bay.

Side Trip on MN 1 to Graded Beds

About 1 mile north of Cook is the intersection of US 53 with MN 1. A low roadcut on MN 1 just 0.4 mile west of the intersection is a small but excellent exposure of metasedimentary rocks of Archean age. The beds were tilted vertically during the Algoman mountain building event 2,700 million years ago. The metamorphosed sandstone beds (now metagraywacke) are light gray, and the metamorphosed mud beds (now slates) are black. Study under a petrographic microscope shows that the grains in the metagraywacke were eroded from volcanoes.

Look on the top surface of the roadcut for well-preserved graded beds in which the grain size changes from coarse sand to fine sand. Such grading is the result of deposition from a thick, swirling turbidity current that carried mud and sand down the sloping ocean floor into deeper water. The larger, heavier grains are first to settle out of such a current when it slows. Thus, the coarser parts of the beds indicate the original bottoms of the beds and the finer parts indicate the original tops. So the top direction of this sequence of beds is roughly to the north.

Graded metamorphosed graywacke sandstone beds (light gray) with beds of darker muds, now slates, on MN 1. Note the irregular base of the metagraywacke bed (at arrows), the result of the sand sinking down into the underlying wet mud at the time of deposition. The sand grains are coarsest there and get finer to the upper left, toward the tip of the hammer handle.

Also visible on the top surface are glacial scratches trending southwest, typical of the general north-to-south flow of the Pleistocene glaciers. Most flat-topped roadcuts will have similar glacial striations. Did you notice the metal survey marker called a benchmark, placed there by the U.S. Geological Survey?

US 53 from Cook to Orr

Between mileposts 97 and 98, about 4.5 miles northwest of Cook, is Olson Road (County Road 540). On the north side of this road just east of US 53 is a gravel pit (not visible from US 53) with unsorted glacial till containing large boulders. This till was deposited directly by glacial ice onto sorted gravel beds deposited by runoff meltwater from a glacier. Glacial ice may have readvanced over previously deposited gravel, or a debris flow from the nearby receding glacier could have deposited the unsorted material. This locality is near the boundary between the St. Louis sublobe of the Des Moines lobe and the Rainy lobe. Geologists are uncertain which glacial lobe the till is from, although the bouldery nature suggests Rainy lobe. The occasional white limestone pebbles in it may have been carried by the Des Moines lobe from Manitoba, where limestone bedrock is abundant, but the limestone could also have come from Hudson Bay, carried by the Rainy lobe. Look for glacial striations, especially on the larger stones. The larger the stone, the more likely it was carried near the base of the glacial ice because its weight would diminish its likelihood of being lifted higher within the ice. Larger stones are thus likely to have been dragged against the bedrock, becoming scratched and gouged.

In the ditch on the east side of US 53, 6.5 miles north of Cook and 2 miles south of the junction of US 53 and MN 73, is an exposure of the Gheen pluton, one of many small plutons shown as "discrete granitoid plutons" on the bedrock geology map on page 75. There are dikes of different composition cutting each other. The rocks here also contain small amounts of copper minerals and gold (but only 16 parts per billion).

A large roadcut at the junction of US 53 with MN 73 is comprised of steeply dipping black biotite schist cut by thin nearly vertical white to pink granite dikes and veins and pods of white quartz. You can see these most clearly on the top of the exposure, along with glacial striations that trend toward the south.

About 5 miles south of Orr, between mileposts 104 and 105, US 53 crosses a high hill of glacial deposits with gravel pits on its top. This is one of the high points on the Vermilion moraine, a 1- to 2-mile-wide end moraine of an advance of the Rainy lobe. It forms the southern shore of Lake Vermilion and extends for 50 miles to the northwest. As the glacier melted, meltwater deposits now mined for gravel were deposited in addition to the till of the morainal complex. Certainly these meltwater deposits were close to the ice margin, for some boulders here are 6 feet in diameter.

Also about 5 miles south of Orr and about 2.5 miles north of Gheen, US 53 crosses the 300-mile-long Vermilion Fault, which extends from north of Ely nearly to the North Dakota border. The fault is buried here under glacial deposits, so don't strain your eyes. The Vermilion Fault separates the western part of the Vermilion District, the greenstone volcanic-sedimentary belt intruded by granite of the Giants Range Batholith to the south, from the Vermilion Granitic Complex to the north. This complex of granites and metasediments (schists)

A maze of dikes cut the Gheen pluton in an outcrop in a ditch on the east side of US 53, 6.5 miles north of Cook. —Mark Jirsa photo

extends to a point about 10 miles south of International Falls. This fault has been best studied in the Vermilion District north of Tower, Soudan, and Ely, where part of it is visible on County 116, the Echo Trail.

About 3.5 miles south of Orr between mileposts 106 and 107, there are high and long roadcuts on both sides of the highway, comprised of minor stringers of black biotite schist cut by two generations of abundant gray and pink granite. This granite, which probably crystallized at a depth of several miles, appears to have melted and incorporated much of the original rock. Because we are north of the Vermilion Fault, it is part of the Vermilion Granitic Complex, rather than the Giants Range Batholith. The Vermilion and Giants Range are similar but separate bodies of rock. The term *granitic complex* is used for the Vermilion because there is so much biotite schist associated with the granite. D. L. Southwick, who studied this region extensively, has mapped this exposure as granite-rich migmatite. Other exposures have been mapped as schist-rich migmatite.

A migmatite is a banded rock comprised of older bands of schist with younger bands of granite. In geological circles, the origin of the granitic portions of migmatites is debatable. Did the granite crystallize from intrusive magma, was it formed by solutions from the magma, or was it melted out of the original country rock during metamorphism? Southwick prefers a magmatic origin for the massive granite and much of the granite-rich migmatite but noted that solutions moving outward from the magma did replace some of the country rock, forming granitic stringers.

The flat and swampy area 2 miles south of Orr is part of the bed of Glacial Lake Koochiching, which was dammed by the Rainy lobe to the northeast, the Des Moines lobe to the west, and high ground to the south. It eventually coalesced with Glacial Lake Agassiz when the Des Moines lobe melted away.

Orr

Orr is on the shore of Pelican Lake, one of the westernmost lakes whose boundaries are in part bedrock controlled, as are most lakes east of this area. Farther to the west, the locations of most lakes are totally controlled by the distribution of glacial deposits. At a pullout on the lakeshore in Orr, you can get a close look at the pink and light gray granite and black biotite schist of the Vermilion Granitic Complex.

On the north side of Orr, US 53 crosses over a high granite knob. Roadcuts here show that the granite contains several horizontal joints that were probably formed during the erosion of the thick cover of overlying rock into which the granitic magma was intruded. As that weight was removed, the solid rock expanded upward, forming the cracks, or joints. The topographic relief of this region prior to glaciation may have been more rugged than at present. Glaciers likely eroded off the tops of knobs, especially the weathered and decomposed rock, and deposited debris in the topographic lows.

Watch for other roadcuts on US 53 of black country rock—biotite or amphibole schist—cut by light-colored pink or gray granite veins. Some roadcuts show distinct layers of black schist that probably represent original bedding.

Side Trip on the Ash River Trail

About 26 miles north of Orr, the 10-mile-long Ash River Trail (County Road 129) leads to resorts and a southern entrance to Voyageurs National Park. This road passes many bedrock knobs separated by flat spruce and cedar bogs, open swamps, and small lakes. The many roadcuts between US 53 and the road that leads to the Voyageurs National Park Visitor Center are in gray granite, banded gray granitic gneiss, or dark gray to black biotite schist of the Vermilion Granitic Complex of Archean age. At the junction with the visitor center road are large roadcuts of the same rocks. The 3-mile-long road to the visitor center has many roadcuts, but it is not safe to stop on this winding road. Instead, stop at the designated overlooks. The Voyageurs Forest Overlook parking area contains an exposure of gray granite. At the Beaver Pond Overlook is a coarse pink to red pegmatitic granite with pink feldspar crystals as large as 4 inches across.

At the end of this road at the visitor center parking lot are excellent exposures of granite. Adjacent to the steps leading up to the visitor center buildings is a pink granite with scattered 2-inch-long crystals of orthoclase feldspar set in a finer-grained granite. By the boat landing is a black biotite schist with two generations of crosscutting gray granite dikes. The largest rock exposure by the parking lot is made up of gray granite with large inclusions of black biotite schist cut by granite dikes.

If you drive to the end of County Road 129, you can see a gravel pit on the north side of the road amid the buildings. The faces of any active gravel pit are continually changing due to removal of material and slumping. However, any freshly dug face in this pit will show glacial sediment of Pleistocene age deposited by meltwater that flowed off a nearby glacier. This gravel pit is near the boundary of two glacial lobes, the Rainy lobe, which moved toward the southwest, and the Des Moines lobe, which moved toward the southeast. Thus it is difficult, without some additional study of pebble types, to determine the detailed history of this particular meltwater deposit.

Side Trip to Kabetogama Lake

Kabetogama Lake, another southern entrance to Voyageurs National Park, is reached via County Road 122, which heads north off US 53 about 3 miles north of the Ash River Trail. About 0.7 mile north of US 53 on the west side of County Road 122 is a low flat exposure of contorted gneiss—migmatite—in which is embedded a survey marker of the U.S. Geological Survey. Another 1.6 miles farther north is a wide dike of black mafic rock cutting across light gray granitic rock. This dike has been traced, by rock exposures and airborne geophysical measurements of magnetism, northward to International Falls and beyond into Ontario. It has a total length of more than 50 miles and has been dated by radiometric techniques at 2,100 million years, about 600 million years younger than the granite it is cutting. This dike, one of hundreds shown on aeromagnetic maps, is part of the Kenora-Kabetogama Dike Swarm. Extensional forces created numerous elongate cracks in the 2,700-million-year-old southern part of the Canadian Shield, and these cracks became passageways for mafic magma rising from the base of the crust.

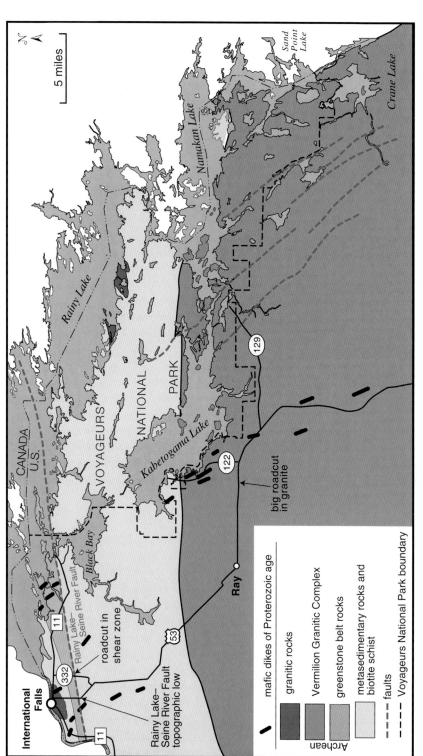

Bedrock geology along US 53 between Orr and International Falls, including Voyageurs National Park. The small area north of the Rainy Lake–Seine River Fault is in the Wabigoon Subprovince; all rocks south of it are in the Quetico Subprovince. —Modified from Ojakangas and Matsch, 1982

Legend (map)

Archean

- mafic dikes of Proterozoic age
- granitic rocks
- Vermilion Granitic Complex
- greenstone belt rocks
- metasedimentary rocks and biotite schist
- faults
- Voyageurs National Park boundary

International Falls

CANADA
U.S.

Rainy Lake

Black Bay

roadcut in
shear zone

Rainy Lake–
Seine River Fault

Rainy Lake–
Seine River Fault
topographic low

VOYAGEURS

NATIONAL   PARK

Kabetogama Lake

Namakan Lake

Sand
Point
Lake

Crane Lake

big roadcut
in granite

Ray

5 miles

Spectacular Roadcut on US 53

About 1.5 miles west of the intersection of US 53 and County Road 122 (about 6 miles east of Ray, between mileposts 140 and 141), is a very large and spectacular roadcut in the Vermilion Granitic Complex. Ignore the vertical drill holes and look at the big black inclusions of country rock that were engulfed by the magma that solidified into the dominantly pink granite. The inclusions are now amphibole-rich schists that probably were volcanic-sedimentary rocks and basaltic rocks prior to intrusion of the granite magma. Some coarse-grained granitic dikes or pegmatites contain crystals of potassium feldspar several inches across. Look for some thin granite dikes that were stretched during mountain building to resemble a string of *boudins*, French for "sausages."

Ray to International Falls

Between Ray and International Falls, the flat terrain is the bed of the southeastern part of Glacial Lake Agassiz, which formed to the south of the retreating ice of the Des Moines lobe. Some areas of slightly higher topography are glacial till modified by wave action. Near International Falls, you may see where black soil, peat, and clay are being removed from the old lakebed.

Just south of International Falls on both sides of the highway are quite small, low roadcuts comprised of biotite schist—metamorphosed clayey sandstone—without granite stringers. This schist is part of the northern edge of the Quetico Subprovince. These metasediments were intruded by the Vermilion granitic rocks. The Quetico Subprovince continues east-northeastward into Canada,

This large roadcut in the Vermilion Granitic Complex is 1.5 miles west of the intersection of US 53 and County Road 122, 6 miles east of Ray.

where it is well-exposed. Based upon geophysical measurements, it is known to continue in the subsurface southwestward across northwestern Minnesota to the North Dakota border. However, rocks of this subprovince are rarely exposed to the west of US 53. They are best seen east of International Falls at Ranier and on the access road to the interpretive center at Voyageurs National Park. See the road guide for **Minnesota 11: International Falls—Voyageurs National Park**

Rainy Lake–Seine River Fault

At about milepost 161, at the southern edge of International Falls, a barely perceptible 200-foot-wide slight topographic low trends across the highway. This is the surface expression of the Rainy Lake–Seine River Fault, a fault zone or shear zone that has an overall length of about 175 miles, 60 miles in Minnesota and 115 miles to the northeast in Ontario. It separates the Quetico Subprovince of metasedimentary rocks to the south from the Wabigoon Subprovince of volcanic-granitic rocks to the north. To the southwest of International Falls this fault merges with the even longer Vermilion Fault.

This fault zone is a major suture between two lithospheric plates that collided about 2,700 million years ago. The ancestral North American continent, which already included the Wabigoon Subprovince of volcanic-granitic rock, was hit from the south (present-day coordinates) by the Quetico Subprovince of metasedimentary rocks. The collision was at an acute angle, so not only was the colliding plate subducted, but it moved laterally as well. It is estimated that the Quetico Subprovince on the south may have moved 50 miles westward relative to the continent on the north.

If you take a short side trip of 1.7 miles off US 53 on County Road 332, just south of International Falls, you will see a very large roadcut exposing the Rainy Lake–Seine River Fault Zone. The rock here is highly sheared or crushed greenstone (metamorphosed basalt), with numerous shear bands defining the trend of the fault zone. The addition and removal of elements by hot water appears to have been extensive, altering the original mineralogy of various bands.

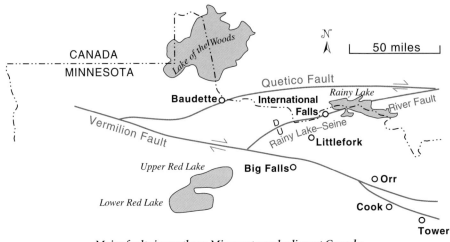

Major faults in northern Minnesota and adjacent Canada.

Quartz veins are especially prominent. The banding, which is not the original bedding, is best observed on the top edge of the eastern roadcut. About 0.5 mile south of this big cut, there is a slight depression about 500 feet wide that trends across the road; this is another surface expression of part of the Rainy Lake–Seine River Fault Zone.

Fault zones commonly form topographic depressions because the crushed and broken rock is more easily weathered and eroded than is solid rock. However, hot solutions in the fault zone can precipitate silica and other minerals that make erosion more difficult. Many of Canada's largest gold mines are in major fault zones. Traces of gold have also been found along the Rainy Lake–Seine River Fault in Minnesota.

Quartz veins in the Rainy Lake–Seine River Fault Zone.

US 169
Twin Cities—Grand Rapids
163 miles
See map on page 61

Between Anoka and Elk River, US 169 is on the braided course of the glacial Mississippi River, which was up to 4 miles wide. Look for flat river terraces marking higher flow levels of the river, when it was carrying water from the glaciers and glacial lakes to the north. These are most easily seen on the north side of the river in the vicinity of Elk River, where the floodplain is narrower.

Between Elk River and Princeton, US 169 crosses drift of the Grantsburg sublobe of the Des Moines lobe, which moved toward the northeast. Between Elk River and Lake Fremont the hilly topography is an end moraine and esker complex that is being extensively quarried for sand and gravel. Such a large deposit near a growing metropolitan area is, quite literally, a gold mine! Subglacial rivers did much of the work of sorting the sediment prior to depositing it in eskers. Between Lake Fremont and Princeton, the highway crosses a much flatter area of glacial sands on the bed of Glacial Lake Anoka—the Anoka Sand Plain, which has sand dunes in places.

About 2 to 3 miles south of Princeton, US 169 crosses a broad tunnel valley formed during the St. Croix advance of the Superior lobe. The valley is now covered with Des Moines lobe drift.

Between Princeton and Mille Lacs Lake, the highway passes over ground moraine of the southwest-moving St. Croix advance of the Superior lobe, with some areas of glacial outwash. Watch for major elongate depressions that cross the highway between Milaca and Page at about milepost 193 and between mileposts 195 and 196. These are channels—tunnel valleys—carved into the till by meltwater flowing westward beneath the melting and retreating glacier. Also in the general area there are elongate hills that trend east-west, roughly perpendicular to the highway; these drumlins were sculpted by the moving glacier and are part of the large Pierz Drumlin Field of 1,600 drumlins.

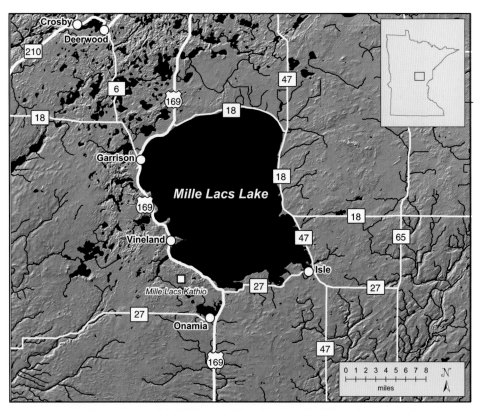

Landscape image of the Mille Lacs Lake area. Note the hilly end moraine of the Mille Lacs advance on the west and southwest sides of the lake.

On the north edge of Onamia, immediately next to the highway, is a rather unique cemetery, with more than fifty identical dark gray granite tombstones in two neat rows. Each marks the grave of a Catholic priest or brother of the Order of the Holy Cross, from the nearby monastery of the Crosier Fathers. The little cemetery is surrounded by walls of mortared round fieldstones, glacial boulders from the Superior lobe till.

The highway crosses the 70-mile-long Rum River several times between Anoka, where it enters the Mississippi River, and its source at Mille Lacs Lake. The Dakota name for Mille Lacs Lake is *Mde Wakon*, which means Spirit Lake. Since the river is the lake's outlet, it became the Spirit River. It seems that Europeans in the area dubbed it the Rum River, after the main alcoholic spirit that they brought into the area.

The Ojibwe called the lake *Missasagaiigun*, meaning "great lake." The name Mille Lacs Lake comes the French fur traders' phrase meaning "the thousand lakes region." The lake covers 250 square miles, has approximate dimensions of 18 by 13 miles, and is 26 to 36 feet deep over most of its area. It is one of the four largest lakes in Minnesota, along with Lake of the Woods and Lower and Upper Red Lake. It exists because the thick glacial deposits encircling it act as a natural dam. The Mille Lacs phase of the Superior lobe reached this area and stalled, depositing end moraine on what are now the west and southwest sides of the lake. The east side is also relatively high because of ground moraine of the same lobe, and to the north is moraine deposited by the St. Louis sublobe of the Des Moines lobe.

Mille Lacs Kathio State Park

Mille Lacs Kathio State Park, located near the south end of Mille Lacs Lake at milepost 221, contains two main lakes—Ogechie and Shakopee—connected by the Rum River. The park has countless hills and topographic lows, as you would expect in an area of end moraine. You may also spot a few boulders in the glacial till.

The park is part of the Kathio Archeological District, which was designated a National Historic Landmark in 1964 by the National Park Service. Humans have inhabited the area for at least 9,000 years and thirty archeological sites have been identified. This area was the prehistoric homeland of the Dakota Nation—the Sioux. They were living here in a village called Kathio when the French explorer Daniel Greysolon, Sieur du Lhut, visited in 1679 and claimed the region for France. Father Hennepin stayed here for six months in 1680. At the campground on the shore of Lake Ogechie, you can stand on the site of a Dakota village. Copper implements were made here about 3,500 years ago, part of the Old Copper Tradition. In excavated clay pots, siliceous plant remains called phytoliths indicate that wild rice, sedges, squash, and corn were cooked here as far back as 200 BC. The Dakota used to travel via the Rum River to the Mississippi River and beyond to hunt buffalo. By the beginning of the 1700s, many Dakota were moving southward to the prairies, and the Ojibwe moved in from the Lake Superior region and have been here ever since. Between Vineland and Garrison on the Mille Lacs Indian Reservation is the Mille Lacs Indian

Museum, operated by the Minnesota Historical Society. Here you can study the journey of the Mille Lacs Band of Ojibwe from the eastern seaboard to Lake Superior and finally to Mille Lacs Lake. In the 1850s, loggers arrived and over the next fifty years cut most of the large white and red pines.

Garrison to Grand Rapids

At Garrison is a lakeside rest area with a monument and a long rock wall, both made out of rounded glacial boulders from the Mille Lacs end moraine. Most of the boulders are granites, but metamorphic rocks are also present. The prominent white vertical stripes on the wall were placed there by the abundant seagulls.

The area between Mille Lacs Lake and Aitkin is hilly end moraine and outwash of the St. Louis sublobe of the Des Moines lobe, which moved southwestward in this area. The bed of Glacial Lake Aitkin, which occupies the large area between Aitkin and Hill City, is a rather flat area of peat bogs, lake sediments, and lake-modified glacial till. Between Hill City and Grand Rapids, US 169 is constructed on hilly end moraine of the St. Louis sublobe, which moved to the southeast here.

US 169/MINNESOTA 169
Grand Rapids—Ely
107 miles

US 169 from Grand Rapids eastward extends over the western three-quarters of the Mesabi Iron Range. About 4 miles north of Virginia, the highway becomes MN 169 and crosses over the Giants Range Batholith of Archean age and ends in the Vermilion District greenstone belt of Archean age. As you drive this route, you will notice numerous signs pointing to the Mesabi Trail, a 132-mile-long paved biking trail, much of it along old railroad beds, that reaches from Grand Rapids to Ely.

The original topography along the Mesabi Iron Range has been very much altered by mining activity that exploits the sedimentary Biwabik Iron Formation deposited in Early Proterozoic time. Today the topographic high points are either mine dumps of iron-formation too low-grade to be economical or dumps of glacial sediments removed from above the ore zones. Many of the dumps are now covered with trees. The waste dumps of ore rock display the purple to red color of oxidized iron-formation. Total relief from the tops of dumps to the bottoms of pits, now commonly filled with water, can be several hundred feet. Many of the pit lakes are stocked with fish.

The twenty towns and cities on the Mesabi, plus several smaller locations, owe their initial existence to either mining or logging, but all eventually became mining centers. There were once 131 high-grade iron ore mines in the iron range between Grand Rapids and the western edge of Virginia.

The glacial sediments along US 169/MN 169 are nearly all products of the Rainy lobe, which moved from northeast to southwest. One exception is the southwestern portion of this route between Grand Rapids and Nashwauk, where end moraine was deposited on the northern edge of the St. Louis sublobe of the Des Moines lobe. More of this end moraine occurs between Hibbing and

Virginia. The St. Louis sublobe flowed to the northeast off the eastern side of the south-moving Des Moines lobe. The bedrock topographic high along the Mesabi Iron Range acted as an obstacle to the St. Louis sublobe. In general, the iron range is the dividing line between Rainy lobe deposits to the north and deposits of the St. Louis sublobe of the Des Moines lobe to the south.

South of the Mesabi Iron Range, from Nashwauk eastward nearly to the eastern end of the range beyond Aurora, the glacial till of the St. Louis sublobe

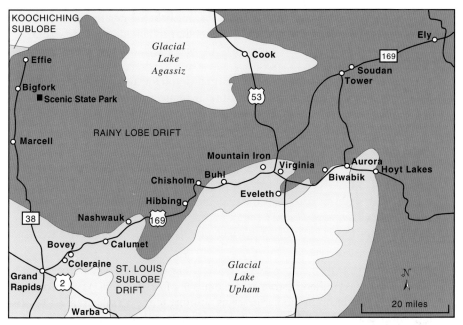

Quaternary geology along US 169/MN 169 between Grand Rapids and Ely.
—Modified from Hobbs and Goebel, 1982

An iron ore dump of waste rock along US 169 between Calumet and Nashwauk.

is blanketed with glacial lake sediments of Glacial Lake Upham. This large lake formed to the northeast of the sublobe as it melted back to the south.

Grand Rapids

Grand Rapids is at the western end of the Mesabi Iron Range, with one mine located 4 miles to the west and others 2 miles to the northeast. These were some of the last high-grade mines to be developed. Grand Rapids began as a lumbering center in the late 1800s, and the Minnesota Historical Society maintains the Forest History Center here. There used to be bouldery rapids at this point on the Mississippi River, which runs through the center of the city, but the rapids is now beneath the dam of a paper mill. The rapids prohibited steamboats from moving upstream beyond this point. You can see a mammoth tusk at the Itasca County Museum in Grand Rapids.

The iron-formation at Coleraine, Bovey, and Grand Rapids at the western end of the range is strongly weathered, so iron ores were not exploited until the Oliver Iron Mining Company developed a washing process to remove the cherty sand from the hematite ore, thereby raising the grade to a commercial level.

Hill Annex Mine State Park

At Hill Annex Mine State Park in Calumet, you can take a tour of the Hill Annex Mine, which is on the National Registry of Historical Places. It closed in 1978, after sixty-six years. It is the sixth largest individual iron mine in the United States, having produced 64 million tons of iron ore. In 1848, Congress passed the Northwest Territorial Act, which provided that sections 16 and 36 of

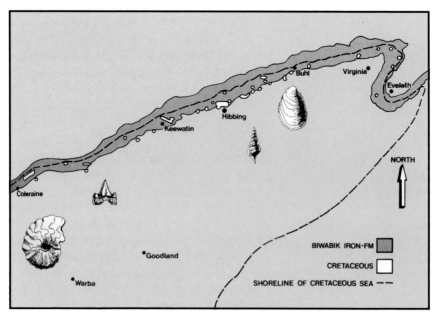

The Mesabi Iron Range formed the eastern shoreline of the Cretaceous sea about 100 to 80 million years ago. Snails and clam fossils are more common in the eastern part of the range and ammonites and shark teeth are more common in the western part. —From Ojakangas and Matsch, 1982

Cretaceous conglomerate with pebbles of high-grade iron ore at the observation stand in Hill Annex Mine State Park.

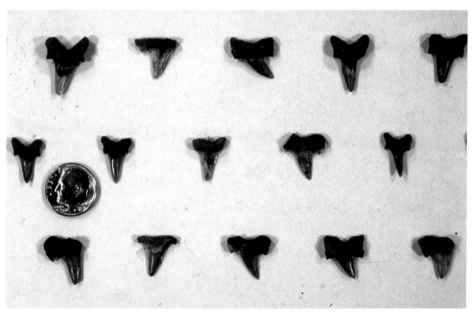

A collection of shark teeth from Cretaceous sedimentary rock overlying the Biwabik Iron Formation of Early Proterozoic age.

every 36-square-mile township would be reserved for educational use. Because the Hill Annex Mine was located in section 16, $27 million in royalties was paid to the Minnesota school trust fund by the mine operators.

At the park, you can also go fossil hunting on mine dumps to search for 100-million-year-old Cretaceous marine fossils. Snails and clams are the most likely find, but shark teeth, reptile teeth and vertebrae, and ammonites have been found. Carbonized wood from coniferous and deciduous trees has also been found.

The comparatively high relief of the Mesabi Iron Range formed part of the eastern shore of the Cretaceous inland sea that covered a wide swath of North America from the Rocky Mountains eastward. The sea reworked some of the high-grade iron ore, and many pebbles ended up in a Cretaceous conglomerate as thick as 18 feet. The alteration of low-grade taconite to high-grade hematite must have occurred before late Cretaceous time in order for the conglomerate to contain high-grade ore. In fact, the conglomerate was mined for iron. During mining, the Pleistocene glacial deposits and the underlying Cretaceous sediments had to be removed to get to the high-grade iron-formation. You can find fossils on the dumps that contain the Cretaceous waste rock.

The walls of the open pit mine clearly show light tan glacial drift overlying red, oxidized iron-formation. The original Cretaceous beds, where still present, are covered by slumped glacial drift.

Nashwauk and Keewatin

Nashwauk started life as a logging town; iron ore was discovered here in 1900. The population in 1902 was 220, by 1910 it was 2,000, and now it is less than 1,000. An observation stand at the very end of Central Avenue in downtown

The Hawkins Mine in Nashwauk now contains a lake. Note the glacial till with boulders over the bedded, red iron-formation.

Nashwauk overlooks the Hawkins Mine, the first mine in Itasca County. Between 1902 and 1962, 25 million tons of ore were removed from this mine. You can see glacial drift deposited by the Rainy lobe above the low-grade iron-formation, or taconite, on the pit walls. George Crosby discovered this mine, the beginning of his fortune. He later went to the Cuyuna Range northeast of Brainerd and built the planned city of Crosby. A taconite mining operation was located 1 to 2 miles west of the Hawkins pit, but it closed in 1984. A larger taconite operation is located at Keewatin, 5 miles east of Nashwauk.

Hibbing

In 1893, Hibbing, the largest city on the iron range, was platted by Frank Hibbing where he discovered iron ore. You can see a statue of Hibbing at Frank Hibbing Park. The Hull Rust Mine, one of the largest open pit iron mines in the world, is sometimes called the Grand Canyon of the North. More than fifty different areas were mined to their boundaries here and thus coalesced. One of the mines, the Mahoning Mine, was the first open pit on the Mesabi when it opened in 1894. When open pits were developed, the miners abandoned underground mines, which could not produce as much ore or do it as inexpensively or as safely. To reach the Hull Rust Mine View, take Third Avenue to the north from Howard Street, the main business street. Or, take Thirteenth Street west off US 169 to reach Third Avenue. Including the present taconite mining operations, the mine is 5 miles long and covers an area of nearly 5 square miles. More than 800 million tons of iron ore have been shipped from this pit, and more than 1.4 billion tons of material have been moved.

Taconite, a low-grade iron-formation, has been mined on the far north side of the pit since 1973. As you look into the pit, you can see the red, oxidized iron-formation, which was mined for high-grade ore, and the dark gray taconite rock now being mined.

The Mahoning pit, the first open pit on the Mesabi Iron Range, in 1894. —From author's collection

Near the north edge of the pit near the processing plant is a knob of Poke-gama Quartzite that is a triple divide watershed point. Rainwater falling at this spot flows in three directions—east to Lake Superior and the Atlantic Ocean, south to the Gulf of Mexico, and north to Hudson Bay. Detailed surveying methods located the point in the 1930s. The hill was a sacred meeting spot for Native Americans, who hundreds of years ago named it the Hill of Three Waters. How did they know this?

Near the Hull Rust Mine View, you can see old streets and foundations of the northern part of Hibbing, then the heart of town. Buildings in this part of town were moved 2 miles to the south when mining operations changed from underground mining to open pit.

Chisholm

Chisholm, which got its start with logging, became a boomtown with iron mining. From a population of 250 in 1901, it grew to over 10,000 in 1923, twice its present size. Archibald Chisholm discovered several Mesabi mines, including the Chisholm Mine. With forty-five depleted iron mines nearby, Chisholm was a logical site for the Ironworld Discovery Center, which was founded in the late 1970s. This center is a must-see for understanding the mining industry and the geology, as well as the immigration, labor, and logging history, on the Mesabi Iron Range. There is an excellent view into a deep high-grade iron ore pit. Also located in Chisholm is the Minnesota Museum of Mining.

It is impossible to miss the 36-foot-tall Iron Man statue on top of a 50-foot-tall base adjacent to US 169 in Chisholm, opposite Ironworld. A plaque bears the following inscription: "The Emergence of Iron Through Steel. This statue,

High-grade iron ore at Chisholm formed along a fault zone. This pit, including several mines, is 3 miles long and almost crosses the entire width of the Biwabik Iron Formation.

the third largest free-standing memorial in the United States, is a lasting tribute to the Mesabi, Vermilion, Cuyuna, and Gogebic Ranges' men of steel, who carved out of a Sylvan Wilderness, the iron ore that made America the industrial giant of the world." (The Gogebic Range is in Wisconsin and Michigan.)

If you want to take a close look at the low-grade iron-formation, the taconite rock, you can walk to roadcuts a few hundred feet behind the statue. From your perspective, the beds will appear to be horizontal, although they are dipping to the southeast at about 10 degrees. Individual beds vary in thickness as you follow them along the roadcut. The waviness of the bedding may have developed during deposition, or it may be the result of postdepositional changes.

The head frame of the Bruce Mine is visible on the north side of US 169 just east of Chisholm, near milepost 348. To the south, you can see the 3-mile-long and quarter-mile-wide Chisholm open pit complex that originally included eight mines. Here, water percolating through the broken rock along a major fault zone removed silica from the low-grade taconite, forming high-grade ore. The numerous waste rock dumps in the area form the highest topography.

Buhl, Kinney, and Mountain Iron

There are more than a dozen high-grade iron ore pits in the Buhl and Kinney area. At the old Judson Mine just south of Buhl, ore was mined from Cretaceous sedimentary rock. Waves along the eastern shoreline of the Cretaceous sea about 100 to 80 million years ago reworked pebbles of the Precambrian high-grade ore into a conglomerate. Fossil clams and snails were abundant in the associated sedimentary rocks.

The iron ore of the Mesabi Iron Range was first discovered in Mountain Iron in 1890 by an employee of Leonidas Merritt, leader of the seven Merritt men involved in iron ore exploration. You can see a statue of Leonidas in the center of town. A shaft was sunk in 1892 and the first ore, shipped on October 17, 1892, was 65 percent iron. An overlook located on a high waste rock dump just east of Mountain Iron provides views of both high-grade pits and a modern taconite operation.

Virginia

Virginia had a history of logging prior to mining, and a museum in Olcott Park depicts the logging industry. About twenty high-grade iron ore mines were located within 2 miles of downtown Virginia. The Enterprise Mine, 1 mile north of Virginia, produced 7 million tons of ore from Cretaceous conglomerate composed of pebbles of high-grade Precambrian ore. There was also a bed of low-grade Cretaceous coal in this mine. You can view a deep open pit mine from the Oldtown-Finntown overlook at the east end of the main street in downtown.

US 169 and US 53 coincide for 4 miles north of Virginia. See the road guide for **US 53: Duluth—International Falls** for details of a side trip to Gilbert to view an excellent pillowed greenstone exposure; a description of the Virginia Horn, the large Z-shaped bend in the iron range; the Mineview in the Sky Overlook just south of Virginia; and the roadside rest area about 3 miles north of Virginia where US 53/US 169 cut through a portion of the Giants Range Batholith at the Laurentian Divide.

About one-half mile north of the divide over the Giants Range, an elongate topographic high, US 169 turns east off US 53 and becomes MN 169. The highway passes over granite of the Giants Range Batholith for about 10 miles, but there are no outcrops or roadcuts. For several miles to the northeast of this intersection, you will be driving on the flat lakebed of Glacial Lake Norwood, meltwater of the Rainy lobe that ponded to the north of the topographically high Giants Range. It eventually drained into Glacial Lake Upham through a gap near the eastern end of the range.

Greenstone of the Vermilion District

A big roadcut between mileposts 382 and 383 is a coarse-grained greenstone, metamorphosed mafic plutonic rock. Note the steep foliation or crude layering, which developed during the Algoman mountain building event 2,700 million years ago. Between this point and the end of MN 169, a few miles east of Ely, you are driving in the Vermilion District, a classic volcanic-sedimentary greenstone belt that is typical of the Canadian Shield and the Precambrian shields of other continents. It is named after Lake Vermilion, the seventh largest lake in Minnesota.

Side Trip to a Classic Exposure

Just north of the junction with MN 1, you can take a short side trip to see a classic exposure of graded graywacke beds and slate. Near milepost 258 (note that mileposts are now for MN 1), turn to the north on County Road 77 and proceed for one-half mile to the bridge over the Pike River. Immediately after crossing the bridge, turn left into a pull-off. This gently sloping exposure is composed of light gray metagraywacke beds (originally clay-rich sandstone) and black slate beds (originally mudstone). The beds were deposited in horizontal layers but are now vertical because of tilting during Algoman mountain building.

If you look closely at the metagraywacke beds, you will see that each one is graded—that is, each bed has a coarse-grained sandy base and a fine-grained top. Each graded bed was deposited by a separate turbidity current, a swirling current of suspended sand and mud. Graded beds allow geologists to determine the original top directions of the beds. I sat on this outcrop several decades ago for most of a day, measuring, studying, and counting the beds. I used empty beer cans from the roadside to carry water to the outcrop because when rocks are wet, it is easier to see the details of the grains under a hand lens. There are 228 metagraywacke beds, of which 146 are graded, with 140 topping to the south. Why did I bother? Because these characteristics help to decipher how the beds were deposited and in what type of environment. That day the walleyes were spawning in the river, and many people were there watching them as well as the crazy guy pouring beer on the rock outcrop and then putting his face close to the rock, apparently to lick up the beer.

The outcrop is crisscrossed by two sets of joints, now filled with silica that stands up in relief. Silica was precipitated from hot water in the joints, or cracks, after deformation, and the silica is more resistant to weathering than metagraywacke. On the left side of the outcrop is a younger series of joints that do not have silica in them.

Microscopic study of the metagraywacke shows that all of the sand-sized grains are volcanic quartz, plagioclase, and fine-grained volcanic rock fragments.

Metagraywacke and slate beds of the Vermilion District at an outcrop near the County Road 77 bridge over the Pike River. Please don't hammer at the rock for a souvenir because it will destroy this classic exposure.

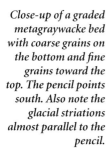

Close-up of a graded metagraywacke bed with coarse grains on the bottom and fine grains toward the top. The pencil points south. Also note the glacial striations almost parallel to the pencil.

Other studies in the area suggest that the source of the sand was probably an explosive volcano in the vicinity of the east end of Lake Vermilion, about 5 to 10 miles to the northeast. Turbidity currents moved downslope and underwater from the volcano to this location.

The Pike River was part of a well-traveled canoe route for both Native Americans and French-Canadian voyageurs. They would come up from Lake Superior via the St. Louis River, and then into the Embarrass River. A 3-mile portage over a height of land led to the northward-flowing Pike River and entry to the lake country of the north. Countless canoes must have passed by this outcrop during the last several hundred years.

Pike Bay Area

Near milepost 259 is a historical marker describing Winston City, a town that existed for three years after the Lake Vermilion gold rush of 1865–1866. It had a post office, stores, and the necessary saloons. Probably no one found any gold.

Near milepost 262, on a curve opposite Pike Bay Drive, is a big roadcut of highly folded metagraywacke and slate beds. Look for the graded metagraywacke beds at the west end of the roadcut. Walk the length of the roadcut along the top to see further evidence of folding.

Between milepost 261 and 262 is a roadcut of white rock. If you stop and look closely at the rock, you might call it a quartzite. Geologists called it a quartzite too, until microscopic studies proved it to be volcanic sandstone or a reworked volcanic tuff. It contains prominent sand-sized volcanic quartz grains, plagioclase grains, and fine-grained volcanic rock fragments. Its source was probably a volcano in the vicinity of eastern Lake Vermilion, 5 to 10 miles to the northeast. At the west end of the roadcut on the south side of the road is a black mafic dike that has been dated by radiometric methods at 1,570 million years. Other similar dikes in northern Minnesota are 2,100 million years old, and it may be that the date on this one is incorrect. However, detailed chemical analyses suggest it is similar to 1,100-million-year-old dikes near Lake Superior.

Immediately west of Tower are high roadcuts of rusty brown rock that is either volcanic fragments exploded from a volcano or a conglomerate eroded from a volcano. The volcano was a few miles to the northeast, at the east end of Lake Vermilion. The rust comes from weathered pyrite, an iron sulfide mineral.

Folded metagraywacke and slate beds in a roadcut on MN 169 near milepost 262. If you look closely at these beds, you will see the beds are graded in opposite directions, indicating intricate folding.

White volcanic sandstone on MN 169 between mileposts 261 and 262 is composed of volcanic fragments erupted from an ancient volcano near Lake Vermilion in the Wawa Subprovince.

Exploration geologists always check this kind of rusty rock for ore minerals that often occur with pyrite. The rust emanates from certain spots that appear to have been pieces of pyrite eroded from a larger body of pyrite and deposited with the rounded volcanic fragments.

Tower

Tower was named for Charlemagne Tower, a financier from Philadelphia who built the railroad from the nearby Soudan Iron Mine to Two Harbors, on the North Shore of Lake Superior. Lake Vermilion, Minnesota's seventh largest lake and the fiftieth largest in the United States, is immediately to the north of town. If you are driving east out of Tower, look for the Soudan Mine high on the hill above the village of Soudan.

Soudan Underground Mine State Park

Soudan Underground Mine State Park is a must-see. Where else can you don a hard hat and ride a nearly vertical incline in a small metal skip to a depth of nearly half a mile—2,341 feet—in three minutes? And where else can you then hop on an underground train and ride three-quarters of a mile to huge underground workings in high-grade Archean iron ore? The mine is a cool place—the temperature is a constant 52 degrees Fahrenheit. The park interpretive center contains excellent historical and geological exhibits.

The Soudan Mine, Minnesota's first and deepest iron ore mine, started as open pits in 1882, with the initial ore shipment in 1884. The operation moved underground in 1892 to continue mining the nearly vertical ore zones. In the 1890s, two thousand miners worked here. The mine operated until 1962, when the U.S. Steel "sold" it and 1,200 adjacent acres to the state for the grand sum of $1, on the condition that it become a park. A total of 14 million metric tons

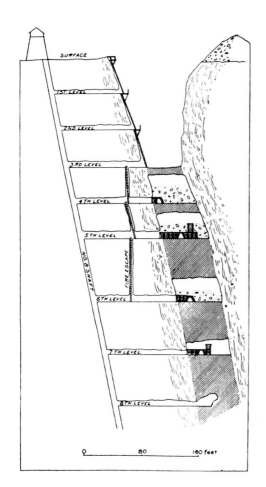

The nearly vertical mine shaft connects multiple levels in the Soudan Mine.
—From Ojakangas and Matsch, 1982, after Clements, 1903

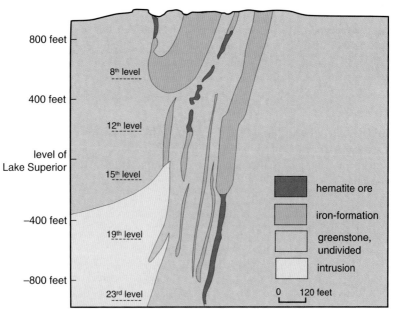

Generalized cross section of the ore in the Soudan Mine.
—From Ojakangas and Matsch, 1982, after Klinger, 1956

of ore containing 63 to 69 percent iron in the form of hematite (Fe_2O_3) was removed from the mine. More high-grade ore remains at depth, but the cost of extraction compared to the lesser cost of making taconite pellets from large open pits doomed the mine to closure. Today the mine serves a dual purpose as a state park and as an underground physics laboratory. Visitors descend to the twenty-seventh level, where they can go on a normal mine tour via the train or enter the physics laboratory at the base of the lift.

The iron-formation at the western end of the Vermilion Iron Range is what geologists call *exhalite*, because iron precipitated as iron-rich hot fluids from volcanism were "exhaled" onto the seafloor. The original rock consisted of layers of hematite or magnetite and layers of red chert or jasper and white chert. In the vicinity of the mine, the silica that makes up chert was removed, probably by hot water during metamorphism. The insoluble iron was thus concentrated to a higher grade, from about 20 or 30 percent to as much as 69 percent iron. Abundant white quartz veins in the vicinity of the high-grade hematite ore may have been part of the original silica of the iron-formation.

You can see a classic outcrop of folded hematite and jasper layers of the iron-formation only a short walk from the mine head frame. This outcrop can also be reached without going into the park entrance. Take Stuntz Bay Road uphill from the church in Soudan. Just past the first old mine buildings, the road bends to the right and climbs up a small hill. At the very top of the hill, turn right onto a flat rock outcrop and park. This highly folded outcrop is perhaps the most photographed in Minnesota, at least by geologists. Hammering on the rock is prohibited. Some geologists think the folding occurred when the still-soft sediment slumped down a submarine volcanic slope. Others think it is the result of two deformational events, while still others say one folding event

Folded iron-formation near the Soudan Mine has layers of white chert, red jasper, and metallic hematite. This may be the most photographed outcrop in Minnesota.

The head frame of the Soudan Mine stands over the deep shaft and supports cables that move up and down the mine shaft transporting loads.

could produce all the features visible here. Look closely—the red jasper layers and the white chert layers have short cracks across them filled with white vein quartz. The chert and jasper bands must have been brittle when they folded, so they cracked. There are no cracks in the gray, metallic hematite layers, so they were more plastic when folded. There are deep open pits near this outcrop where high-grade ore was removed, but this outcrop was not mined because it had not been transformed into high-grade ore.

Deep underground is a good place to do physics experiments that are sensitive to background radiation, so an underground laboratory was built in the Soudan Mine. Nearly a half mile of rock above the experiments blocks the constant storm of cosmic radiation at Earth's surface. In 2009 there were two experiments taking advantage of this site: one watching a beam of neutrinos originating from Fermi National Accelerator Laboratory near Chicago, 455 miles away; the other using a few kilograms of ultrapure silicon and germanium crystals chilled to almost absolute zero to look for dark matter, particles that appear to make up much of the mass of the universe but have not yet been directly observed.

Side Trip to the Mud Creek Shear Zone

Mud Creek Road (County Road 408) intersects MN 169 between mileposts 273 and 274. If you drive 3.6 miles up this gravel road, you will cross a broad, quarter-mile-wide, east-west-trending valley, occupied by Mud Creek and Mud Lake, that is 200 feet lower than the ridges on either side. Water and ice eroded the valley here because it is a broad fault zone of sheared rock. The fault, called the Mud Creek Shear Zone, is more than 6 miles long and continues beneath Lake Vermilion at its western end. Its east end joins the Vermilion Fault, which extends across Minnesota to North Dakota. The shear zone appears to be a splay off of that major fault. Sheared rocks provide passageways for ore-bearing solutions and space for the deposition of ore minerals, including native gold. Traces of gold have been found along the shear zone during mineral exploration. Look for the sheared rock in a brownish, oxidized roadcut on the north side of the valley. Fresher, less-weathered banded rock can be seen on the south edge of the valley about 50 feet west of the road in a small open area.

Banded rock in the Mud Creek Shear Zone. The bands look like original bedding, but they formed by pervasive shearing during movement on the fault.

Soudan to Ely

The roadcuts between Soudan and Ely are all in the Soudan Iron Formation Member of the Ely Greenstone or in the greenstone, which is commonly metamorphosed pillowed basalt extruded underwater. Between mileposts 269 and 270, on a hill with a big radio tower, there is a big roadcut in the iron-formation. The bedding is nearly vertical. At the east end of the roadcut, the iron-formation is cut by a light-colored felsic dike with big quartz and plagioclase crystals that crystallized at a greater depth than the rest of the magma that formed the dike. Dikes such as this were probably feeders to explosive volcanoes that formed on top of the pillowed greenstone.

At the junction of County Road 88 at milepost 282, look for a big pile of crushed greenstone protruding above the trees on the north side of the highway. This is the remnant of a failed venture of the 1920s to make green granules for roofing paper and shingles. The development of artificial coloring techniques for roofing granules made this approach obsolete. Also note the large gravel pit in a glacial kame at this point on the highway.

Between milepost 283 and Ely, there are several roadcuts in pillowed Ely Greenstone. Just west of Ely at the top of the highest roadcut on the north side of the highway, immediately beneath a crossing power line, vertical pillows have been accentuated by weathering. They are harder to delineate in the fresher rock at road level. Pillows are positive evidence that the lava poured out underwater, in this case in a deep ocean about 2,700 million years ago.

In Ely there is an excellent three-dimensional exposure of pillowed Ely Greenstone. Near the east end of Ely, turn north on Thirteenth Avenue East,

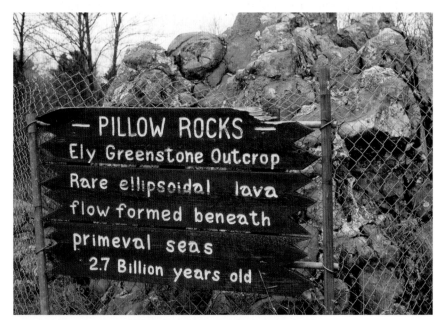

Pillowed greenstone on Main Street in Ely.

Pillowed greenstone in a roadcut just west of Ely.

then left on Camp Street, then turn right on Twelfth Avenue East, and then turn right on Main Street. There it is! It is not an outcrop but a big glacial boulder that has been moved a short distance southward from an outcrop by the last glacier.

About 1.3 miles east of Ely and 0.3 mile east of the junction with County Road 88 are more roadcuts in the Ely Greenstone. The top part of the roadcut on the north side of the road shows excellent pillows in two dimensions. Like most rocks in the Vermilion District, they have been tilted into a vertical position. So there are pillowed greenstone roadcuts on both the north and south sides of the highway both east and west of Ely.

Logging is still important in Ely, but not as important as it was in the late 1800s, when the white pine forests were being logged. Iron mining was important from the late 1880s until 1964, when the last of five mines closed. The head frame of the Chandler Mine is still standing. Ely, a major gateway to the Boundary Waters Canoe Area Wilderness (BWCAW), now survives mainly on tourism. The Dorothy Molter Museum is on Hidden Valley Road at the east edge of town. Dorothy (1907–1986) was the last year-round resident of the BWCAW before it was designated a wilderness in the 1970s. She lived on Isle of Pines on Knife Lake for fifty-six years. Near her museum is the Ely Joint Public Works Facility, where you can see high cuts of glacial outwash material where glacial drumlins are being mined for gravel. The drumlins were sculpted by the Rainy lobe and contain boulders as large as 6 feet in diameter.

MINNESOTA 1
Illgen City—Ely
61 miles
See map on page 129

Minnesota 1 is a hilly, winding road that crosses a fairly unpopulated terrain of rugged topography formed by glacial morainal deposits over buried bedrock. The till in this part of the state is generally less than 50 feet thick except in end moraines. Within 0.5 mile of the intersection with US 61 are two roadcuts in the Palisade Head Rhyolite, the same rock that forms a high North Shore viewpoint 2 miles southwest of the intersection with US 61. This 200-foot-thick, 3-mile-long felsic lava flow is a minor component of the North Shore Volcanic Group, which consists of about 90 percent mafic flows. The flow is very important to geologists, though, because it contains small crystals of zircon that have been dated at 1,096.6 million years, one of the dates that is the basis of the 1,100-million-year age of the North Shore Volcanic Group. Look for banding at the top of the northernmost roadcut, which formed as the hot volcanic ash and magma flowed across the land. Some small black or gray elongate particles in the reddish rock may be flattened pieces of pumice, a vesicular, glassy volcanic rock. If you stop here and inspect the reddish rock closely, you will see small dark spots that are quartz crystals and lighter spots that are orthoclase crystals, all enclosed in a finer-grained matrix.

By driving east out of Finland on County Road 7, you can see another point of both historic and geological interest. One mile east of Finland, turn north on Airbase Road and follow it uphill for 1.7 miles to the remains of a U.S. Air

The Palisade Head Rhyolite along MN 1. Note the banding that formed while the magma flowed.

Force radar station built during the Cold War to detect Soviet bombers that might be flying over the polar route to reach the United States. Along County Road 7 are roadcuts in deep red granitic rock of the Duluth Complex dated at 1,097.8 million years.

If you look closely at the somewhat grassy roadcuts on MN 1 in glacial till, you will see many bright red rocks. These were eroded from the granitic portion of the Duluth Complex. Most of the stones, however, are composed of dark gray basalt. Note a distinct lack of pink to gray granitic rocks, which would have come from the Archean terrain to the northeast. This till is derived mostly from local rock.

Between mileposts 333 and 334, at Murphy City, MN 1 crosses the railroad that extends from the taconite pits of the eastern Mesabi Iron Range to Taconite Harbor on Lake Superior's North Shore. Taconite pellets were shipped from this harbor to steel mills in the lower Great Lakes area, but the taconite company declared bankruptcy and this railroad is no longer in use.

Between Illgen City and Isabella, the till was deposited by the Superior lobe. Near milepost 326, in Isabella, a community based on the logging industry, there is a large gravel pit in Rainy lobe drift in which you'll find cobbles and boulders of red granitic rock, gabbro, and basalt, with a few light pink or gray granites mixed in. Between Isabella and the bridge over the South Fork of the Kawishiwi River at about milepost 298, MN 1 crosses till deposited by the Rainy lobe, which passed over the main part of the gabbroic Duluth Complex. Watch for large dark gray boulders of gabbro, some several feet in diameter, along the roadside. When there is an abundance of large boulders of one type of rock in a till, it usually indicates the boulders come from nearby bedrock. It also indicates that the glacial sediment is fairly thin, so that the ice was eroding bedrock, not just older till.

Roadcuts in gabbro of the Duluth Complex are present between mileposts 305 and 297. However, it is extremely difficult and even dangerous to stop at any of them because of the narrow shoulders on this curving, hilly road.

The South Branch of the Kawishiwi River near milepost 297 is about the dividing line between the 1,100-million-year-old gabbro of the Duluth Complex on the south and the 2,700-million-year-old granitic rock of the Giants Range Batholith on the north. This northern edge of the Duluth Complex has been of economic interest since the mid-1900s because it contains iron-bearing sulfide minerals, which are often associated with ore minerals. Chalcopyrite, the main ore mineral of copper, and pentlandite, a major ore mineral of nickel, are indeed present. International Nickel Company removed many tons of rock from a point a few miles down Spruce Road (National Forest Road 181) for metallurgical testing during the 1960s. However, the ore proved to be low-grade, averaging only 0.5 to 1 percent total copper and nickel.

Several mining companies have explored elsewhere along the northern and western boundary of the Duluth Complex and located a lot more low-grade copper-nickel ore. At the time of this writing (2009), they are also exploring for platinum group elements and gold. Rocks similar to the Duluth Complex occur in Montana, Canada, South Africa, and Russia and are sources of such ore minerals. The Duluth Complex is one of the largest bodies of this type in the world.

At milepost 292, about 5 miles south of Ely on the east side of the road, is a large gravel pit in which nearly all the stones are composed of granite from

Close-up of pieces of gabbro of the Duluth Complex containing sulfide mineralization. The brownish piece has been weathered.

the Giants Range Batholith. The portion of the Rainy lobe that deposited this material had traversed a terrain composed mainly of this granite. It is typical for thin tills to be loaded with local bedrock, and the thin Rainy lobe till in this area dramatically changes in composition within a short distance of passing over a new type of bedrock.

Large roadcuts in the Giants Range Batholith between mileposts 288 and 289 are an ideal place to stop and look at granite. The many joints, or cracks, were caused by either contraction during cooling or by Earth movements. With a close inspection, you might spot a few small purple fluorite crystals. These road-cuts are at the northern edge of the batholith, and low roadcuts and exposures between here and Ely are all comprised of Ely Greenstone—metamorphosed basalt of the Vermilion District, part of the Wawa Subprovince.

MINNESOTA 11
International Falls—
Voyageurs National Park
10 miles
See maps on pages 90 and 117

MN 11 leads to the main entrance to Voyageurs National Park. About 2.5 miles east of the intersection of US 53 and MN 11 in downtown International Falls is a turnoff to Ranier, marked by a big statue of a voyageur. If you drive the half-mile into Ranier, you will find a roadcut on the side of a low rock knob just south of the railroad tracks. On this exposure, you can see vertical beds of

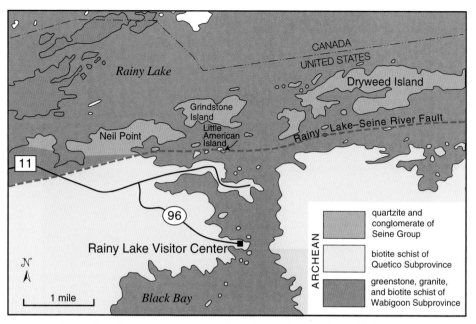

Bedrock geology of the eastern portion of MN 11 and adjacent Rainy Lake.
Note the Rainy Lake–Seine River Fault. —*Modified from Ojakangas and Matsch, 1982*

metamorphosed graded graywacke sandstone and thin mudstones. In graded beds, the coarser, heavier grains settled out of the water first, so they are at the bottom of the beds and fine sediment is at the top. A very close inspection of the coarser beds here indicate their tops are toward the north.

The fairly flat surface that MN 11 crosses along much of its 10-mile length is the eastern extremity of the bed of Glacial Lake Agassiz. Gray clay deposited in the lake may be visible in some ditches. The few rock outcrops, some of which were likely islands in Glacial Lake Agassiz, are mostly dark greenstone that was once a thick sequence of basaltic volcanic rocks. In this area, the rocks are highly sheared because of proximity to the Rainy Lake–Seine River Fault. Most of the bays that the highway passes over are topographic lows eroded in splays of the fault zone.

Side Trip to Neil Point

About 9.5 miles east of the junction of US 53 and MN 11 is Gold Shores Drive (County Road 138), which leads northward to Neil Point. This 2.5-mile round trip passes by some unique rocks and a fault. The first rocks are greenstones. A short 0.4 mile to the north of MN 11 is a very distinct topographic low, filled with a swamp about 500 feet wide. This depression marks the Rainy Lake–Seine River Fault. Traces of gold have been found in drill cores from this fault zone farther to the west.

North of the fault zone, a long roadcut in conglomerate is on the left (north) side of the road. This conglomerate is part of the Seine Group of sedimentary rocks that extends to the northeast into Ontario along the Seine

Conglomerate of the Seine Group of Archean age on Neil Point.

River. The conglomerate has rounded pebbles, cobbles, and boulders of mostly volcanic and granitic rocks. These were deposited by fast-flowing streams on alluvial fans near a relatively high area uplifted on the north side of the Rainy Lake–Seine River Fault. The stream had to be a fast-moving stream in order to transport and round such large rocks. The conglomerate has been metamorphosed, and the beds are now vertical.

At a fork in the road, take the main road to the left (north)—don't go down the one-way road. Just beyond the junction you can see gray arkose sandstone, also of the Seine Group. The bedding is hard to discern in these fresh roadcuts, but detailed studies of cross-bedding in the region indicate the currents were generally moving from north to south. Look for nearly vertical zones of sheared and cracked rock, especially on the first roadcuts after the just-mentioned fork in the road. The sheared zones are about parallel to the Rainy Lake–Seine River Fault.

The conglomerate and the arkose sandstone make up what is likely the youngest Precambrian rock unit in the region. Besides the abundant volcanic and granitic pebbles, the conglomerate also contains minor amounts of pebbles of biotite schist. The conglomerate is therefore younger than the volcanic and granitic rocks and the biotite schist in this area, and the schist had to have already been metamorphosed before the conglomerate was deposited. All of these Archean rocks are about 2,700 million years old. The granites in the region range in age between 2,750 and 2,686 million years, and the biotite schist is older than 2,752 million years. The depositional age of the conglomerate cannot be ascertained, but it apparently was metamorphosed about 2,685 million years ago.

Biotite Schists along County Road 96

About 10 miles east of the junction of US 53 and MN 11 is prominently marked County Road 96, which leads to Voyageurs National Park. There are numerous roadcuts of biotite schist—metamorphosed sedimentary rock—on this 2-mile stretch of road. Some of the black rock contains prominent white quartz veins deposited in cracks by hot water, probably during the Algoman mountain building event. Larger quartz veins are common in fault zones and may contain gold.

The biotite schists, part of the Quetico Subprovince, were interbedded graywacke sandstones and mudstones before they were metamorphosed. The mudstones formed from the slow settling of fine-grained particles in water, probably in an ocean. The graywacke sandstones are poorly sorted sands probably deposited by swirling turbidity currents that moved from the sides of large volcanoes into deep water offshore. As the turbidity currents slowed and lost velocity, the coarser grains settled first, forming graded beds with the larger grains on the bottom and the finer grains on the top. Because metamorphism causes minerals to recrystallize, the original grading is commonly obscured, although the beds are clearly visible. Deformation associated with the Algoman mountain building event moved these beds from a horizontal position into a more vertical orientation. Geologists think the Quetico Subprovince was an accretionary wedge of sediment scraped off a subducting plate.

The Rainy Lake–Seine River Fault separates the Quetico Subprovince of metasedimentary rocks on the south from the Wabigoon Subprovince of volcanic and granitic rocks to the north. The fault appears to be an important collisional boundary of these two terranes. It may have been a low-angle thrust fault that dipped northward but was later steepened to its present vertical position by further northward compression. This collision about 2,700 million years ago

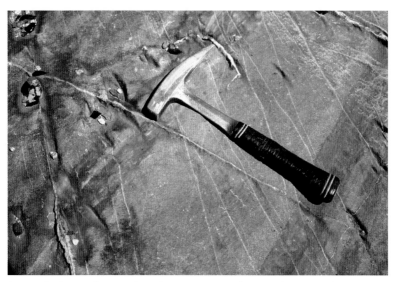

This steeply dipping biotite schist along County Road 96 was formerly sedimentary rock.

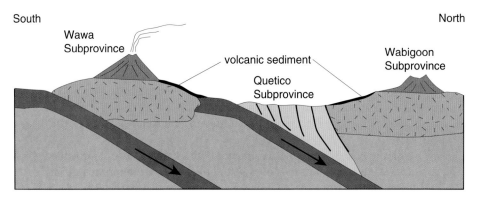

South   North

Wawa
Subprovince   volcanic sediment   Wabigoon
                                                                        Subprovince
                                        Quetico
                                        Subprovince

An accretionary wedge of rock skimmed off a subducting plate is now the biotite schist of the Quetico Subprovince.

was not at a right angle to the continental landmass of the Canadian Shield but rather at an acute angle, resulting in some horizontal motion along the major fault zone. The north side is estimated to have moved eastward several miles relative to the south side. In addition, the south side may have been uplifted a mile or so relative to the north side, as evidenced by the higher degree of metamorphism on the south side.

Voyageurs National Park

Voyageurs National Park encompasses more than 50 miles of the major fur trade route of the French-Canadian canoemen (voyageurs), who in the 1700s transported furs between northwestern Canada and Montreal. The voyageurs traveled in 26-foot-long birch bark canoes, each manned by several men who not only paddled but also carried the canoes and 90-pound packs of furs over portages.

The Rainy Lake–Seine River Fault cuts through the northwest corner of the national park. In 1893 gold was discovered in the fault zone on Little American Island, the only authentic gold mine ever discovered in Minnesota. George Davis, grubstaked by Charles Moore to prospect Rainy Lake, found the gold in a 6-foot-wide quartz vein that assayed at $98 a ton. Moore quickly sold the island for $10,000 to a group of Duluth businessmen. About $5,600 worth of gold was produced in 1894–1895 from a 200-foot-deep shaft.

Rainy Lake City, the boomtown that sprang up during the gold rush, was located on the east side of Black Bay Narrows about 1 mile southeast of Little American Island. Both the mine and the now-vanished city are in the national park. Numerous other mine adits and shafts in the park, part of the "Rainy Lake Gold Fields," failed to produce any gold. International Falls has been called the "city whose streets are paved with gold," because some tailings from the mine on Little American Island were used in construction of the town's main street.

North of the Rainy Lake–Seine River Fault and west of the Seine Group, 1 to 3 miles wide in this area, is a thin, 1-mile-wide sliver of 2,700-million-year-old volcanic and sedimentary rocks that make up a greenstone belt. These underlie a small northwestern portion of the park. The rocks were originally deposited as horizontal layers but are now in a vertical position. This volcanic-sedimentary belt is 10 miles wide on the Canadian portion of Rainy Lake.

South of the fault are vertical biotite schists of the Quetico Subprovince that once constituted a sequence of graded sandstone beds and mud beds totaling thousands of feet in thickness. The shorelines and islands of Rainy Lake and northwestern Kabetogama Lake are mostly comprised of these biotite schists with minor granite dikes. The metamorphism and tilting from a horizontal to a vertical position occurred about the same time as the intrusion of granitic magma that now makes up part of the Vermilion Granitic Complex.

The southern part of the park, including southern Kabetogama and Namakan Lakes, is mostly migmatite composed of contorted alternating bands of schist and granite, all part of the Vermilion Granitic Complex within the Quetico Subprovince. Sand Point Lake in the southeastern part of the park is mostly located on the Lac La Croix granite, a granitic part of the Vermilion Granitic Complex.

The interior of Voyageurs National Park is rugged and difficult to traverse. The elevations are not great, but there are countless areas of high and low ground. The low ground is often occupied by ponds formed by beaver dams. The rock of the high areas is jointed and faulted. There are thirty lakes within the park. A string of four small lakes in the interior is probably situated along a major fault. Running water and glaciers eroded away the broken rock along the fault, leaving behind a linear trough. The bedrock map for the northern part of US 53, on page 90, shows Voyageurs National Park.

Much of the surface area of this park is water, so to really see it necessitates using some type of watercraft. If you have time to take a boat tour or canoe trip on the big lakes—Rainy, Kabetogama, Namakan, or Sand Point—you will see countless rocky islands and shorelines. However, most rock exposures are covered with dark lichen that obscures the finer details, except where waves have washed the rocks clean.

MINNESOTA 23
Duluth—St. Cloud
141 miles
See map on page 61

Minnesota 23 is built upon a series of glacial deposits of the Superior lobe, ranging in age from about 21,000 years old to 10,000 years old. All of the deposits are red because the ice lobe eroded red sedimentary rocks deposited in the Midcontinent Rift in Late Proterozoic time, including the Fond du Lac Formation. The ice lobe also eroded red clays of early glacial lakes in the Lake Superior Basin.

Minnesota 23 between Duluth and its intersection with I-35 west of Askov is Veterans Evergreen Memorial Scenic Drive, a Minnesota scenic byway. The northern end of MN 23 is at the Grand Avenue exit of I-35 in western Duluth. As you drive south, watch for the scenic overlook on the curve between Gary–New Duluth and Fond du Lac. The overlook offers a good view of the wide

St. Louis River. The westward tilting of the Lake Superior Basin since the glaciers melted back about 10,000 years ago has drowned the St. Louis River Valley here.

Fond du Lac

Fond du Lac, which in French means "head of the lake," was the site of an Ojibwe village when Daniel Greysolon, Sieur du Lhut, the first European in what is now Duluth, visited here in 1679. In about 1817, John Jacob Astor's American Fur Company built a trading post here.

You can see the Fond du Lac Formation along Mission Creek in Fond du Lac Park. Drive northward to the end of 131st Avenue West in the village of Fond du Lac to a gate from where you can walk or drive a short distance to a damlike structure across the creek. On the opposite side of the creek is a high cut in tan to red, cross-bedded sandstone and red shale of the Fond du Lac Formation. More sandstone is exposed a few hundred feet upstream. This sandstone was probably deposited in an ancient river in Late Proterozoic time. The cross-beds indicate that the currents were generally flowing from west to east, into the valley formed by the Midcontinent Rift System about 1,100 million years ago.

You can see an old quarry in red sandstone of the Fond du Lac Formation on the bank of the St. Louis River near Chambers Grove Park by the MN 23 bridge, but to see it requires a walk. Beginning at the far end of the boardwalk along the river is a fisherman's path. Follow it for about 750 feet upstream along the wooded bank and you will come to an old quarry in the red sandstone. This type of rock, either from this area or from a similar formation near Bayfield, Wisconsin, was used to build many buildings in downtown Duluth, including old Central High School, First Presbyterian Church, and the Board of Trade Building. Pillsbury Hall on the Twin Cities campus of the University of Minnesota, which houses the Department of Geology and Geophysics, was also constructed out of this stone. The Minnesota Brownstone Company provided the "brownstone" from a large quarry just across the river from Fond du Lac. Buff-colored Hinckley Sandstone was used for windowsills and other trim on Pillsbury Hall.

Red Clay of Glacial Lake Duluth

Glacial Lake Duluth formed in the Lake Superior Basin about 11,000 years ago when glacial ice still blocked the eastern outlet of the basin. Shorelines of that lake were about 450 feet higher than present-day Lake Superior, which has an elevation of 602 feet above sea level. Fine clay dumped into Glacial Lake Duluth by streams draining receding glaciers accumulated on the lakebed. The sediments are more than 300 feet thick, but some of them were deposited in earlier glacial lakes in the basin. A small amount of fine-grained iron oxide (hematite) mixed in with the clay gives it a red color. This clay is now situated at an elevation higher than Lake Superior, so modern streams flowing into the lake are dissecting it.

Just to the north of the bridge over the St. Louis River at Fond du Lac is a large, bare artificial cut in the red clay north of the highway. South of the river and south of the highway is a ski area developed on hills in the deeply dissected red clay. At the scenic overlook between mileposts 333 and 334, you can look northward across a broad low area from which the clay was removed by the St. Louis River.

Between Fond du Lac and County Road 8, which leads to Holyoke, the topography is relatively rugged because the St. Louis and Nemadji Rivers and their tributaries have deeply dissected the easily eroded red clay and carried it into Lake Superior. In an example of geological recycling, clay minerals originally deposited on the lakebed of Glacial Lake Duluth about 11,000 years ago are now being deposited in its successor, Lake Superior. Many sideroads and driveways along this stretch of highway are reddish. The large, grassed-over roadcuts between mileposts 324 and 325 at the Nemadji River are composed of the red clay. The clay is so unstable and easily eroded that the roadcuts must have a low angle and be grassed over to prevent slumping and erosion.

Just 2.4 miles down County Road 8 (east of MN 23) is a small park on a branch of the Nemadji River where the water cascades over layers of Hinckley Sandstone. Notice the red clay in the roadcut at the park entrance.

At about the junction with County Road 8, there is a distinct topographic change between the lower, flatter Glacial Lake Duluth lakebed to the north and hills to the south. The high ground is the Nickerson moraine, which extends southward to Duquette. At about milepost 313, near a fire tower and about halfway between Nickerson and Duquette, the highway crosses the drainage divide between waters flowing into Lake Superior and waters flowing southward into the St. Croix River and hence to the Mississippi.

Between Duquette and I-35 to the south, including the villages of Kerrick, Bruno, and Askov, MN 23 crosses drift of the Cloquet advance. In a gravel pit near milepost 306, you can see that the till is red, typical of material derived from the Lake Superior Basin.

Hinckley Sandstone

The glacial deposits at Askov are thin, and the Hinckley Sandstone that makes up the bedrock is exposed. The sandstone contains numerous sinkholes through which contaminants such as sewage have polluted local water wells. Sinkholes are common in limestone, which is soluble in acidic groundwater, but rare in sandstone. The sinkholes in the sandstone are apparently related to underlying joints that were widened by dissolution or erosion.

About 2 miles west of Askov and about 1 mile east of I-35, MN 23 crosses the valley of the Kettle River, cut deeply into the buff-colored Hinckley Sandstone. Just east of the MN 23 bridge, there are excellent roadcuts in this formation but the shoulder is narrow and dangerous. A more relaxing place to stop and look at the sandstone is Banning State Park, off MN 23 just east of I-35. This park has numerous trails along the sandstone gorge of the Kettle River, as well as old quarry workings. For detailed information about the park, the Hinckley Sandstone, and the towns of Sandstone and Hinckley, see the road guide for **I-35: Duluth—Twin Cities**.

MN 23 coincides with I-35 for the interval between exits 195 and 180. The terrain north of Sandstone is deposits of the Superior lobe—the Cloquet ground moraine—and between Sandstone and Hinckley it is Mille Lacs ground moraine.

For nearly the entire distance between Hinckley and St. Cloud, MN 23 passes over gently rolling St. Croix ground moraine. North-trending glacial river valleys cut across the ground moraine at Mora, Ogilvie, Milaca, Foreston, and Ronneby. Look for the big boulders in the river valleys at Foreston and Ronneby. Meltwaters of the slightly younger Mille Lacs advance of the Superior lobe, located about 20 miles to the north, scoured these valleys. Between Ogilvie and Milaca, MN 23 crosses several low-relief glacial drumlins, or flutes, that trend about perpendicular to the highway. There is a gravel pit in a drumlin between mileposts 243 and 244, and another at milepost 253.

MINNESOTA 38
Grand Rapids—Effie
47 miles
See map on page 97

Minnesota 38 is a national scenic byway known as the Edge of the Wilderness. About half of MN 38 is within the Chippewa National Forest. Glacial outwash and end moraine of the Rainy lobe cover the area. Look for cobbles and boulders from the moraine in roadcuts, rearranged along flowerbeds of homes, in rock walls, and in the rock and log structures marking natural history and cultural discovery sites along the byway. At Site 00 in Grand Rapids, only a short block from the intersection of MN 38 with US 2, the rocks include granites, banded gneisses, metamorphosed volcanic rocks, and some cherty iron-formation.

Lind and Greenway Iron Mines
Only 3.4 miles north of Grand Rapids is Site 3.4, where you can read some history on local iron mining. One mile east of the highway on County Road 61, you can get a glimpse of the Lind and Greenway Iron Mines, which operated from 1940 to 1976. They produced 7.7 million tons of high-grade ore. The adjacent West Hill Mine operated from 1953 to 1973 and produced 9 million tons. You can't miss the high dumps of bright red waste rock. The old pits are out of sight and off-limits behind steel fences, but you can spot some old mine buildings. This mine complex is near the western end of the 110-mile-long Mesabi Iron Range, which has had several hundred mines and from which more than 3 billion tons of iron ore have been shipped. Only one small mine was situated farther to the west, by about 6 miles. The dumps are slowly being removed by the Minnesota Department of Natural Resources and sold as rock aggregate.

The Prairie River flows southward between the Lind and Greenway Mines on its way to the Mississippi River just east of Grand Rapids. Along the river near County Road 61 and the dam that impounds the Prairie River just upstream from the bridge are exposures of the Early Proterozoic Pokegama Quartzite, a pink to white quartzite deposited in a sea about 1,900 million years ago. It underlies the Biwabik Iron Formation, which was deposited in the same sea. Just west of the County Road 61 bridge over the Prairie River and opposite the building on the south side of the road is a gravel road leading to the dam. Walk around the locked gate and take one of several paths down to the riverbed where the quartzite is exposed just below the dam. Look for glacial striations trending southwest, crescentic gouges indicating the ice moved toward the

Iron ore dump at Greenway Iron Mine.

southwest, and small-scale cross-bedding. In the river valley just south of the County Road 61 bridge are scattered outcrops of south-dipping iron-formation that overlies the Pokegama.

Just east of the bridge is a parking place on the south side of County Road 61 for access to the nonmotorized, hard-surfaced Mesabi Trail. If you walk south on it for a few hundred feet, you can see the open pit, now a lake, of the Lind Mine. The far side of the pit is a high cut in glacial deposits. You can find pieces of waste rock iron-formation along the sides of the trail.

About a half-mile west of the bridge is a parking lot on the north side of the road at another access point to the Mesabi Trail. The lot is surrounded by large boulders of granite, greenstone, and iron-formation. Look for the only boulder of Pokegama Quartzite; the marks on its top surface may be ripples from a current. About 0.2 mile farther west as you are driving back to MN 38, there are some low, hard-to-spot roadcuts of quartzite in the south ditch. And slightly farther west, in the southeast corner of the junction of County Road 61 and MN 38, are outcrops of Archean Giants Range Batholith. Although you can't put your hand on these relationships, the Pokegama Quartzite was deposited on an eroded surface of the Archean granite, and the iron-formation was deposited on top of the quartzite.

Over the Laurentian Divide

Between Grand Rapids and milepost 12, the terrain is generally quite flat, for most of this stretch of MN 38 is on glacial outwash. Between that milepost and Marcell, the terrain is markedly hillier end moraine of a minor sublobe of the Des Moines lobe, and the highway has many sharp curves as it winds between a myriad of hills, lakes, and potholes. Locals once called it "Highway Loop-de-Loop."

At about milepost 21 is a rest area on the Laurentian Divide at an elevation of 1,524 feet. From this continental divide, waters flow northward to Hudson Bay and southward to the Gulf of Mexico. Here you can see neat split-rock walls made of dozens of boulders of different rock types collected from the glacial drift. There are coarse-grained granites in various shades of red, pink, and gray; fine-grained volcanic rocks in black and shades of red; and gneisses with prominent banding. Look for a gray granite boulder cut by a thin cross-cutting pink granite dikelet; a black basalt boulder with a thin white quartz veins; a red granite boulder with large, 1-inch crystals of orthoclase; and a gray to black biotite schist cut by a pink granitic dike.

Bear in mind that sometimes signs are wrong. One sign at this rest stop reads as follows: "Where you stand today was once a mountain range. It eroded when the glacier melted, leaving behind this curving range of hills called the Laurentian Divide." The glacier that was here about 14,000 years ago had nothing to do with the demise of the Algoman Mountains, which formed about 2,700 million years ago.

County Road 48 intersects MN 38 near milepost 22. About 0.1 mile off MN 38 on County Road 48, also known as Suomi Road, is the entrance to a very large gravel pit located in glacial till and outwash. The sediments here may include minor deposits of the Koochiching sublobe of the Des Moines lobe, but Rainy lobe drift appears to dominate.

About halfway between Marcell and Bigfork the terrain changes from the hilly area of end moraine of the Koochiching sublobe, an eastern offshoot of the Des Moines lobe north of the Giants Range, to lower-relief ground moraine of the same lobe.

Rainy lobe drift in a gravel pit along County Road 48, off MN 38 near milepost 22.

Scenic State Park

Scenic State Park, 7 miles east of Bigfork on County Road 7, contains virgin white pines and red (Norway) pines near two lakes. Chase Point, which forms the boundary between Coon and Sandwick Lakes, is a magnificent example of a glacial esker. It is 0.65 mile long, is as wide as 0.1 mile, and has an undulating and curving crest that is several tens of feet above the lake level. A 0.9-mile-

Chase Point in Scenic State Park is an esker, deposited by a river in a tunnel beneath an ice sheet.

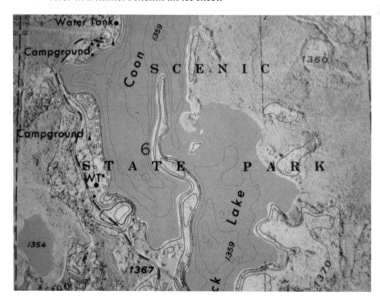

Chase Point, on the U.S. Geological Survey Coon Lake 7.5-minute quadrangle, is an esker. The contour interval is 10 feet.

long trail along the crest of the esker is a most worthwhile geologic walk in this beautiful setting admidst pine trees. The esker was deposited by a meltwater river that flowed beneath the ice sheet.

Big Fork River

The Big Fork River, an important waterway for floating logs in the late 1800s and early 1900s, is a major tributary of the Rainy River, which forms the border with Ontario. MN 38 crosses the Big Fork River at Bigfork, but if you'd like to see a waterfall on the river, continue north on County Road 5 from Effie for about 5 miles and cross the bridge over the river at the now-deserted logging townsite of Craigville. Continue north about 1 mile to a fork in the road, choose the one on the left, and continue for about 1 mile to a gravel entrance to a high overlook on the south (left) side of the road. Little American Falls spills over Archean mica schist and gray granite. The granite is probably related to the Effie pluton, an Archean granitic intrusion of about 100 square miles that is mostly hidden by glacial drift.

MINNESOTA 61
Duluth—Canadian Border
153 miles

MN 61 extends the full length of the Minnesota portion of the North Shore of Lake Superior. Officially known as the North Shore Scenic Drive, a Minnesota scenic byway, the road is known informally as the North Shore Highway. Lake Superior is the largest freshwater lake in the world, having 31,700 square miles of surface area and 1,026 miles of shoreline. It contains 40 percent of the nation's fresh surface water, and 10 percent of the world's freshwater, about 3 quadrillion gallons. However, it is not the largest lake in terms of water volume—that honor belongs to Lake Baikal in Russia, which occupies a deeper rift basin. The Ojibwe called the lake *Kitchi-gumi*, meaning "big lake." The French explorers and voyageurs called it *le lac superieur*, which means "upper lake," because it was the last and highest of the five large lakes that they traversed as they paddled westward from Montreal.

Lake Superior is as deep as 1,333 feet, and its average temperature is about 40 degrees Fahrenheit. Its drainage basin is only half again as large as its surface area, so the replenishment rate is low. Water loss to evaporation and drainage out of its east end is about equal to the annual input, so a few years of drought can lower the lake level. In 2007 it was down by 2 feet. This decline affected the amount of cargo that ships could carry because of the water depth in key places. Any diversion of Lake Superior water to other parts of the country would quickly exceed the replenishment rate.

Lake Superior is centered over the Midcontinent Rift, a structural basin filled with volcanic rocks overlain by sedimentary rocks. The various advances of the Superior lobe glaciers scoured out much of the softer sedimentary rocks deposited on top of the volcanic rock, forming the present depression that is filled with the waters of Lake Superior.

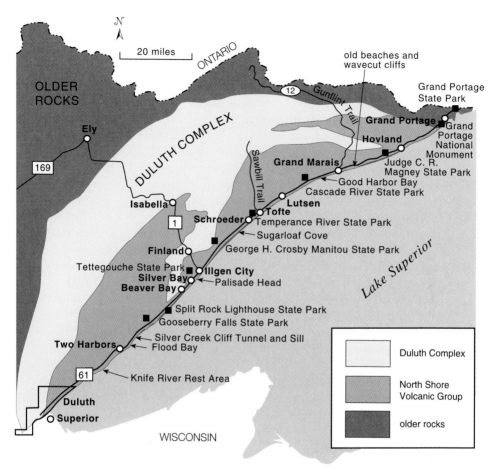

Bedrock geology map of northeastern Minnesota and the North Shore of Lake Superior. —After Green, 1996

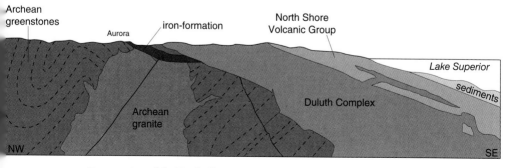

Cross section of the North Shore. Note the southeast-dipping North Shore Volcanic Group. —After Green, 1996

Except for the 5 miles adjacent to the international border, where the rocks include the Early Proterozoic Rove Formation, about 1,850 million years old, all of the rocks you will see on this route are either part of the 1,100-million-year-old North Shore Volcanic Group or related intrusive rocks. An abortive splitting of the central part of the North American continent produced the magmatic activity of the Midcontinent Rift System. Basaltic lava flows dominate, but the more silica-rich rhyolites comprise 10 percent of the flows of the southwestern half of the North Shore and 25 percent of the northeastern portion, with Tofte at about the dividing line. Some gabbro sills were intruded between lava flows. The basaltic magmas were derived from melted mantle rock from great depths. The rhyolites are thought to have been produced by partial melting of Archean basement rocks. The volcanic rocks sunk, or bowed down, forming the Lake Superior syncline as the magmas beneath them were extruded. The few hundred flows exposed along the North Shore of Lake Superior are all tilted at an angle of about 20 degrees toward the center of the lake. If they were stacked one on top of the other in a vertical pile, the pile would be about 6 miles thick!

The glacial drift along MN 61 is relatively homogeneous, consisting mostly of reddish, clay-rich glacial till—the Nickerson moraine—deposited by the Superior lobe 12,000 to 11,500 years ago. However, an even clayier till of the Marquette advance is also present, deposited about 10,000 years ago. Just inland from the Nickerson moraine is the Highland moraine, as wide as 10 miles, which was deposited by the slightly older Mille Lacs advance of the Superior lobe, but you cannot see it from MN 61. Both moraines were deposited along the northern side of the southwestward-moving Superior lobe as the ice moved a short distance toward the west and northwest out of the Lake Superior Basin. This indicates that the ice was thick enough to overflow the basin. Because the bottom of western Lake Superior is in places at or below sea level and much of the terrain just inland from the lake is higher than 1,500 feet, the ice was probably more than 2,000 feet thick.

Some of the glacial sediment was reworked by waves along the beaches of Glacial Lake Duluth, the 11,000 to 10,000-year-old predecessor to Lake Superior. You will be able to spot these beaches where the highway has been constructed on and along them. The highest beach is as much as 450 feet above the current elevation of Lake Superior, which is about 602 feet above sea level. Also present along the lakeshore, as any gardener along the North Shore knows, is sticky red lake clay and clayey till.

Anyone who plans to spend time on the North Shore of Lake Superior, with its eight Minnesota State Parks, needs *Geology on Display: Geology and Scenery of Minnesota's North Shore State Parks* by John C. Green, a professor at University of Minnesota Duluth who has spent more than forty years studying the rocks of the North Shore. The book provides much more geological detail than can be included in this roadside survey.

An alternative way to observe the geology and other aspects of the North Shore is to hike the Superior Hiking Trail. Soon you will be able to hike from Jay Cooke State Park west of Duluth all the way to the Canadian border, a distance of about 200 miles!

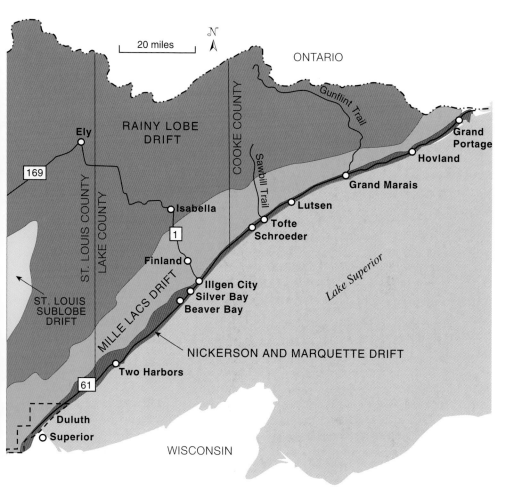

Glacial geology of northeastern Minnesota and the North Shore of Lake Superior.
—*Modified from Hobbs and Goebel, 1982*

Old North Shore Highway

Less than 1 mile east of Lester River is the junction of the MN 61 expressway between Duluth and Two Harbors and the Old North Shore Highway (County Road 61), which extends for 20 miles between Duluth and Two Harbors. This scenic drive follows the lakeshore and is the route over which Grandma's Marathon, one of the nation's ten largest, is run each June. This route provides numerous excellent views of the lake, and there are several parking and picnic areas from which you can walk down to the lakeshore beaches or lava flows. A historical marker 2 miles west of Knife River describes the short-lived town of Buchanan, which was platted and named after President Buchanan in 1856. The marker is made of blocks of gabbro and diabase, rock that is similar to the Stony Point Sill, which you can observe by walking down to the lakeshore just behind the monument.

Duluth to Two Harbors on the MN 61 Expressway

The expressway, the faster route between Duluth and Two Harbors, passes several roadcuts in basaltic lava flows near Duluth, but only a few others between Duluth and Two Harbors. The expressway crosses several North Shore streams. All North Shore streams are quite short; most have their sources within 10 miles of Lake Superior.

A historical marker at the French River describes the first townsite surveyed on the United States portion of the North Shore. Clifton was platted in 1855 after copper exploration brought in many prospectors. The town was never developed, even though several exploratory shafts were dug in the search for native copper, which had been found on Isle Royale and on the Keweenaw Peninsula of Michigan.

The Knife River Rest Area and historical marker between mileposts 18 and 19 is worth stopping at. Walk the stairs down to the river, where you can see basalt flows. They are reddish because weathering oxidizes iron in the basalt, but are black on recently broken surfaces. Notice the rounded rocks exposed in the streambed during low water. The occasional roaring floods are capable of transporting and rounding these large rocks.

Two Harbors, the Agate City

Two Harbors has two natural bays, Agate Bay and Burlington Bay, separated by a point comprised of a thick basalt lava flow upon which you can easily walk. In 1884, the first iron ore mined in Minnesota was transported by rail from Soudan, in the Vermilion District of northeastern Minnesota, to Two Harbors. The *Three Spot*, the small, wood-burning locomotive that hauled that first ore in ten small cars, stands by the bay in downtown Two Harbors. Two Harbors is still a major port from which taconite pellets manufactured on the Mesabi Iron Range 60 miles to the north are shipped to the lower Great Lakes ports. Huge

Taconite is loaded onto ships that would dwarf this small boat at the ore docks at Two Harbors.

docks in the main harbor—Agate Bay—accommodate the large ore boats, which are as long as three football fields.

You can get to an excellent exposure of the contact between two lava flows at the municipal Two Harbors Tourist Park at Burlington Bay on the east edge of town. Park near the picnic shelter in the park and walk the paved path eastward for a few hundred feet to a low point on the path where it is near the beach. There, you'll see the massive base of one flow on top of the vesicular, porous, and more easily eroded top of another. The vesicles formed by gas bubbles in the cooling lava. When filled with minerals, the vesicles are called amygdules.

Agates in a basalt flow in Burlington Bay. To the left of the leaf is an impression left by an agate freed by weathering of the basalt.

Close-up of a large agate that weathered out of a lava flow.

With a little luck, you may find agates in the beach gravels on the swimming beach nearer MN 61, and on other beaches. Agates are composed of fine-grained silica precipitated from hot water in the vesicles. When the basalt flows are weathered, these resistant agates are freed from the basalt. You can see amygdules in the top part of a lava flow at the west end of the swimming beach, but these are made of soft orange zeolite minerals rather than the resistant agates made of silica. Look very closely at this amygdule-rich rock and you may find some bluish green amygdules that contain copper minerals, and others composed of a darker green chlorite. You can also see small agate amygdules still within a basalt flow on the shore below the water treatment plant at the western end of Burlington Bay, but this requires a bit of walking. Note that most agates are orangish red because of a small amount of iron oxide.

Flood Bay

At Flood Bay, between mileposts 27 and 28 just northeast of Two Harbors, is a Minnesota wayside rest where you can walk on a typical gravel beach and search for agates. Most of the pebbles are volcanic rocks; notice the lava flows on the far side of the bay on a rocky point. The big pieces of rock that have been placed between the parking lot and the lake are mostly coarse-grained gabbroic rocks that do not occur naturally at this locality.

Stewart River

A pullout at the Stewart River between mileposts 28 and 29 is a convenient place to stop and examine the lava flows. A very precarious path leads down to a spot at the mouth of the river, where you can see the massive base of one flow on the softer eroded top of the underlying flow. The tops of the flows are more easily eroded because gas rises to the top of liquid lava, and some of it

These vesicles in the upper portion of a lava flow are filled with minerals, which may be agate, calcite, chlorite, or various zeolite minerals.

gets trapped in the cooling lava as gas bubbles. These are commonly filled with minerals precipitated out of hot water moving through the rock after it was buried. Many of these minerals are soft and easily eroded, unlike resistant agates composed of silica, which weather out of the flows in one piece.

Silver Creek Cliff Tunnel and Sill

Between mileposts 30 and 31 is the 1,400-foot-long Silver Creek Cliff Tunnel through an imposing topographic high formed by black diabase. For the most part, the magma intruded parallel to the layered flows so the diabase is a sill, here more than 200 feet thick. In places, however, there is a slight angle between the sill and the flows, showing a slight crosscutting relationship, which is more typical of a dike.

When the highway along the shore was being built, this cliff was the final obstacle to overcome. The original highway at this point, completed in 1925, was located on the side of the cliff dangerously high above the lake. Frequent collapses finally necessitated the construction of the tunnel, which was completed in 1994.

From the parking area at milepost 31 at the east end of the tunnel, walk the paved, fenced path (a segment of the Gitchi-Gami State Trail for hiking and biking) up the slope on the lake side of the highway. From this walkway you can look across the highway at two highly altered basalt flows beneath the sill. The pink and white coloration is the result of metamorphism by the sill, as well as

A dark gray diabase sill overlies the pinkish basalt flows visible at the east end of the Silver Creek Cliff Tunnel.

the presence of calcite and other minerals that precipitated out of hot solutions. Note that the flows appear to have been deformed by the forceful injection of the magma that formed the sill.

The magma of the sill cooled slowly because of the insulating effect of the overlying lava flows. The solidifying magma contracted and fractured as it cooled because rock occupies less volume than magma. The fractures, called joints, are perpendicular to the top and bottom of the sheetlike body of magma and intersect, forming very large columns of rock. Note that the columnar joints are not vertical, as the entire sequence of rocks has been tilted at an angle of about 20 degrees toward the center of Lake Superior, as nearly all of the lava flows along the North Shore have been. If you could get a top view of the columns, you would see that a majority have five sides. Also present are prominent horizontal joints, which may also be the result of the cooling of the magma or due to vertical expansion after erosion of the overlying lava flows relieved some of the pressure. You can see the columnar joints and the large columns more easily along the Gitchi-Gami State Trail than in the fresh roadcuts by the tunnel because weathering along the joints over many decades has made them more pronounced.

Where the Gitchi-Gami State Trail is next to the sill, you can see its relatively coarse-grained texture. The magma cooled slowly enough for the crystals to have time to grow to a visible size, typical of the mafic rock called diabase.

Vertical fractures in the Silver Creek Cliff Sill form columns
along the Gitchi-Gami State Trail, a paved path.

Where the crystals have grown larger, the rock is gabbro. The magmas involved have the same composition as the lava that formed the basalts of the North Shore. The sill has smaller crystals near its contact with the underlying flow because magma cooled faster against the already cooled lava flow.

At the high point on this walkway is the Silver Creek Cliff Overlook, with signs describing Lake Superior and the local geology. From this point, if the weather is good, you can see for long distances both up and down the lakeshore.

Lafayette Bluff

At milepost 34 is a highway tunnel through Lafayette Bluff, a topographic high formed by the Lafayette Bluff Sill. The steamer *Lafayette* was wrecked near this bluff on the treacherous lakeshore in 1905. For a few hundred feet east of this tunnel, the upper portions of the dark diabase exposed in the roadcuts have weathered to a distinctive yellowish brown, crumbly material. Air and water have oxidized the iron-bearing minerals in the diabase to limonite, a yellow iron oxide mineral.

Gooseberry Falls State Park

Between mileposts 39 and 40 is a turnoff into Gooseberry Falls State Park. The Gooseberry River cascades over lava flows, forming several waterfalls. Upper Falls is just north of the highway. Middle Falls, the most spectacular and the easiest to observe, is just below the highway. Lower Falls is closer to Lake Superior. All can be reached on paved, handicap-accessible trails.

Middle Falls at Gooseberry Falls State Park cascades over three lava flows of the North Shore Volcanic Group.

From the visitor center, take the short path to Middle Falls. Just below the falls, you are standing on the undulating top of a basalt flow that is about 10 feet thick. The billowy top is very fine-grained because it cooled rapidly in contact with air when the lava extruded onto the land surface. Beneath this chilled top are numerous amygdules, mineral-filled gas cavities. Gases rose in the hot lava flow but were trapped beneath the already cooled flow top, forming gas cavities. Later, after the lava flow was covered by younger flows, minerals precipitated out of hot water, filling the gas cavities.

You can distinguish three different flows at Middle Falls: the one you are standing on, a thinner one above that, and the one at the top of the waterfalls, with prominent cooling joints that form in five- or six-sided columns. You can get a top view of the columns and actually walk on them above the falls at low-water stage.

Near the highway in the park, you can see superb workmanship in the stone walls built by the Civilian Conservation Corps from black gabbro. Thick lava flows are exposed on MN 61 on both sides of the bridge over the Gooseberry River.

Iona's Beach

Iona's Beach Scientific and Natural Area is 3 miles north of Gooseberry Falls State Park at milepost 42 and the Twin Points Boat Launch. The 900-foot-long beach is composed of flat, pink pebbles called shingles. At its northern end is a shore cliff of pink rhyolite, the source of the pebbles, and at its southern end is

Iona's Beach is composed of pink rhyolite pebbles from a cliff at its northern end.

a protruding point composed of dark gray basalt. This point acts as a natural barrier to the southwestward-moving longshore drift along Lake Superior, so the pink pebbles are trapped here. Just southwest of this barrier is a sandy beach without any pink rhyolite pebbles.

Split Rock River and Split Rock Lighthouse State Park

Between mileposts 43 and 44 is the Split Rock River. Look for the well-developed gravel bar at the mouth of the bay. High-energy waves and currents in the lake form such bars from sediment carried in by rivers.

A wayside rest near milepost 45 is a good spot from which to get a view of Split Rock Lighthouse, completed in 1910, with all the materials brought in by ship and hoisted up the 168-foot-high cliff. The necessity for a lighthouse at the top of this cliff had become evident in a huge storm in 1905 that damaged thirty ships, including four near this spot. Newer technology resulted in its closure in 1969, but not until 3 billion tons of iron ore from Minnesota's mines had passed by and the United States had become an industrial giant.

Most of the cliff is made up of a single large block of anorthosite, a rock composed of more than 90 percent plagioclase. Because anorthosite lacks appreciable iron-bearing minerals such as pyroxene or olivine, it is quite resistant to chemical weathering. The inclusion was carried upward by the buoyant force of the rising magma during the rifting event that formed the Midcontinent Rift

Split Rock Lighthouse as viewed from the wayside rest on MN 61 near milepost 45. There are better views within Split Rock Lighthouse State Park.

System 1,100 million years ago. The magma crystallized into dark gray diabase, a medium-grained version of gabbro, forming the thick sill that intruded between basalt lava flows at Split Rock. If you want to see more inclusions in the diabase, walk down to the lakeshore along the long wooden stairway just to the west of the lighthouse. One study suggested that they are 800 million years older than the sills and lava flows. Such inclusions are common between Split Rock and Tofte, about 35 miles to the northeast.

The sill at Split Rock, part of the Beaver Bay Complex of mafic intrusive rocks, has large near-vertical columns that formed as the solidifying magma contracted and fractured as it cooled. The sill and its columnar joints are visible in all the roadcuts between mileposts 45 and 50. Note also that the top portions of most roadcuts in the sill are yellowish because chemical weathering has oxidized some of the iron-bearing minerals. The newer high roadcut between mileposts 46 and 47 does not show the columns well, both because of the vertical drill holes and because weathering has not yet had time to accentuate the columns.

Also within the park boundaries are the remains of a mining operation of the Minnesota Mining and Manufacturing Company, now known as 3M, in the early 1900s. The mined mineral was thought to be corundum, a very hard mineral used in abrasives. On the Mohs scale of hardness, corundum has a hardness of 9. However, the rock proved to be anorthosite, composed of anorthite plagioclase with a hardness of only 6. Could we say that this well-known international company had a rocky start?

Beaver Bay

Beaver Bay is the oldest European settlement on the North Shore, dating back to 1856. Look for the waterfalls in Beaver River just upstream from the highway bridge. A large tree-covered peninsula forming the south shore of Beaver Bay is diabase of the Beaver Bay Complex. The massive, shallow diabase intrusions are more resistant to weathering and erosion than are the lava flows into which they intruded. These diabase rocks have a radiometric age date of about 1,096 million years, about 3 million years younger than the Duluth Complex. We know the lava flows are older than the diabase because of crosscutting by the diabase.

Silver Bay

Between mileposts 53 and 54 is a huge complex of large buildings. Adjacent to a very large building on the lower side of MN 61, opposite a large roadcut on the upper side of the highway, is a wide pull-off where you can park and observe the two rock types of the Beaver Bay Complex in the roadcut, one nearly black and the other light greenish gray. The black rock is diabase, a mafic rock intermediate in grain size between basalt and gabbro. The light rock is anorthosite, which contains more than 90 percent plagioclase feldspar of the calcium-rich variety called anorthite. The anorthosite is a huge inclusion, a piece of previously crystallized rock carried upward by the rising mafic magma. Its source may be the lower crust at a depth of 15 to 25 miles. Look for the thin, 1- to 2-inch-wide, red granitic dikes that cut across both the diabase and the anorthosite.

In this Silver Bay roadcut, the huge, light gray anorthosite inclusion was carried by magma that solidified into the black diabase at left.

In Silver Bay, just off the highway, there are signs directing you to a high viewpoint from which you can get a good look at the great dimensions of the Silver Bay taconite plant, Minnesota's first such large facility. It was built in the mid-1950s by Reserve Mining Company to process magnetic iron-formation from a mine near Babbitt, at the eastern end of the Mesabi Iron Range. The ore, which comes to the plant via a 40-mile-long railroad, is ground to a very fine size so strong magnets can remove the magnetite grains. The fine particles are then bound with bentonite into marble-sized taconite pellets and heated at high temperatures to convert the magnetite to hematite. The pellets are shipped by huge ore boats to the steel mills in the lower Great Lakes region.

The first version of the taconite process required great amounts of water, and therefore the facility was built on the shore of Lake Superior. (The subsequent seven plants built in Minnesota were all on the iron range, adjacent to or close to the mines.) The nonmagnetic fractions of the ground rock—the tailings that amounted to about two-thirds of the original rock—were initially disposed of in Lake Superior. The coarse-grained fraction of the tailings flowed down the slope into the deep offshore trough on the lake bottom. However, the finest-grained fraction, probably less than 1 percent of the total, did not settle to the bottom but was held in suspension in the water and was distributed around western Lake Superior by waves and currents. These fine grains included needlelike asbestiform crystals—the amphibole mineral cummingtonite and not asbestos—that were judged to be carcinogenic. Years of legal maneuvering during the 1970s finally ended with the company disposing of the tailings at a site a few miles inland from Lake Superior.

Palisade Head

At about milepost 57, a narrow, winding paved road leads to the top of Palisade Head and its spectacular viewpoint, but it is impassible for buses and trailers. Palisade Head is an erosional remnant of a lava flow, the Palisade Head Rhyolite, that is as thick as 310 feet. The flow is 3 miles long and 2 miles wide. Palisade Head is one of the highest points on the North Shore, rising about 350 feet above the lake. It is higher than adjacent basalt flows because, compared to basalt, rhyolite contains little iron and more silica, and therefore does not weather as easily via oxidation. The rhyolite has a radiometric age date of 1,096.6 million years.

From the top of Palisade Head, look to the northeast up the shore to see Shovel Point, also known as the Little Palisades. This topographic feature is formed of the same eroded rhyolite flow. If the weather is clear, you will see the jagged profile of the Sawtooth Mountains in the far distance on the northeastern skyline. Most of these peaks are formed of resistant lava flows and diabase sills dipping toward the center of Lake Superior at angles of 10 to 20 degrees.

When you are at the top of Palisade Head, you are standing on the tops of big columns bounded by joints that formed as the rhyolite cooled. Shovel Point to the northeast also contains large columns, visible even from this distance. The joints that form the polygonal columns are weaknesses in the rock and provide access for water that freezes and expands, thus widening the joints. During storms, waves pound the base of the cliff, eroding the rock. Glaciers of the last 1.8 million years certainly removed many columns. And erosion by

Palisade Head in the foreground and Shovel Point in the distance are part of the same rhyolite flow. Note the vertical columns that formed when the rhyolite cooled.

running water during the 1,100 million years since volcanism ceased has removed much of the rhyolite.

If you look very closely at the rhyolite upon which you are standing, you can see small pink to white rectangular crystals of orthoclase feldspar and the more rounded dark gray crystals of glassy quartz, both in a finely crystalline matrix. These crystals formed in the magma when it was below the surface. Once the upward-moving magma reached the cooler surface, it crystallized rapidly and formed smaller crystals invisible to the naked eye. Detailed studies indicate the top and bottom of the rhyolite lava flow cooled so quickly at Earth's surface that only glass formed—there was not time for even small crystals invisible to the naked eye to grow. Glass is unstable over time, and this glass has since "deglassed" or devitrified, forming microscopic crystals.

Tettegouche State Park

The entrance to Tettegouche State Park and the Baptism River Rest Area is between mileposts 58 and 59. From the parking lot, you can walk a well-maintained, half-mile trail to Shovel Point on the shore of Lake Superior. From the observation stand on the point, look to the southwest down the shore and you will see Palisade Head. Both Shovel Point and Palisade Head are made of the Palisade Head Rhyolite flow that is as thick as 310 feet. Look for a wave-cut arch at lake level a short distance southwest of Shovel Point. Look toward the northeast up the shore from the northeast side of the point and you will see several basalt lava flows younger than the rhyolite upon which you are standing. They are tilted southeastward toward the center of the lake at about a 20-degree angle, as are most flows on the North Shore. The tilting occurred

Lava flows of the North Shore Volcanic Group dip about 20 degrees toward the lake center. View to the northeast from Shovel Point at Tettegouche State Park.

because magma was removed from beneath what is now Lake Superior and extruded on the land surface, and the overlying lava flows then sagged downward. On the south shore of Lake Superior in Michigan and Wisconsin, the flows dip northwestward at much steeper angles—about 70 degrees.

Illgen City Area

At Illgen City, MN 1 heads northwest to Ely. The reddish rock in the big roadcut at this highway intersection is the Palisade Head Rhyolite, the rock that underlies Palisade Head and Shovel Point. Note the vertical drill holes in the rock face. They were packed with explosives to blast the road through this massive rock, which is thought to be the product of a hot ash flow. Drive less than 0.1 mile north on MN 1 to see the banding in the uppermost portion of the thick rhyolite flow that formed as the hot ash flowed. The first roadcut contains folded layering, and you might also see some flattened pieces of pumice, a vesicular, glassy volcanic rock.

Between mileposts 61 and 62 are high vertical roadcuts in reddish, coarsely crystalline anorthosite, a rock comprised of more than 90 percent calcium-rich plagioclase feldspar. This huge inclusion of already cooled rock was carried upward, probably from a depth of 15 to 25 miles, by rising magma that crystallized to form the Beaver Bay Complex. The large grain size of the anorthosite is a result of slow cooling at depth.

Sugarloaf Cove

Between mileposts 73 and 74, about 4 miles southwest of Schroeder, is a turnoff to Sugarloaf Cove, a unique spot on the North Shore, complete with hiking trails and an interpretive center. The cove is a beautiful small bay between Sugarloaf Point and the mainland. The rocky point is roughly parallel to the shoreline and is connected to the mainland by a strip of wave-deposited pebbles, cobbles, and boulders that make up a topographic feature called a tombolo. The rocks on both the point and the mainland are basalt lava flows. The cobble beach at the head of the cove is composed of many rock types, mostly from the bedrock of the North Shore, but also others, including various granites that were carried here by glaciers and rounded by wave action on the beach.

Sugarloaf Point was designated a state Scientific and Natural Area by the Minnesota Department of Natural Resources in 1992, largely because of the beautifully preserved examples of basaltic lava flows. Features in the flows include columnar joints and the associated rock columns, ropy tops of lava flows, "dikes" of fine sand that infiltrated downward into cracks in the lava flows, and pipe amygdules, gas-escape structures formed in the basal parts of cooling lava flows and later filled by minerals. Also present here are some rare plants—this is the only known Minnesota locality for three unique species of moss.

Between 1943 and 1971, pulpwood sticks were dumped into the cove and encircled by log-and-chain booms to form large pulpwood rafts. The rafts of several thousand logs were then towed 62 miles across Lake Superior to a paper mill in Ashland, Wisconsin. Large metal rings embedded in the rock on both sides of the cove are visible reminders of that pulpwood operation. Back in the late 1800s, there were rafting operations associated with many of the North Shore streams that were used for floating logs down to the lakeshore.

Contact of two lava flows at Sugarloaf Point. The white curving lines are mineral-filled pipes, called pipe amygdules, that formed where water at the base of the hot flow formed steam, which moved upward into the liquid lava.

Sugarloaf Cove was used much later when pulpwood logs were hauled to the lake by truck.

Taconite Harbor

Between mileposts 77 and 78 is Taconite Harbor, a former shipping point for a now-closed taconite pellet plant on the Mesabi Iron Range. A small gravel road near the railroad trestle over MN 61 leads to an observation area where you used to be able to observe the loading of pellets into large ships. The harbor was constructed by building a breakwater between the shore and two existing islands using large blocks of anorthosite quarried from Carlton Peak near Tofte.

Cross River Wayside

Near milepost 79 at Schroeder, MN 61 passes over the Cross River, which cascades over lava flows above, beneath, and below the bridge. At the parking area just to the west of the bridge there is a well-defined boundary between two lava flows. The upper flow is massive, whereas the lower flow contains amygdules of soft, easily eroded zeolite minerals.

Temperance River State Park

Between Schroeder and the Temperance River a few miles to the northeast, MN 61 is located on an old Lake Superior beach with an elevation of about 670 feet, about 70 feet above today's lake level. Lake Superior has at various times had higher lake levels than today because glacial ice blocked drainage via the

St. Lawrence River. The highest level of ancestral Glacial Lake Duluth was about 1,050 feet above sea level, which is 450 feet above the present level. Geologists have identified strandlines of beaches and wave-cut cliffs of twenty-seven lower lake levels since Glacial Lake Duluth, including one below the present lake level.

Between mileposts 80 and 81 is the Temperance River, Temperance River State Park, and a state wayside. Most streams have a sand or gravel bar where they empty into a lake, a product of deposition by the river and wave action on the lakeshore. The Temperance River, however, has no bar at its mouth because the lake bottom drops off steeply at the river mouth. Also, the river is not bringing in enough sediment through its very steep, deep, rocky gorge. Do you suppose the lack of a bar is how the river got its name?

Trails lead both upstream and downstream from the highway. If you walk the trail for some distance upstream from the highway, you can view a deep gorge with potholes carved by swirling stones in high-velocity waters. Downstream, over the very short distance between the highway and the lakeshore, you can observe many interesting features along the trail.

Ropy flow tops, formed as the fluid basaltic magma flowed, are present below the footbridge over the river, just below the highway. They are red because

The deep gorge of the Temperance River below the MN 61 bridge. Note the curved outlines of large potholes. Photo taken from the footbridge.

Ropy flow top of a basalt flow in Temperance River State Park just below the footbridge.

of oxidation of the iron in the flow tops when the lava was still hot. Look for the columnar joints below the far end of the footbridge and on the footpath immediately west of the footbridge. The steep gorge here has more large potholes carved in the swirling water. And with this short walk, you can verify for yourself the absence of a gravel bar at the river's mouth.

At about milepost 81 opposite a large Superior National Forest sign, a 1.5-mile-long unimproved gravel road leads inland and uphill to an inactive rock quarry high on Carlton Peak, which provides spectacular views on a clear day. This topographic high, 924 feet above Lake Superior, is a part of Temperance River State Park. The reason it is high is that it is composed of resistant anorthosite inclusions in diabase. If you drive to the quarry, look for the large, light green inclusions in the dark gray diabase. Anorthosite is composed of more than 90 percent calcium-rich plagioclase and comes from deep within Earth's crust. The quarry provided resistant rock for the breakwater at Taconite Harbor, a former taconite shipping facility.

Tofte

Tofte is where the youngest lava flows of the North Shore Volcanic Group are found. This stack of a few hundred lava flows is about 6 miles thick and Tofte is on the top. Whether you drive northeast or southwest from Tofte, you are descending in the volcanic pile.

Eagle Mountain

If you want to stand on the highest point in Minnesota—Eagle Mountain at 2,301 feet above sea level—take the Caribou Trail (County Road 4) north from Lutsen. After about 15 miles, this road ends at a T with Superior National Forest Road 170. Follow this road eastward for about 4 miles to the Eagle Mountain parking lot. The footpath to the mountaintop is about 3 miles long. The red rock that makes up the mountain is a granitic component of the generally gabbroic Duluth Complex. Its radiometric age is 1,095.4 million years. This highest point in Minnesota is only about 13 miles from the lowest point in Minnesota—the surface of Lake Superior at about 602 feet above sea level.

Cascade River State Park

Cascade River State Park extends for more than 10 miles along MN 61 between mileposts 96 and 106. Between mileposts 101 and 103, look at the tops of roadcuts for soil that developed in place by the weathering of the iron-bearing volcanic rocks. This soil has developed in the last several thousand years since the glaciers left and the lake level dropped. The formation of soil from solid rock is a slow process, especially in this northern climate. The more iron in the volcanic rock, the faster it will weather because the iron combines with oxygen to form iron oxide or rust. This oxidation is why the weathered rock and the overlying soil are brown to tan. Some of the basalts in the North Shore Volcanic Group, including these, contain more crystals of iron-bearing olivine, which is oxidized more easily than other minerals. Like most of the streams along the North Shore, the Cascade River drops over ledges of basalt flows, forming waterfalls.

At about milepost 104 is an excellent roadside observation point overlooking Good Harbor Bay. This high point is due to the presence of the hard, 160-foot-thick Terrace Point basalt flow. The lava flow is well exposed in the roadcut on both sides of the highway and can be traced inland for 15 miles. Some columnar joints are present. Look closely at the contact zone between the lava flow and the underlying red sediment. As the lava poured out on top of this soft sediment, it pushed or dragged the originally horizontal layers of sediment into steeper angles. Also present at the eastern end of the cut is a volcanic debris flow containing various volcanic rock types. Look for orangish amygdules of the semiprecious zeolite mineral thomsonite in the basalt.

The 130-foot-thick unit of red sandstone and siltstone beneath the lava is an interflow sediment deposited by streams during a lull in the volcanism. The parallel, thin, fine-grained layers probably formed in a lake. This quiet period between volcanic outbursts may have lasted for thousands of years in order for so much sand to accumulate. There are more than one hundred interflow sedimentary units on the North Shore, mostly quite thin and probably stream deposits, but this is the only one that can be easily seen from the highway and it is one of the thickest. The sand grains in these interflow sediments are mostly volcanic grains eroded from previously deposited lava flows. Therefore, the drainage basins of those ancient streams seem to have been entirely within the rift zone of lava flows. The red color of the interflow sedimentary rocks is from the oxidation of iron minerals because the original sediments were deposited on land.

A gray basalt flow overlies an interflow sedimentary unit in a roadcut on MN 61 near milepost 104, in the vicinity of Good Harbor Bay.

There is a rest area at the base of the hill where Cut Face Creek crosses the highway. If there is not too much water flowing in the creek, you can see good examples of ripple-marked surfaces on the red sandstone layers in the creek bottom immediately north of the highway. Ripple marks are small features formed on the surface of the sediment as currents and waves in the overlying water moved the individual sand grains. Look at them, but don't remove them, for this area is protected as part of Cascade River State Park.

The beach of Good Harbor Bay by this rest area is a place to search for thomsonite, a banded, green, pink, and white zeolite mineral that is harder than many zeolites. However, this is part of Cascade River State Park and removing anything from parks is prohibited. There is a commercial outlet where you can buy thomsonite a short distance southwest of this locality along the highway. The thomsonite was deposited in gas vesicles in the thick Terrace Point basalt flow. Vesicles are cavities formed where gas bubbles were trapped in the cooling lava. After the flows were buried, the vesicles were filled by minerals precipitated from hot water circulating through the volcanic pile. Such filled

Ripple marks in sandstone at Cut Face Creek, which flows into Good Harbor Bay.

vesicles, called amygdules, have different compositions. Agate, chlorite, calcite, epidote, and zeolite minerals are the most common. As the lava flow weathers, the iron-rich rock decomposes and the amygdules are freed.

Grand Marais

About 1 mile west of Grand Marais, between mileposts 107 and 108, is a roadcut in columnar basalt. Low roadcuts near the top of the hill on the west edge of Grand Marais are comprised of a pink to red rhyolite. This rhyolite lava flow, nearly 500 feet thick, contains angular crystals of pink orthoclase, rounded crystals of clear and glassy quartz, and a few oxidized iron-rich minerals, all in a fine-grained matrix. These larger crystals grew in the magma while it was still beneath Earth's surface. When the magma was extruded as lava, it cooled quickly in contact with air, resulting in the finer-grained matrix.

Grand Marais has one of the best natural harbors on the North Shore, so it attracted fur traders and early settlers. The harbor was probably a marsh in the early days of settlement because Grand Marais is French for "great marsh." The harbor was created by the erosion of a softer lava flow located between more resistant volcanic rocks. The resistant outer flow, an island, is connected to the mainland by a gravel bar formed by wave action. This connecting bar is called a tombolo. If you walk beyond the U.S. Coast Guard station on the harbor, you will see small, five-sided cooling columns in a basalt flow. Look southwestward from the harbor and you will see the Sawtooth Mountains on the skyline. This jagged profile is due to the fact that harder lava flows and sills are standing in relief, compared to softer, more easily eroded flows.

An outcrop of rhyolite near Grand Marais has large crystals of pink orthoclase, round crystals of quartz, and some dark minerals surrounded by a fine-grained matrix.

The jagged profile of the Sawtooth Mountains as viewed to the southwest from the harbor at Grand Marais is made by hard lava flows and sills protruding above softer flows, all dipping about 20 degrees toward the lake.

Old Beaches and Wave-Cut Cliffs

East of Grand Marais between mileposts 112 and 120, MN 61 is located on a flat, old beach terrace of Lake Superior about 16 feet higher than the present lake level. Beach pebbles are visible along the highway in the shallow ditches. Look for a wave-cut cliff just above the beach terrace, visible in many places just inland from the highway. Bear in mind that highway construction has altered some of the wave-cut cliffs. Croftville is situated on a slightly higher and older beach. These beaches are the products of higher water levels of Lake Superior a few thousand years ago. Geologists have delineated a total of twenty-seven higher stands on the basis of elevated beaches, deltas, wave-cut terraces, and cliffs. Shorelines of a given lake stand are as much as 250 feet higher in elevation here than at Duluth because Earth's crust had been depressed more here and for a longer time, so as the ice receded, the land beneath rebounded further.

Wave Energy and Beaches

Between mileposts 139 and 140 is a picturesque bay with an excellent pebble beach that records the piling up of pebbles by the last storm. On each side of the bay are rocky points of basalt jutting into the lake. As waves approach a shoreline, they drag on the shallow bottom and tend to approach the beach at right angles. Because of this wave refraction, wave energy is concentrated on the rocky points and erosion occurs there. Wave energy is spread out in the bays, so depositional features form—a pebble beach in this case.

Gravel beach and outcrops along MN 61 between mileposts 139 and 140.

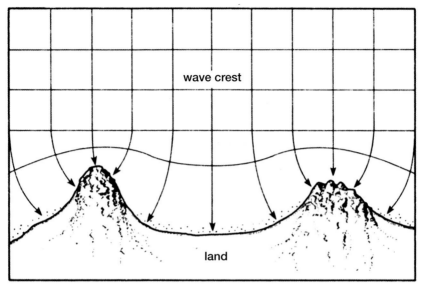

Waves refract as they near the shore, so the energy is concentrated at points of land and deposition occurs in the bays.

Judge C. R. Magney State Park

Judge C. R. Magney State Park is 1 to 1.5 miles wide and extends inland for more than 5 miles along the gorge of the Brule River. Upstream from the highway the river crosses a number of alternating basalt and rhyolite flows. Hikers moving inland on the hiking trails will cross all of the old strandline features formed during the various higher stands of Lake Superior. At an elevation of about 1,400 feet, these are features of the shoreline of Glacial Lake Duluth. See J. C. Green's book on North Shore state parks for details on the strandlines.

The rock most easily observed without extensive hiking is intrusive ferrodiorite, an intermediate rock that is more silica-rich than gabbro but does not contain as much silica as granite. You can see it at the footbridge near the parking lot. A hike of about 1 mile will pass the Upper Falls and bring you to the Devil's Kettle, a truly unique feature. Part of the flow of the river pours into a large circular pothole or kettle abraded into the rhyolite by rocks swirled about in high-velocity water. This part of the river disappears, and where it exits is a mystery.

Hovland

Hovland was established by immigrant Norwegian fishermen in the late 1800s. Looking inland from the highway, you will see high hills on the skyline. They are composed of mafic intrusive rocks—diabase and gabbro—that are more resistant to weathering and erosion than the adjacent lava flows. This same massive, black rock is visible in roadcuts between the western boundary of the Grand Portage Indian Reservation near the Reservation River at milepost 134 and milepost 142 near Grand Portage. Volcanic rocks in this area, part of the North Shore Volcanic Group, have radiometric ages of 1,107.7 million years.

Grand Portage National Monument

Signs on the highway between mileposts 144 and 145 will direct you to Grand Portage National Monument, which commemorates eighteenth-century fur trade history and even older Native American history. The Grand Portage is an 8.5-mile-long portage between Lake Superior and a navigable portion of the Pigeon River that allowed early travelers to bypass 21 miles of unnavigable rapids and three major waterfalls on the lower Pigeon River. You can see where the trail crosses MN 61 near milepost 146, about 1 mile east of the road into the national monument. The drop in elevation along the Pigeon River between the north end of the portage and Lake Superior is about 660 feet. The first Euro-pean to leave a record of having used the portage was Pierre Gaultier de Varennes, Sieur de la Verendrye, in 1731. Native Americans used this por-tage for hundreds of years before the French voyageurs arrived on the scene. They may have guided the first French explorers over this land route in the late 1600s. The Ojibwe called it *Git-che o-ni-ga-ming*, which, like the French *Grand Portage*, means "a great carrying place." A fur-trading post was established on Grand Portage Bay, the most protected bay on Minnesota's North Shore, per-haps as early as the late seventeenth century. The trading post was very active in the eighteenth century, and in 1793, the peak year for the fur trade, 182,000 beaver pelts reached Grand Portage from the west and were then transported by large canoes to the supply center at Montreal on the St. Lawrence River.

An excellent vantage point from which to view the reconstructed build-ings at the monument is Mt. Rose, a high knob of 1,850-million-year-old Rove Formation with a 1,110- to 1,105-million-year-old diabase dike of the Pigeon River Dike Swarm of Logan Intrusions at the crest. Note that the Rove Forma-tion within 10 feet of the contact with the dike has been baked by the dike, an example of contact metamorphism. Look for black clots of biotite that grew during the metamorphism. Signs along the Mt. Rose nature trail point out vari-ous geologic features, including benches and bluffs cut by wave action during higher stands of Lake Superior.

Grand Portage to the Canadian Border

The wayside rest between mileposts 145 and 146 is one of several places to see the approximately 1,850-million-year-old sedimentary Rove Formation, the oldest rocks along MN 61. The nearly horizontal beds of gray to black shale, mudstone, siltstone, and muddy sandstone called graywacke were deposited in an ancient ocean. The sediment was originally black because of organic mat-ter from microscopic life of that time, but the rock is now somewhat oxidized to reddish brown along joints. G. B. Morey, in a detailed study that included mineralogy and paleocurrent measurements, showed that the sediments were derived from the older Archean rocks to the north. The Rove sediments were deposited in the Animikie Basin.

Between the wayside rest and the international border, a distance of about 8 miles, all roadcuts are either in the 1,850-million-year-old Rove Formation or in the approximately 1,110- to 1,105-million-year-old Grand Portage and Pigeon River mafic dike swarms that crosscut the Rove Formation. The Rove is easily recognized by its well-developed beds of dominantly muddy rocks. The intru-sives are black, massive, nearly vertical dikes and horizontal sills of diabase.

There are two places to stop to get great views of Lake Superior: a well-marked scenic view parking place on a high point on the highway and a pull-off near milepost 148, opposite a very high roadcut in the Rove Formation on Mt. Josephine. The crest of this mountain is nearly 750 feet above Lake Superior. At this stop you can see Wauswaugoning Bay just below you, and the rugged topography of this eastern part of Minnesota. Susie and Lucille Islands are visible to the southeast. Pigeon Point, the easternmost bit of Minnesota, is also visible. On a clear day, you can see Isle Royale National Park (part of Michigan) 20 miles to the east.

The layered, nearly horizontal rock in the lower part of the high roadcut near milepost 148 is the muddy Rove Formation, but the upper part of this hill is more massive. The highest points are part of a vertical diabase dike that cuts through the Rove Formation, part of the mafic dike swarm. The hot, intruding magma baked the adjacent parts of the Rove. Look closely at some of the rock pieces in the ditch, and you may find some with very thin pink stringers of granite, probably the result of partial melting of some of the Rove Formation by the 2,000-degree-Fahrenheit mafic magma. Such rock pieces were probably adjacent to the dike but have fallen down the steep slope. Also look for some thin, vertical white quartz veins crossing the Rove in the roadcut.

If you look closely at low roadcuts on the north side of the highway near milepost 149, you can see three vertical mafic dikes 3 to 6 feet wide that cut across the horizontal beds of the Rove Formation. Both rock types are black here, so the relationships aren't very obvious from a passing vehicle.

High roadcut in the Rove Formation on Mt. Josephine.

Pigeon Point

A mafic sill of diabase, a resistant rock, is responsible for Pigeon Point, which protrudes 5 miles eastward into Lake Superior. The sill is part of the Logan Intrusions, a swarm of sills and dikes that intruded 1,115 million years ago. They are named after Sir William Logan, the first director of the Geological Survey of Canada. Dikes of the Logan Intrusions hold up several hills in this region, such as Mt. Josephine. The high, flat-topped mesalike hills between the international border and Thunder Bay are capped by Logan sills of diabase and gabbro. These mafic sills, which are as thick as 500 feet and have prominent columnar joints, protect the underlying Rove Formation from erosion.

The Logan Intrusions contain a dark green or brownish pyroxene mineral called pigeonite, which is named after Pigeon Point. Pigeon Point and the Pigeon River were named for the once abundant but now extinct passenger pigeon. Huge flocks frequented the North Shore as recently as 1879, eating blueberries. Flocks would arrive in April, raise their young, and fly south in the fall. The last verified sighting in Minnesota was in 1895, and the last passenger pigeon died in the Cincinnati Zoo in 1914.

Grand Portage State Park

Grand Portage State Park is on the Minnesota side of the Pigeon River, adjacent to Ontario's Middle Falls Provincial Park on the northeast side of the

High Falls, also known as Pigeon Falls, spills over a resistant dike of diabase in Grand Portage State Park.

river. The Pigeon River, the largest stream on Minnesota's North Shore, forms the north border of the easternmost part of Minnesota. The most impressive thing to see in the park is High Falls, also known as Pigeon Falls, the highest waterfall in Minnesota at about 90 feet. You can reach it by a half-mile-long handicap-accessible, paved trail. The same big diabase dike that caps Mt. Josephine at milepost 148, about 3 miles from High Falls, is the resistant rock over which the water spills here. Below the falls, the river has eroded the softer Rove Formation, forming an impressive gorge. Above the falls you can see a diabase sill overlying the Rove sedimentary rocks, thereby preserving them from total removal at that spot. By walking a much longer trail, you can also see Middle Falls, a lower waterfall.

MINNESOTA 210
Fond du Lac—Brainerd
104 miles
See maps on pages 61 and 158

MN 210 primarily passes over glacial deposits of the Superior, Des Moines, and Rainy lobes, but you can see bedrock at its eastern end, which passes through Jay Cooke State Park. Here, MN 210 has been designated the Rushing Rapids Parkway, a Minnesota scenic byway. The western park boundary is just east of Carlton and is easily reached via exit 235 from I-35.

Jay Cooke State Park

In Jay Cooke State Park, you can see where thick, red silty clay deposited in Glacial Lake Duluth about 10,000 years ago overlies bedrock of the approximately 1,850-million-year-old Thomson Formation. The St. Louis River, the largest river in Minnesota that discharges into Lake Superior, has cut deeply through the red clay and into the underlying bedrock.

As you drive along the winding, hilly MN 210 through the park, you will see several high roadcuts in the red clay. MN 210 has a somewhat uneven surface in places because the clay is unstable and is continually sliding and slumping downhill. If you look closely, you should be able to spot some cobbles or boulders, called dropstones, enclosed in the clay. These stones sank onto the lakebed from melting icebergs floating in Glacial Lake Duluth. Some of the large stones are scratched or striated from being dragged along bedrock at the base of glacial ice. Be forewarned, however, that in addition to the lake clays, this area has clay-rich glacial tills that also contain boulders, so not all stones enclosed in clay are dropstones.

Another kind of "stone" in the red, silty clay is concretions, better-cemented parts of the silty clay. They are formed by groundwater moving through the upper, near-surface portions of the sediment and depositing calcium carbonate between the fine grains. The concretions range from spheres to very irregular shapes.

The Thomson Formation is visible in the river bottom where the highway is adjacent to the river in the western few miles of the park. This part of the river was not navigable for the canoes of the Native Americans and the voyageurs, so they carried their stuff 6.5 miles over the Grand Portage of the St. Louis.

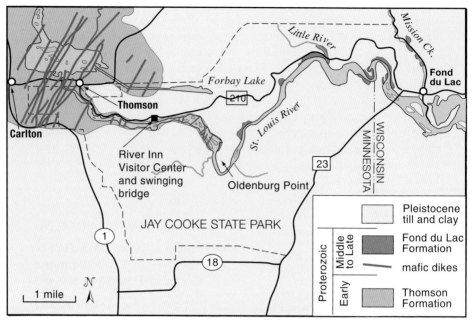

Bedrock geology of Jay Cooke State Park. —From Ojakangas and Matsch, 1982

Roadcuts along MN 210 expose red lakebed clay deposited in Glacial Lake Duluth and clayey tills.

The Thomson Formation is made up of slates, metamorphosed siltstones, and metamorphosed graywackes deposited as mud, silt, and dirty (clayey) sand in a deep sea about 1,850 million years ago. The sands were deposited by turbidity currents—swirling dense currents that moved from shallower water on the north edge of the basin southward onto the deep ocean floor. There, where the slope angle became more horizontal, the turbidity currents lost their velocity and deposited their sediment loads. The sand beds are coarser at the bottoms and finer at the tops because the larger grains settled faster than the smaller grains. The mud deposited between turbidity current deposits settled slowly over long periods of time in calm water.

The sedimentary rock layers were originally deposited in near-horizontal attitudes but were tilted by the Penokean mountain building event about 1,850 million years ago. During this event, high pressures and temperatures metamorphosed the muds into slate, the silts into metasiltstones, and the dirty sands or graywackes into metagraywacke.

There are two places from which you can view the Thomson Formation from a short distance. One is the Oldenburg Point overlook and the other is the 200-foot-long swinging bridge over the St. Louis River at the River Inn Visitor Center. Both are marked by signs along the highway, and both have buildings made of gabbro of the Duluth Complex, constructed by the Civilian Conservation Corps in the 1930s and early 1940s.

The best place for you to really see the rock types up close is in the vicinity of Thomson Dam and the river gorge at the west edge of the park. Just east of the MN 210 bridge, 1 mile east of Carlton, is a parking lot near the dam. Park here, cross the road, proceed up a short bank on a few stone steps, and follow the trail for a few tens of feet. From here you will have a view of a classic anticline, or upfold, in the rock as you look westward across the gorge. The anticline is elongated in an east-west direction and is the result of strong compressional forces directed from the south toward the north. These forces were related to the Penokean mountain building event that occurred along the south side of what is now Lake Superior. Successive volcanic arcs collided with the continental nucleus as the oceanic crust on which they were riding was subducted.

For additional views of the Thomson Formation, follow the primitive path southward through the pines on the top of the bank high above the river gorge for another few hundred feet to the old railroad grade, now a paved bicycle trail. In the railroad cut immediately east of the old railroad trestle, a nearly vertical basaltic dike about 2 feet wide is clearly visible. Stand on the trestle for other good views of this formation. The river gorge between the highway bridge and the trestle is quite straight because it follows the course of a weathered mafic dike. If you walk another 100 feet or so westward on the tarred grade, you will see a path into the woods on the right. Follow this path and you will end up back at the highway bridge.

At the west end of the highway bridge, on the north side of the highway, is a large pod of white quartz in the black Thomson Formation. Native gold is sometimes found in quartz veins, so geologists have indeed checked out this large quartz pod. A speck of gold supposedly found in this quartz proved to be a small bit of alloyed gold, probably from someone's wedding band.

*Anticline in the Thomson Formation viewed from the east side of the St.
Louis River near the MN 210 bridge.*

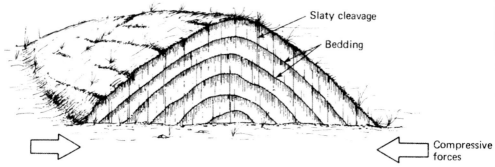

*Sketch of a typical anticline, showing vertical cleavage cutting across
the bedding. Cleavage develops when microscopic mica crystals form
perpendicular to the regional pressures.* —From Ojakangas, 1991

While standing on the highway bridge, look upstream toward the dam. If the
water is low, look for a 20-foot-wide dike of black diabase rock adjacent to the
east bank of the river. It contains horizontal columns, the result of joints that
formed perpendicular to the dike walls during cooling. This dike, one of many
in the area, is about 1,100 million years old, the same age as the volcanic rocks
on the North Shore of Lake Superior. The dikes were paths along which magma
rose, feeding overlying lava flows that have since eroded away.

The diabase dike that runs through the center of the photo from bottom to top cuts across the Thomson Formation and therefore is younger. Note the horizontal columnar fractures that formed when the magma cooled. View looking upstream at the Thomson Dam from the MN 210 bridge over the St. Louis River.

From I-35 to McGregor

Between I-35 and a point about 4 miles east of Cromwell, MN 210 crosses generally flat terrain of glacial outwash deposits or younger peat deposits. Watch for a slight topographic rise between mileposts 180 and 181, formed by a sandbar or a beach of a glacial lake. Look for bouldery fields and boulder piles near milepost 186 and between mileposts 199 and 201. The boulders are part of the unsorted ground moraine deposited beneath the glacial ice of the Mille Lacs advance of the Superior lobe. Also watch for an agricultural peat mining operation near milepost 202, barely visible behind the trees.

At Sawyer, between mileposts 208 and 209, and near Iverson, at milepost 214, there are modest yet sharp breaks in elevation. These are interpreted as places where the front of a glacial lobe was melting, with meltwater carrying the sediment outward from the glacier and depositing it nearby as glacial outwash. Later, when the ice was completely melted, the piles of sediment remained as higher areas.

Cromwell is located on the northern edge of an area of northwest-trending drumlins within the ground moraine of the Mille Lacs advance of the Superior lobe. Between a point a few miles west of Cromwell and Crosby, a distance of about 60 miles, you are driving on drift of the younger St. Louis sublobe of the Des Moines lobe.

Flatter areas, as at Tamarack and McGregor, are parts of the lakebed of Glacial Lake Aitkin, which existed about 11,600 to 7,400 years ago. The lakebed contains peat deposits 5 to 10 feet thick. The Rice Lake National Wildlife Refuge is located a few miles south of McGregor on the Glacial Lake Aitkin lakebed, which here is mostly wave-washed till rather than lake sediment. Some slightly higher portions of the glacial lakebed are likely either sandy beaches or sandbars, as at milepost 169. The roadside rest area at McGregor has a sign describing Glacial Lake Aitkin.

Savanna Portage State Park
Savanna Portage State Park is 17 miles northeast of McGregor. To get there, take MN 65 north from McGregor for 7 miles, and then turn east on County Road 14 and follow it for 10 miles. This park contains an important portage between Lake Superior and the Mississippi River on a route used for hundreds of years by Native Americans and during the 1700s and 1800s by French fur traders. They would canoe up the St. Louis River to the East Savanna River at what is now Floodwood, canoe up that river, and then traverse the Savanna Portage across the marshy grassland or savanna.

The portage took five days of wading through water and muck, in places waist deep. Tamarack logs were occasionally laid end to end to provide footing. After crossing the continental divide, travelers utilized the West Savanna River, the Prairie River, and Big Sandy Lake before reaching the Upper Mississippi. Called a "boundless swamp" by one traveler in 1854, the Savanna was the western portion of the bed of Glacial Lake Upham. The lake formed east of the St. Louis sublobe of the Des Moines lobe as it stagnated. It existed about 11,600 to 9,800 years ago.

The continental divide in the park is formed by till of the St. Louis sublobe of the Des Moines lobe draped over an end moraine of the Rainy lobe. As you are approaching the park on County Road 14, a 7-mile-long esker several tens of feet high is on your left. It is probably a Rainy lobe esker overlain by Des Moines lobe ground moraine. This esker forms the southeast shore of Big Sandy Lake and is a major reason why the lake is here. You can walk along the dry crest of the esker on the esker trail within the park. Too bad an esker like this didn't cross the Savanna to aid voyageurs on their portage.

Glacial Lake Aitkin
Near the MN 210 junction with US 169, 8 miles northeast of Aitkin, is an excellent example of the flat glacial lakebed of Glacial Lake Aitkin. The black, sandy loam soil is ideal for cropland. Some of the sand was probably brought to the lake by a river. Waters of the glacial lake winnowed more sand from the underlying St. Louis sublobe of the Des Moines lobe. Peat beds that formed as the lake filled in with vegetation are also common in this area. The southern margin of the lake is located between mileposts 155 and 156.

Aitkin is located on the lake plain just north of the end moraine deposited on the south side of the eastward-moving St. Louis sublobe of the Des Moines

Farmland on the bed of Glacial Lake Aitkin near the junction of MN 210 and US 169.

lobe. This end moraine of till formed the southern shore of Glacial Lake Aitkin. Watch for boulders a few miles east of Aitkin. This hilly end moraine also underlies the area between Aitkin and Crosby. The many lakes are kettle lakes formed where glacial ice that was buried by glacial debris subsequently melted and formed depressions. The numerous swamps formed in the same way.

Cuyuna Iron Range

The Cuyuna Iron Range, between Deerwood and Brainerd, is one of three iron ranges in Minnesota that produced ore. Its discovery is attributed to Cuyler Adams. While surveying land that he was planning to log in the 1880s, he noted that his compass needle was deflected at specific places. He reasoned that perhaps magnetic iron-formation beneath the glacial drift was causing the needle to act strangely. He then spent some years measuring these magnetic variations by means of a super dip needle. There were no rock outcrops in the area to verify his idea, for the glacial drift is 50 to 300 feet thick. Adams realized that places along the magnetic lines that were not magnetic may have been oxidized to high-grade hematite ore.

In 1903 he chartered a mining company, and in 1904 drills penetrated the first hematite ore body. The initial ore was transported by rail in 1911 from the Kennedy Mine to the Duluth-Superior ore docks. By 1912, more than 2,500 exploration holes had been drilled in a four-county area and sixty drill rigs were operating.

Cuyler Adams's wife suggested that the newly found range be named "Cuyuna," for Cuyler and his St. Bernard Una who accompanied him on his surveys in the early 1900s. The Cuyuna consists of two parts: the North Range north of MN 210 and the South Range south of MN 210. The much more important North Range mining area is about 10 miles long and 6 miles wide.

Many new towns were platted soon after the discovery of iron ore. Cuyuna was the first in 1908, followed by Deerwood, Crosby, Iron Hub, Ironton, Barrows, Manganese, Orelands, Riverton, Trommald (formerly Iron Mountain), Steelton, Wolford, and Pershing. Only six remain on a modern Minnesota highway map. George H. Crosby, a Duluthian who was an early explorer on the Mesabi Iron Range, developed Crosby. It was a well-planned city located on the shore of Serpent Lake, a well-known scenic spot. Crosby even drilled the site to verify that it did not overlie iron ore, which might cause the city to be moved in later years. Miners rented new homes for $12 a month.

Unlike the Mesabi Iron Range, where the iron-formation is gently dipping, the ore of the Cuyuna Iron Range dips steeply, thus necessitating underground mining. The thick glacial drift was also a factor until improved machinery allowed for its economical removal and the development of open pits. Thus, many underground mines became open pits, and the last underground production was in 1967. The east half of Rabbit Lake, 2 miles north of Cuyuna, was

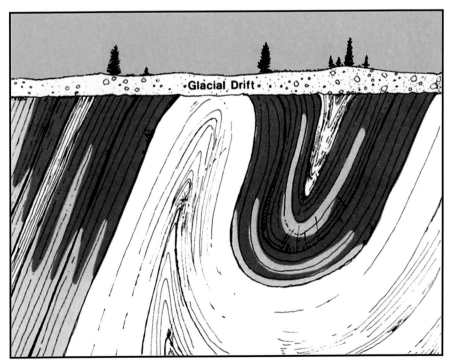

Cross section of the Cuyuna Iron Range. The dark areas are high-grade iron ore. The folding occurred during the Penokean mountain building event about 1,850 million years ago. —From Ojakangas and Matsch, 1982, after U.S. Steel

drained to get at iron ore; this became the Kennedy open pit mine. Some of the ore contained as much as 69 percent iron, which is very high-grade.

Much ore on the North Range was high-grade hematite and contained manganese, whereas South Range ore was the iron oxide goethite. The manganese ranged from 4 to 14 percent. The Cuyuna Iron Range was essentially closed by the early 1980s, but small tonnages of manganiferous ore were shipped from stockpiles of the Algoma-Zeno Mine for another decade or so. Manganiferous iron ore is valuable for the manufacture of certain types of steel. The Cuyuna contains the United State's largest resource of manganese. It is economically difficult to separate the manganese from the iron, but during World War I, manganese was separated with the help of a government subsidy.

Driving through the range on MN 210, you will see little evidence of the iron ore heritage of this area. On the west edge of Ironton, a reddish waste rock dump is visible about one-quarter mile north of the highway, already quite overgrown with trees. The best places to see the historic mining activity are a short distance off MN 210. If you drive north on MN 6 from Crosby for 0.6 mile, you can park at the Portsmouth Mine overlook. The open pit, now a lake more than 450 feet deep, produced 13 million tons of iron and manganese ore containing up to 65 percent iron and up to 20 percent manganese. Across MN 6 from this overlook is the Croft Mine Historical Park, with underground mine tours on certain days. Or to reach the Croft Mine, look for the sign in downtown

Block of iron-formation from the Cuyuna Iron Range at the Portsmouth Mine overlook along MN 6 north of Crosby.

Mahnomen Mine on the Cuyuna Iron Range near Ironton circa the 1950s. —From author's collection

Crosby—the mine, now a park, is a few blocks north of MN 210. Many small pits, now lakes, and old underground shafts are hidden by the forest.

The Cuyuna Country State Recreation Area north of Crosby and Ironton includes six natural lakes and fifteen deep lakes that were iron ore pits, thirteen of which are now trout lakes. To see some of this area, drive north on Irene Avenue in Ironton. This leads to County Road 30, which you can follow to the villages of Trommald and Manganese.

The worst mine disaster in the Lake Superior area happened on February 5, 1924, at the Milford Mine, 2 miles north of Crosby. Forty-one miners perished when the underground mine was suddenly inundated and filled with water, mud, and quicksand from a nearby lake. Within 25 minutes, the 200-foot-deep mine had filled to within 15 feet of the surface. Only seven miners managed to escape by climbing ladders from the work area at the 165-foot level.

In 1922 at the Sagamore Mine, an open pit operation near Riverton, about 4 miles southwest of Crosby, a buried forest was found in the glacial drift beneath 170 feet of glacial sand. The remains of extinct horses, bison, and huge beaver were also found. Carbon-14 dating of the wood has shown it to be at least 35,000 years old. This date is similar to other dated wood from elsewhere in central Minnesota.

VERMILION TRAIL
(COUNTY ROAD 4 AND MINNESOTA 135)
Duluth—Biwabik—Tower
90 miles
See maps on pages 75 and 97

County Road 4, between the upper end of Mesaba Avenue in Duluth and Biwabik on the Mesabi Iron Range, is also known by two other names: Vermilion Trail and Governor Rudy Perpich Memorial Drive. The road, which follows a Native American trail, was built between Duluth and Lake Vermilion because of the Lake Vermilion gold rush of 1865. The 1,100-million-year-old Duluth Complex of gabbroic rocks underlies the southern half of County Road 4, but the only roadside exposures north of Duluth are low roadcuts on the west side of the road between mileposts 21 and 22, north of Island Lake. There are larger exposures in the woods behind the low roadcuts.

The Mille Lacs end moraine of the Superior lobe is present between Duluth and Island Lake, which is an artificial reservoir on the dammed Cloquet River. The flatter terrain between Island Lake and County Road 49, a distance of about 7 miles, is glacial outwash deposits.

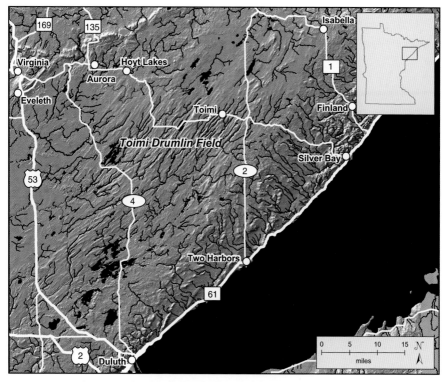

County Road 4 passes through the Toimi Drumlin Field, formed beneath the southwest-moving Rainy lobe. The southwest-flowing streams there are controlled by the drumlin topography. Note that the many streams flowing into Lake Superior are short and have small drainage basins compared to other streams in northern Minnesota.

The hilly topography between County Road 49 and County Road 547 is glacial drumlins formed beneath glacial ice of the Rainy lobe. They are part of the Toimi Drumlin Field, which is about 75 miles long and as wide as 25 miles. The hundreds of individual drumlins in this northeast-trending set are generally about 1 to 2 miles long, less than 0.5 mile wide, and 30 to 50 feet high.

Watch for three large gravel pits on the east side of the road within a distance of 6 miles. These are in ground moraine and drumlins and probably associated outwash deposits of coarse gravel. The many varieties of pebbles, cobbles, and boulders in these pits are mainly composed of different types of granitic and volcanic rocks, plus black slate, all eroded from Archean and Proterozoic bedrock to the northeast. The absence of carbonates indicates these pits are not located on drift of the St. Louis sublobe of the Des Moines lobe, which contains pebbles and cobbles of white to buff Paleozoic limestone and dolomite from the Winnipeg region.

The gently undulating 9-mile-long stretch of the highway between the Whiteface River and County Road 16 overlies end moraine of the St. Louis sublobe. Between the Whiteface River and Markham, the western end of the Whiteface Reservoir is barely visible behind an earthen berm adjacent to the highway. Damming the Whiteface River created this reservoir. Between the reservoir and Biwabik, the underlying unexposed bedrock is the 1,850-million-year-old Virginia Formation.

Between County Road 100 and Biwabik, the flat, farmed land is mostly sand and gravel at the northern end of Glacial Lake Upham, which formed on drift

Gravel pit in glacial drift of the Rainy lobe. The light-colored cobbles are granites.

of the St. Louis sublobe as the glacier melted back to the west. The sand seems to be a large delta formed by the inflow of meltwater from Glacial Lake Norwood, which formed north of the Giants Range. That water flowed through a gap in the range now occupied by the Embarrass River. The northern boundary of Glacial Lake Upham is the topographically high Giants Range, which also stopped the northeastward advance of the St. Louis sublobe.

About 4 miles south of Biwabik, near the highway by the Lakeland store, are some well-preserved Indian mounds. About 2 miles south of Biwabik is a large gravel pit in the Des Moines lobe. MN 4 ends at Biwabik at the junction with MN 135. Between Biwabik and Aurora, 4 miles to the east, MN 135 follows the Mesabi Iron Range. Note the high, red, overgrown waste rock dumps of low-grade iron-formation and tan-colored dumps of glacial overburden, reminders of the early mining years.

North of Aurora, MN 135 crosses the topographically high Giants Range, formed of Archean granite of the Giants Range Batholith. The granite solidified from magma several miles beneath the 2,700-million-year-old Algoman Mountains. Between mileposts 20 and 21 are low roadcuts in black biotitic schist, the Archean country rock into which the granite intruded. Stop at the roadcut near milepost 23 to get a close look at this granite. The magma cooled slowly enough for large crystals to form. The black elongate inclusions are remnants of the country rock into which the granite intruded. The granite has a faint foliation formed by the parallel grains of elongate, black hornblende. They probably grew while the granite was subjected to directional pressures during the Algoman mountain building event.

The dark area is a hornblende-rich country rock inclusion in granite of the Giants Range Batholith, exposed on MN 135 near milepost 23. The granite is composed of pink potassium feldspar, gray quartz, and black hornblende crystals.

The few rock exposures in the lower terrain between the Giants Range and Tower are greenstone of the Vermilion District. These metamorphosed 2,700-million-year-old volcanic rocks were here before the magma of the Giants Range granite intruded them.

A thin cover of glacial drift of the Rainy lobe blankets northeastern Minnesota between the Giants Range and the Canadian border, 50 miles to the north. Most of the glacial cover consists of ground moraine, but there are some flat areas of glacial outwash and glacial lake sediments. For a distance of about 5 miles just north of the Giants Range, you are crossing the bed of Glacial Lake Norwood. Some higher ground along the southwestern margin of Lake Vermilion is part of the Vermilion end moraine.

At milepost 26, MN 135 crosses the Embarrass River. Although a small stream, it served as a water highway for Native Americans, explorers, and French voyageurs who canoed up from Lake Superior via the St. Louis River to its confluence with the Embarrass River. They then followed the Embarrass River through a chain of lakes that included Esquagama, Embarrass, and Wynne Lakes. From near the present-day site of the MN 135 bridge over the river, they portaged a few miles to the north over the Laurentian Divide into the Pike River, which flows northward into Lake Vermilion. From there, the Vermilion River flows northward to the lakes on the Canadian border. The French called the river *River des Embarrass,* meaning "river of difficulties" because jams of driftwood gave the travelers a bit of grief and hard work.

The town of Embarrass, 3 miles east of the highway on County Road 21, was settled by Finnish immigrants in the late 1800s and early 1900s who liked the looks of the flat glacial lake and outwash terrain that did not contain bothersome glacial boulders. Nearly all of the sideroads have Finnish names, such as Koski, Lehto, Hanka Nevela, and Waisanen.

About 1 mile north of the junction of County Road 21 with MN 135, you will cross the unmarked Laurentian Divide, which separates waters flowing northward to Hudson Bay from those flowing southeastward to Lake Superior and the Atlantic Ocean.

GUNFLINT TRAIL (COUNTY ROAD 12)
Grand Marais—Trails End Campground
60 miles

The Gunflint Trail (County Road 12) intersects MN 61 in eastern Grand Marais, but it can also be reached by driving uphill on Fifth Avenue West. The original trail headed north from Grand Marais to a point near Gunflint Lake on the Canadian border where the Paulson Mine was being developed in the late 1880s in the Gunflint Iron Formation. Although there are many resorts tucked into this lake country, it remains wild. From several points along the northern half of the trail, you can enter the Boundary Waters Canoe Area Wilderness by canoe. Boat motors are generally restricted to a few corridors.

If you stop at the scenic overlook a few miles north of Grand Marais, you will have an excellent view of the harbor. Note the curved gravel bar—a tombolo

The gravel bar connecting Grand Marais to the island is a tombolo and helps protect the harbor, which is on the right side of the photo.

connecting the mainland to a resistant lava flow that was once an island. This natural feature protects the harbor from strong northeast winds.

The large sawmill near the Devil Track River, about 3 miles north of the scenic overlook, is located on a flat area of the uppermost beach gravels of Glacial Lake Duluth, the ancestor to Lake Superior. About 11,000 years ago, the Superior lobe still occupied the lake basin to the northeast and meltwater filled the southwestern portion. The lake surface was more than 450 feet higher than it is today.

A thin layer of glacial drift blankets the bedrock here. The roadcuts in glacial material are not always obvious because they are grown over with grass and weeds, but watch for large glacial boulders protruding through the grass. Some of the glacial cuts are tills, and some are sorted glacial outwash sediments. The boundary between a 6-mile-wide strip of Superior lobe glacial drift along Lake Superior and the widespread Rainy lobe glacial drift to the north, which extends into Canada, is located about 9 miles north of Grand Marais, just south of the intersection of National Forest Road 140 with the Gunflint Trail.

About 10 miles north of Grand Marais, the Gunflint Trail passes through a grove of big white pine, the species nearly removed from the landscape by the logging industry in the late 1800s and early 1900s. Other scattered white pines along the road escaped the saw because they were poorly located, too scattered, or a bit on the small side a century ago.

The "arrowhead" of Minnesota has more rock exposure than the rest of the state because the glacial drift is generally thin. For the first 10 miles inland from Lake Superior, the rock outcrops are black basaltic lava flows about 1,100 million years old. However, between the North Brule River bridge and Gunflint

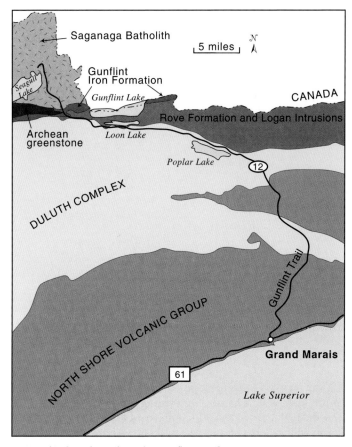

Bedrock geology along the Gunflint Trail. —Modified from Green, 1982

Lake, the black rocks are coarse-grained gabbro of the Duluth Complex, one of the largest accumulations of mafic intrusive rocks and associated felsic rocks in the world. The gabbro crystallized from mafic magma about 1,107 million years ago, at depth beneath lava flows that have long since been eroded away. The complex covers a large arc-shaped area of nearly 2,000 square miles between Duluth and the Gunflint Trail region. Watch for roadcuts in glacial till near the bridges over the South Brule River and the North Brule River. The distinctive red glacial boulders at the North Brule River were derived from the granitic rocks of the Duluth Complex and are mixed in with the dominant dark gray to black boulders of gabbro.

Be sure to stop at the well-marked Laurentian Divide scenic overlook at Birch Lake and read the signs. Waters northwest of this vicinity flow northward to Hudson Bay, and waters southeast of this vicinity flow eastward into the Atlantic via the St. Lawrence River. Here you can learn about the 90-mile-per-hour winds during the megastorm on July 4, 1999, that flattened an 8- to 12-mile-wide swath of the surrounding forest. Logging and controlled burns of the windfall took several years.

Gunflint Lake Area

In the vicinity of Gunflint Lake, the rocks are the Gunflint Iron Formation, which is 1,878 million years old; the overlying Rove Formation, which has an enigmatic age range between 1,850 and 1,777 million years; and the Logan Intrusions, which are 1,115 million years old and intruded and metamorphosed the Rove Formation. The Rove Formation and Gunflint Iron Formation were deposited in the Animikie Basin.

The Gunflint Lake scenic overlook is a "must-stop" for the impressive view to the north across Gunflint and Magnetic Lakes toward light-colored granite exposures of the Saganaga Batholith on the far ridges. Signs at the overlook describe the history of the Paulson Mine in the Gunflint Iron Formation. Early explorers and voyageurs picked up pieces of black chert (better known as flint) from this rock for use in their flintlock guns to produce the spark needed to ignite the gunpowder. Iron ore was discovered near here in 1886 by Henry Mayhew, and a mine opened in 1888. However, the mining venture failed in 1893 because the much richer ore of the Mesabi Iron Range was already in production, there was a financial panic in 1893, and there was some dishonesty among the investors. The Paulson Mine was a prime factor in the rapid construction of the Port Arthur, Duluth, & Western Railroad to the mine. It also failed.

About 150 feet south of the Gunflint Lake scenic overlook is the northernmost roadcut in gabbro of the Duluth Complex. On the Gunflint Trail just to the north of this overlook, a few feet north of South Gunflint Lake Road (County Road 50), is a roadcut in metamorphosed and laminated Rove Formation overlain by a massive diabase sill of the Logan Intrusions.

County Road 46, between County Road 50 and National Forest Road 1347, passes a few interesting roadcuts. Along this road about 0.5 mile off the Gunflint Trail, you will see a roadcut in slate of the Rove Formation, which overlies the Gunflint Iron Formation. Slate is metamorphosed clay-rich sedimentary rock. Here you can see original bedding rather than slaty cleavage. The Rove Formation here has been metamorphosed by an underlying Logan diabase sill. If you drive in a bit farther, you will cross a bridge. Just across this bridge on the left is a flat exposure of the diabase sill. Look for glacial striations that trend nearly north-south. Farther along this 1.2-mile-long road, you will pass many

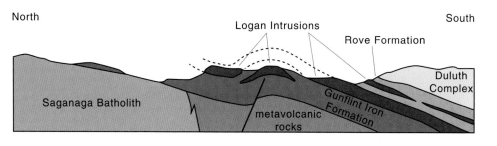

Geologic cross section of the northern part of the Gunflint Trail. —After Jirsa, 2008

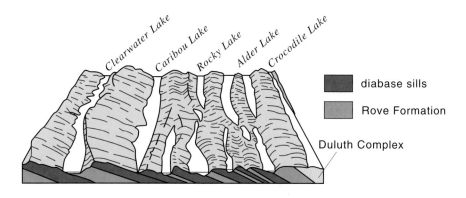

Block diagram showing how sills control the elongate shapes of the lakes along the border. —From Wright, 1972b, after Zumberge, 1952

low exposures of the sill, and at the end of the road you can see a roadcut in the sill on the entrance to a private driveway.

Breccia from Impact

National Forest Road 1347, about 1 mile west of County Road 46, is partially built on the old railroad bed that led to the Paulson Mine, which was located about 2 miles west of the Gunflint Trail. About a quarter mile in on this road is a large gravel pit in well-bedded glacial outwash of the Rainy lobe. On the north and east edges of the pit are excellent exposures in the uppermost part of the Gunflint Iron Formation on a southerly sloping surface.

On your left as you enter the gravel pit is a rock exposure about 10 feet across that is a coarse breccia composed mainly of angular pieces of Gunflint Iron Formation. This breccia is interpreted by Minnesota Geological Survey geologist Mark Jirsa as a submarine debris flow deposit triggered by impact-related earthquakes. It formed along the shore of the sea in which the Gunflint Iron Formation was being deposited. The impact was that of an asteroid that hit Earth at Sudbury, Ontario, about 450 miles to the east about 1,850 million years ago. The Sudbury impact event was the second largest terrestrial impact of about 170 on Earth that are scientifically verified. The asteroid was 6 to 12 miles in diameter and hit Earth with a force equal to several billion Hiroshima-sized atomic bombs. The temperature reached 10,000 degrees, 6,500 cubic miles of Earth's crust melted, and a huge crater 150 miles in diameter was formed. Most of the material fell back into the crater, but some was thrown 500 miles to the west, including this area. There are other, larger exposures of this breccia farther in on National Forest Road 1347, 1.3 miles from the Gunflint Trail and 0.2 mile beyond Cut Across Trail, which intersects the forest road. At that point there is an opening in the trees. If you walk in about 50 feet, the opening (a clear-cut) gets larger. Look for exposures of the breccia there.

Fine-grained ejecta thrown into the air likely circled the globe, but only remnants of that ejecta exist, such as here on the Gunflint 500 miles west of the impact. When looking at thin sections of the finer-grained matrix with petrographic microscopes, scientists have seen shocked quartz, which has been found only at impact sites. The ejecta also includes small, less than half-inch-diameter spheres of ash and possibly once-molten material.

As you drive to the end of this 2.5-mile-long road, you will see several old railroad cuts in massive diabase sills, some tens of feet high. Near the end of the road there are also cuts in the Rove Formation.

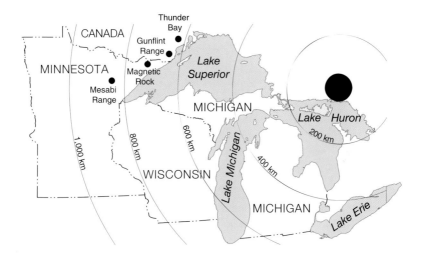

A meteorite impact 1,850 million years ago at Sudbury, Ontario, affected the area hundreds of kilometers to the west. —Courtesy of W. F. Cannon, U.S. Geological Survey

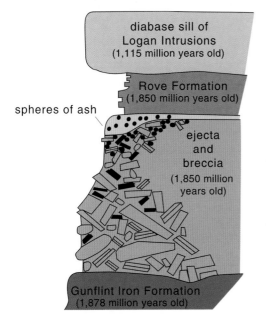

The stratigraphy of the Gunflint Lake breccia and adjacent rocks, with approximate ages. The polygons of various shapes represent fragments of chert-rich Gunflint Iron Formation. Circles represent cemented ash particles. —From Jirsa, 2008

In the breccia, some slabs of iron-formation are bent, suggesting it was still soft when the asteroid triggered the debris flow. However, the Gunflint Iron Formation is 28 million years older than the Sudbury impact, so more research is required.

Pellets of ash formed in the impact cloud and were carried west from Sudbury, Ontario.

Magnetic Rock

About 1 mile north of National Forest Road 1347 along the Gunflint Trail is a parking area and a sign indicating the location of the Magnetic Rock Hiking Trail. Nearby is a roadcut in the Gunflint Iron Formation. The meandering, 1-mile-long, uphill walk to Magnetic Rock is over dark, 1,878-million-year-old Gunflint Iron Formation deposited near the shoreline of an ancient sea. Look to the north of the high ridge that you are on, and you will see whitish granite outcrops of the Saganaga Batholith. They were light-colored in 2007 because a recent forest fire burned off the lichen and moss. You will also be stepping over glacial boulders of this granite, dropped here by the southwestward-moving Rainy lobe. Look closely at the Gunflint Iron Formation that you are walking on, especially high on the ridge. It contains thin silica-rich beds of chert that vary in color from white to gray to green to black. These alternate with thin, black iron-rich layers.

The iron-formation also contains stromatolites, circular to elliptical algal mounds as large as a few feet across. Blue-green algae, now called cyanobacteria, are microscopic plantlike life-forms that grow as sticky fibrous mats on the seafloor and trap sediment. Modern algal mounds exist in hypersaline waters where algae-eating snails and other animals cannot live. The algae use carbon dioxide (CO_2) in their life processes, and the removal of CO_2 from the seawater can cause precipitation of thin layers of calcium carbonate ($CaCO_3$). The algae then grow through the mat and build another layer that again traps and binds sediment. Tidal and longshore currents can erode these layers, thus developing the algal mounds. However, the mounds here are composed of silica (SiO_2) rather than carbonate. Although this remains an unsolved problem, many

Stromatolites in the Gunflint Iron Formation along the trail to Magnetic Rock.

geologists think that the silica replaced the carbonate during changes in the sediment soon after deposition. If so, the replacement was virtually complete.

Magnetic Rock is a spire of iron-formation about 25 feet high. The bedding in this rock exposure is nearly vertical, but the other outcrops near here have horizontal bedding. Glaciers probably left this block in its vertical position. If you hold a magnet or a compass next to the rock, you will find that certain layers are magnetic. If the French voyageurs who traveled the border lake route in the 1700s had compasses, which were rare at that time, they may have had a bit of trouble navigating in the vicinity of Magnetic Lake, just north of Gunflint Lake and east of Magnetic Rock.

The bedding layers are nearly vertical in Magnetic Rock, a chunk of Gunflint Iron Formation, probably because a glacial ice sheet tilted it on edge. A forest fire burned through here in 2007.

The Gunflint Iron Formation is world-famous among geologists. In 1965, E. Barghoorn and S. A. Tyler found cyanobacteria preserved in very fine-grained black chert in the 1,878-million-year-old Gunflint Iron Formation at Schreiber, Ontario, east of Thunder Bay. At the time, these were the oldest known fossils in the world. Since then, algal mounds have been found in rocks 3,500 million years old in Australia and southern Africa.

Saganaga Batholith (Saganaga Tonalite)

Between the Gunflint Iron Formation at the Magnetic Rock trailhead and the end of the Gunflint Trail, a distance of about 10 miles, all roadcuts and exposures on hills visible from the road are in light-colored, coarse-grained granitic rock of the Saganaga Batholith. It is named for Saganaga Lake on the border, part of the water highway between Montreal and the west that was traveled by Native Americans, explorers, and voyageurs at least since the 1600s. The granitic rock is distinctive among granitic rock of the region because it has large mineral grains of gray quartz. The major rock type is a tonalite, or quartz diorite, rather than true granite because it is composed of quartz, plagioclase, and hornblende, and generally lacks potassium feldspar. This rock body has a radiometric age of 2,689 million years and occupies about 270 square miles in Minnesota and Ontario. It crystallized at a depth of a few miles beneath the 2,700-million-year-old volcanic rocks of the eastern Vermilion District. Isotopic studies indicate that the magma from which it crystallized was from the base of Earth's crust rather than from the melting of rocks higher in the crust. Some very good roadcuts and natural exposures can be examined along the highway and in the Trails End Campground.

Light-colored granitic bedrock of the Saganaga Batholith in an area burned by a forest fire in 2007 at the northern end of the Gunflint Trail.

Close-up of granitic rock of the Saganaga Batholith. Note the distinctive large gray quartz grains and pink and white feldspar.

Exposures have become more plentiful because of the megastorm of 1999, with its 90-mile-per-hour winds, which flattened an 8- to 12-mile-wide swath of forest through this area and the adjacent Boundary Waters Canoe Area Wilderness. Later, controlled burns in the area and wildfires such as the 2006 Cavity Lake Fire just south of Seagull Lake (53 square miles) and the 2007 Ham Lake Fire to the west and north of Gunflint Lake (115 square miles) exposed much bedrock in both the Boundary Waters Canoe Area Wilderness and in the adjacent Quetico Provincial Park in Canada. Some geologists may like this lack of vegetation, but no one else does!

ECHO TRAIL (COUNTY ROADS 88 and 116)
Ely—Echo Lake
50 miles
See map on page 75

The Echo Trail is a real wilderness drive through the Superior National Forest and the Kabetogama State Forest. Though part of the Echo Trail is gravel, it is well maintained. In places, large white pines (with black bark) and red (Norway) pines are present. The road passes over Archean rocks about 2,700 million years old, covered with thin ground moraine deposited by the Rainy lobe.

To reach the Echo Trail, drive about 1 mile east of Ely on MN 169 and turn north on County Road 88. Roadcuts on both roads near the intersection are in pillowed Ely Greenstone, lava cooled beneath water and later metamorphosed.

The pillows are now in a vertical position because they were tilted during the Algoman mountain building event about 2,700 million years ago.

On the northeast edge of Shagawa Lake, 1.5 miles north of MN 169 and 0.8 mile from the intersection with County Road 116, is a tan to brown roadcut in the Shagawa Lake Fault, a major fault and shear zone. Thin slices of broken and sheared rock moved past each other, and the resultant rock is composed of thin, shiny mica-rich layers. Hot, hydrothermal, ore-bearing solutions passed through the shear zone, leaving behind elements, such as the potassium that is now in the mica. Drill holes near this roadcut showed traces of gold. The brownish color of the roadcut is probably due to oxidized pyrite and iron carbonate.

Weathering and erosion by running water for nearly 2,700 million years, and by glacial ice in the past 1.8 million years, have formed the topographic low over this shear zone. Both this roadcut and Shagawa Lake are located on this relatively low ground. The fault is on the boundary between metasediments of the Knife Lake Group on the south and greenstones of the Newton Lake Formation on the north, both of Archean age. The sheared rock could have originally been either rock, now greatly altered by the hydrothermal fluids.

A little over 0.5 mile west of this exposure of the shear zone, and within 0.2 mile of the Echo Trail junction, are roadcuts in greenstone of the Newton Lake Formation. In the middle roadcut is a vertical shear zone about 6 feet wide. Note the quartz veins that were likely precipitated from hot waters. The greenstone on either side of this thin shear zone is more massive.

A narrow shear zone between more massive greenstones along
County Road 88 just east of the Echo Trail junction.

The terrain just north of the Echo Trail junction is topographically much higher than the shear zone because it is massive greenstone of the Newton Lake Formation. Several roadcuts are present in the greenstone along the southern-most 3 miles of the Echo Trail.

It is worth stopping about 3 miles from the south end of the Echo Trail at the intersection with Somero Road. That side road and a power line are located in what may appear to be an artificial trench, but this natural topographic low was formed by weathering and erosion along the Burntside Fault, one of several major faults that splay off the east end of the Vermilion Fault. The Burntside Fault separates lower-metamorphic-grade greenschist rocks of the Newton Lake Formation on the south from higher-metamorphic-grade amphibolitic rocks of the Vermilion Granitic Complex on the north. The north side has been uplifted about 1 mile and has been moved horizontally many miles to the northeast. Other studies to the west of this locality indicate that there has been about 20 miles of similar (right-lateral) movement along the Vermilion Fault, one of the major boundaries between terranes of the Canadian Shield. The Vermilion Fault separates the Vermilion District greenstone belt of the Wawa Subprovince (a volcanic-plutonic terrane) on the south from the Quetico Sub-province (a metasedimentary-plutonic terrane) on the north.

Somero Road follows a topographic low over the Burntside Fault.

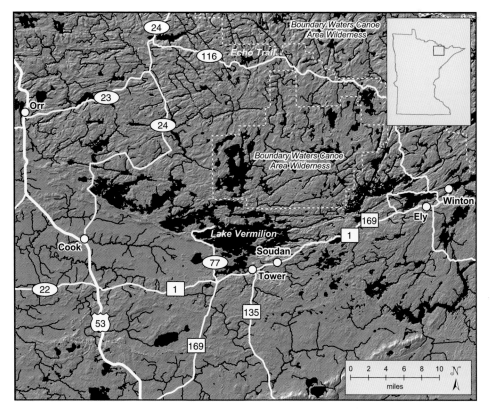

Landscape image of the Archean terrane north of Ely. Glacial deposits are thin here, so features in the bedrock are visible in the northern half of the area. Many of the straight lines are faults. The flat area between Cook and Lake Vermilion is the eastern end of Glacial Lake Agassiz. The flat area southeast of Tower is partly outwash and partly the bed of Glacial Lake Norwood.

A large gravel and sand pit in a glacial outwash deposit is present east of the Echo Trail at the east end of Burntside Lake. On the ridge just north of and above Burntside Lake, there are several roadcuts in migmatite, part of the Vermilion Granitic Complex. The migmatite contains older black bands of biotite schist interbedded with light gray or pink bands of younger granite that crystallized at depth.

The bedrock from about 6 miles north of Burntside Lake to the intersection of the Echo Trail with County Road 24 is massive pinkish granite of the Vermilion Granitic Complex. You can see numerous small outcrops along the Echo Trail, but other evidence of the granitic bedrock is the presence of abundant glacial boulders of granite along the road. These are especially prominent in cutover areas where logging operations have made them more visible.

The granite forms a large batholith that is surrounded by migmatite, which covers a large area west of the batholith. D. L. Southwick, who has studied the Vermilion Granitic Complex in detail, has suggested that the migmatite formed

Migmatite of the Vermilion Granitic Complex in a roadcut on County Road 116 just north of Burntside Lake.

Massive granite of the Vermilion Granitic Complex in a roadcut along the Echo Trail.

Granitic boulders in glacial till are more visible in cutover areas. The bedrock in this area of thin till is granite, so the boulders are locally derived.

Schist-rich migmatite of the Vermilion Granitic Complex along County Road 23. The light-colored rocks are veins of granite. The vertical lines are holes drilled for blasting the roadcut.

the roof above the major granite body. During regional deformation, the eastern part of the complex was uplifted more than the western part, thus exposing the deeper batholith.

From the junction of County Road 116 (Echo Trail) and County Road 24, you could continue 7.5 miles northward on County Road 24 to Crane Lake and one entrance to Voyageurs National Park, the Boundary Waters Canoe Area Wilderness, and Ontario's Quetico Provincial Park. Several excellent roadcuts of migmatite are present along this road.

If you head toward Orr on County Road 23, all the roadcuts are in schist-rich migmatite of the Vermilion Granitic Complex. All glacial deposits are from the Rainy lobe except for about 2 to 3 miles immediately east of Orr on County Road 23, where the easternmost ground moraine of the Des Moines lobe is present.

NATIONAL FOREST HIGHWAY 11
(COUNTY ROADS 15, 16, AND 110)
Silver Bay—Hoyt Lakes
61 miles

The route between Silver Bay and Hoyt Lakes, once used mostly by seasonal logging trucks, was upgraded and designated the Superior National Forest Scenic Byway in 2003. Most of the land it crosses is part of the Superior National Forest. Glacial deposits blanket the bedrock along this route, but a few roadcuts and exposures of gabbro protrude through the drift. The bedrock formed 1,100 million years ago in the Midcontinent Rift System, the major rift that started to split North America. Near Silver Bay and Lake Superior, the rocks are mafic lava flows, but most of the bedrock between Silver Bay and a point a few miles south of Hoyt Lakes is intrusive coarse-grained gabbro of the Duluth Complex. See **MN 61: Duluth—Canadian Border** for information about the Silver Bay area.

Between Silver Bay and Forest Service Road 397 near the bridge over the Beaver River (about 12 miles from Silver Bay), you may be able to see the reddish color of glacial deposits through the grassed-over roadcuts. This color is the main clue these are deposits of the Superior lobe, which moved down the Lake Superior Basin from northeast to southwest. The color was mainly derived from red glacial lake clays deposited in early glacial lakes in the Lake Superior Basin. In contrast, the glacial deposits between this point and Hoyt Lakes are a tan color, indicative of deposition by the Rainy lobe, which also moved toward the southwest but did not have access to the red sediments.

About 8 miles from Silver Bay, watch for a low, flat gabbro outcrop on the north side of the road, across a broad ditch. The obvious glacial striations are oriented west-northwest, as are the crescentic gouges, indicating that the thick Superior lobe ice spilled up and out of the rock-sided Lake Superior Basin.

Tan glacial deposits are visible near the intersection with Forest Service Road 397 and the Beaver River bridge, and especially in two large gravel pits located within 1 mile of this intersection on the south side of the road. On the glacial map of this area, this gravel pit is shown in Mille Lacs moraine, which should

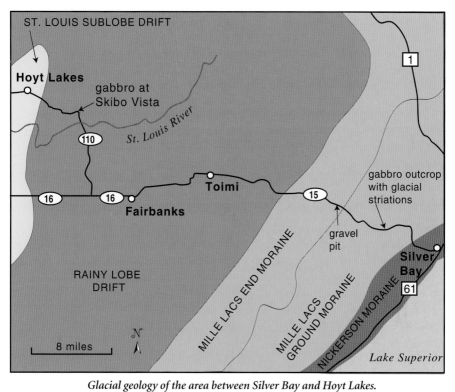

Glacial geology of the area between Silver Bay and Hoyt Lakes.
—Modified from Hobbs and Goebel, 1982

The west-northwest orientations of glacial striations on this gabbro, about 8 miles west of Silver Bay, are from rocks embedded in ice of the Superior lobe as it overflowed the Lake Superior Basin.

be reddish deposits. The tan deposits you can see are likely from the underlying Rainy lobe. You will find abundant cobbles and boulders of black gabbro and a bright red rock eroded from the granitic portion of the Duluth Complex.

Just west of County Road 2 on the north side of County Road 15 is a deep gravel pit in glacial till of a drumlin, with the access road blocked by large gabbro boulders displaying a variety of textures. Some of the boulders have crystals of plagioclase as large as 1 inch in diameter. Drive northward about 2.5 miles on Country Road 2 to see a grove of 300-year-old pines.

Over a 25-mile-wide area between the Cloquet River on the southeast and the St. Louis River on the northwest, the drainage is controlled by northeast-southwest-oriented drumlins of the Toimi Drumlin Field. Hundreds of teardrop-shaped hills were sculpted beneath the southwestward-moving Rainy lobe about 15,000 years ago. The drumlins are 1 to 2 miles long, one-quarter mile wide, and 30 to 50 feet high. All of the many streams in this area flow toward the southwest along rather straight courses. Several small lakes and swamps have the same orientation, and their locations are clearly controlled by the drumlins. The drumlin field gets its name from Toimi, a century-old Finnish community.

Fairbanks is located near two elongate lakes, Bassett Lake and Cadotte Lake, whose locations are controlled by drumlins. The railroad that crosses

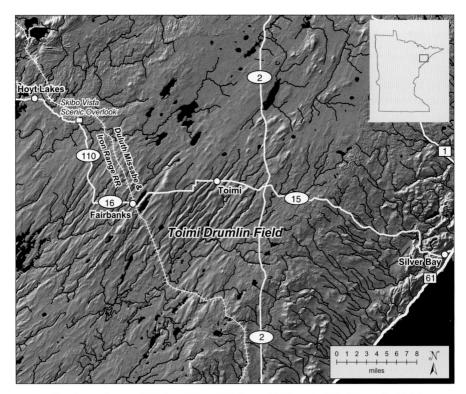

Landscape image of National Forest Highway 11. Note the Toimi Drumlin Field.

View to the northwest of the Giants Range, a ridge of granite, from Skibo Vista.

the highway near Fairbanks was built as the Duluth, Missabe & Iron Range Railroad to haul iron ore from the Vermilion Iron Range near Soudan to the port at Two Harbors for shipment to the steel mills on the lower Great Lakes.

Don't miss the view from the Skibo Vista Scenic Overlook, about 9 miles south of Hoyt Lakes. The overlook is on the highest point south of the Giants Range, and a fire tower (now gone) was once anchored to the solid gabbro bedrock here. From the overlook, you can see the topographically high Giants Range about 10 miles to the northwest. On this hilltop, cobbles and boulders of pink granite show that glacial ice once covered this high point. You can see glacially polished gabbro in a roadcut just south of the vista. Glacial striations on this outcrop range from azimuth 200 to 240 degrees, indicating the southwesterly movement of the Rainy lobe, under which the numerous glacial drumlins of the region also were formed.

About 5 miles south of Hoyt Lakes, the highway crosses the St. Louis River. Note how small it is here, compared to its large size where it enters Lake Superior at Duluth. The many tributaries along its course have greatly increased the water volume. Hoyt Lakes is situated on the 1,870-million-year-old Virginia Formation, which overlies the Biwabik Iron Formation, both deposited in a sea in the Animikie Basin. However, the Virginia Formation is not exposed, and only one natural exposure of it exists on the entire Mesabi Iron Range.

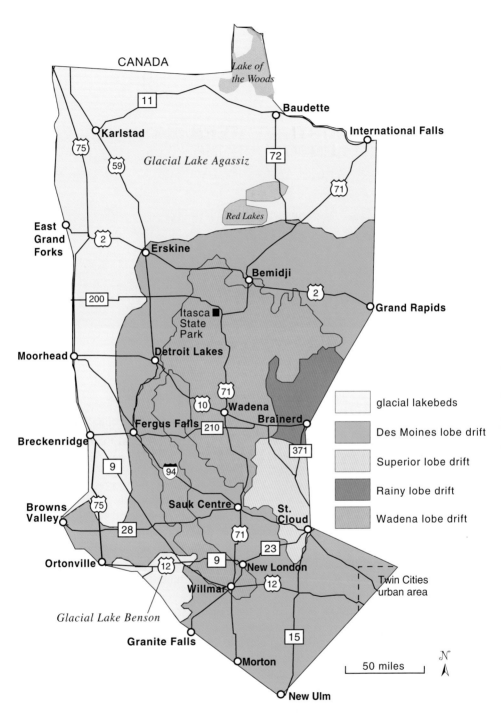

Glacial geology of northwestern and central Minnesota.

NORTHWESTERN AND CENTRAL MINNESOTA
Glacial Moraines and Lakes

Most of Minnesota's 10,000-plus lakes are located in the northwestern and central part of the state, which we could call "lake and moraine terrain." While most are kettle lakes, some of them, including Lake of the Woods and Upper and Lower Red Lakes, are remnants of Glacial Lake Agassiz, which existed in Minnesota from about 11,700 to 9,400 years ago. Though there a few outcrops of bedrock in this region, particularly along the Rainy River, you'll have more luck finding ancient shorelines, drumlins, and kames.

GLACIAL GEOLOGY

The flat country of northwestern Minnesota is only the small southern portion of the lakebed of Glacial Lake Agassiz. It extends from central Minnesota north nearly to Hudson Bay and covers parts of Saskatchewan, Manitoba, and Ontario, although not all the lakebed was covered by water at the same time. The lake's history and demise were complex and sometimes catastrophic. It had several major outlets, one far to the northwest in Canada, one to the north to Hudson Bay, and one to the east via Lake Nipigon and Lake Superior. Glacial ice covered these outlets in the lake's early years. Its southern outlet was Glacial River Warren, which cut the broad valley now occupied by the Minnesota River. At times, Glacial River Warren was a huge river—the size of its valley suggests catastrophic floods as the lake emptied.

Glacial Lake Agassiz formed about 11,700 years ago when the Des Moines lobe melted back north of the modern continental divide. The meltwater was trapped between the ice to its north and moraines to its south. Eventually the lake became deep enough that it overtopped the glacial till and cut the valley where Big Stone Lake now sits. As the ice retreated northward, the lake covered the land. When lower outlets were exposed in the north about 10,700 years ago, the water drained to the north and the southern outlet was abandoned temporarily. When ice readvanced about 10,000 years ago, the northern outlets were closed and Glacial Lake Agassiz reappeared in Minnesota for a couple hundred years at least.

The water level in Glacial Lake Agassiz fluctuated as the ice receded northward and at times readvanced. The water level also changed when the northern outlets were exposed and when the southern outlet was lowered by erosion. When the water level was constant for a while, beaches developed on the shores of the lake. Waves and currents reworked the underlying Des Moines lobe glacial drift during these times, so the subtle beach landforms are made up largely of sand and gravel. The beaches are as wide as about 500 feet but rise only 10 to 15 feet above the adjacent lakebed.

Four major beaches have been identified in Minnesota, each named for a village where it is prominent. The highest and oldest beach is the Herman beach, at an elevation of 1,075 feet. The Norcross beach is at 1,040 feet, and the Tintah beach is at 1,020 feet. The topographically lowest and youngest beach is the Campbell beach, at about 981 feet. Much of the bed of Glacial Lake Agassiz in the northwestern part of the state is at an elevation of 800 to 900 feet, so when the lake was at its highest level, lake depth was probably as much as 300 feet in places. The most continuous beaches are the Herman and the Campbell.

The weight of the thick ice sheet depressed Earth's crust, so after the ice melted, the land rose slowly. The postglacial rebound tilted the once-horizontal beaches up toward the north. For example, the Herman beach at the town of Fertile, 75 miles north of Herman, is about 100 feet higher than at Herman. Also, a beach 250 miles to the north in Manitoba that is correlated with the Herman beach in Minnesota is about 175 feet higher than the Herman beach at Herman. The glacial ice was thicker to the north and persisted for a longer time, so the crust there was depressed more than it was in the southern Lake Agassiz region and therefore rose more once the ice melted.

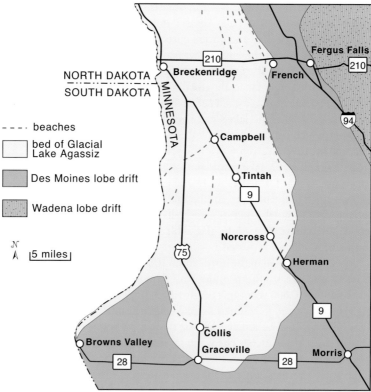

Generalized map of beaches in the southern portion of Glacial Lake Agassiz. Note the four beaches that cross MN 9, each named after the nearby town.
—Modified from Hobbs and Goebel, 1982

The ages of the beaches have been determined by radiocarbon dating of pieces of wood buried in the beach deposits. The Campbell beach, the youngest of the four, dates at 11,000 to 9,500 years before the present. The Herman, the oldest, is closer to 12,000 years old.

The Red River of the North meanders northward along the lowest part of the original lake basin, now excellent farmland with nutrient-rich soil formed from the fine-grained silt and clay and the prairie plants. The river technically begins at Breckenridge where the Bois de Sioux and Otter Tail Rivers merge. The Red River Valley is 40 to 50 miles wide and about 160 miles long in Minnesota, but the river itself is 395 miles long because it meanders so much on the flat lakebed. It loses less than 200 feet in elevation between its origin and the Minnesota-Manitoba border. The valley is very susceptible to flooding in the spring, with record floods in 1997 and 2009.

Whereas much of the lakebed of Glacial Lake Agassiz is ideal for farming, some of the former lakebed is bog, too low and too wet. The most notable example is the Big Bog crossed by Minnesota 72 north of Upper Red Lake.

All four glacial lobes—Rainy, Superior, Wadena, and Des Moines—lived and died in central Minnesota, ending their active lives, so to speak, with the building up of end moraines as monuments to their former existence. These end moraines include the Alexandria moraine, the St. Croix moraine, the Itasca moraine, and the Mille Lacs moraine, all formed during the last major

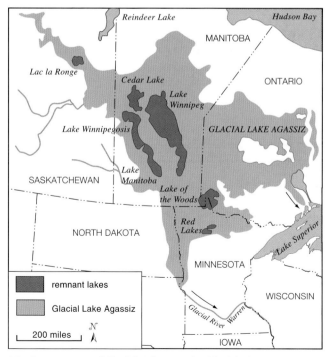

Maximum extent of Glacial Lake Agassiz. Glacial River Warren was the lake's southern outlet. —From Ojakangas and Matsch, 1982

ice advance, the Wisconsin glaciation. The Alexandria moraine, deposited by the Wadena lobe about 24,000 years ago and then blanketed again by the Des Moines lobe about 14,000 years ago, is the highest. The glacial sediments in the moraine are as thick as 500 feet. Note on the glacial map on page 197 that drift of the southwest-moving Des Moines lobe flanks the Alexandria moraine on both sides. The Des Moines lobe made thirteen separate advances, each shorter than the previous one.

Drumlin fields are nearly as prominent as moraines in central Minnesota. They are comprised of hundreds of teardrop-shaped hills formed under the ice lobes and are excellent indicators of the directions of glacial movement.

BEDROCK GEOLOGY

Bedrock exposures are rare in northwestern and central Minnesota because of the thick glacial drift. Some occur as scattered outcrops along the Rainy River, some just south of Lake of the Woods, others in the Northwest Angle, (the northernmost point in the Lower 48), and still others in the St. Cloud area.

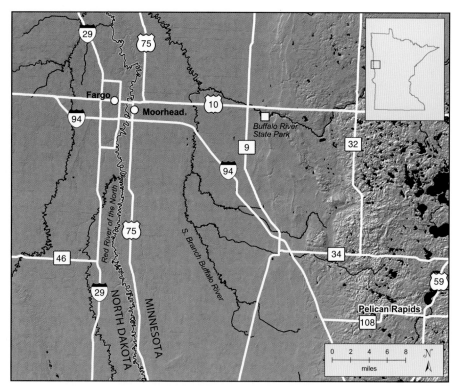

Landscape image of a portion of northwestern Minnesota, showing hilly glacial moraine with numerous lakes, the bed of Glacial Lake Agassiz, and beaches within the eastern portion of the lakebed. Note how the rivers meander over the flat lakebed.

However, gravity measurements taken on the land surface and magnetic measurements taken from specially equipped airplanes provide much information on the bedrock beneath the glacial drift. The generally basaltic volcanic rocks are distinguished by higher densities and higher magnetic signatures relative to the granites and metasedimentary rocks. The thick glacial drift may be masking valuable ore deposits, for mines are present in similar rocks to the east-northeast in Canada.

Nearly all the buried bedrock in northwestern Minnesota is Archean in age, about 2,700 million years old. These include volcanic rocks of the Wabigoon Subprovince exposed to the north in Ontario and the poorly exposed Quetico Subprovince of metasedimentary rocks to the south. These two subprovinces are separated by the Rainy Lake–Seine River Fault Zone, formed where the Quetico Subprovince was added to the continent when it collided from the south about 2,700 million years ago. The collision was not at right angles, so there was also a horizontal component of movement along the fault, a little like that on the San Andreas Fault in California.

The only rocks that are not about 2,700 million years old are northwest-trending gabbro dikes that are as wide as 400 feet and can be traced intermittently for about 200 miles in Minnesota and Canada. The dikes are about 2,100 million years old based on ages of similar dikes near Lake Kabetogama, Minnesota, and in Ontario. This swarm of parallel dikes is called by two names: the Fort Frances Dikes and the Kenora-Kabetogama Dikes. The magma came up along large cracks that apparently formed when the continent started to break up; however, the breakup was an abortive one. The dikes cut across all the other rocks in the region. They are more resistant to erosion than the older Archean rocks and protrude out of the low-lying countryside. Geologists checking the edges of the dikes can find exposures of the Archean country rock into which the dikes intruded, thus adding to their knowledge of the bedrock geology.

The southern part of this large region also contains a few rock exposures, especially in the St. Cloud–Mille Lacs Lake area. These are Archean gneisses, Early Proterozoic metasedimentary rocks such as those in and south of Little Falls, and Early Proterozoic granitic rocks such as those near St. Cloud. The granites are quite undeformed, indicating that they were intruded into the other rocks after the deformational phase of the Penokean mountain building event. Radio-metric dates suggest that the granites are 1,800 to 1,700 million years old.

Road Guides in Northwestern and Central Minnesota

INTERSTATE 94
Twin Cities—Moorhead
224 miles

Between the Twin Cities and St. Cloud, I-94 is on glacial drift deposited by the Grantsburg sublobe of the Des Moines lobe. Where the topography is gently rolling or hilly, the drift is till; where it is flat, the drift is outwash. In the vicinity of Monticello, the highway is on a terrace of the Mississippi River for a few miles.

There are no bedrock exposures along I-94, but there are many exposures of granite just east of the highway in the St. Cloud area and several miles to the west at Cold Spring and Rockville. About one hundred quarries have been in operation in this area at one time or another, but only four are presently active. For discussion of the granite, see the road guides for **US 10: Twin Cities—Moorhead** and **MN 23: St. Cloud—Granite Falls**.

West of St. Cloud, look to the north and south for higher hills a few miles in the distance. These hills, and those on the highway between St. Joseph and Avon, are composed of the westernmost end moraine deposits of the Superior lobe. Here the lobe stopped its westward movement. This glacial drift, reddish in color, was derived from the Lake Superior Basin and Ontario, farther to the northeast. It is quite distinct from the deposits of the Des Moines lobe, which are gray to tan and were derived from the northwest. Grass covers most of the drift, so you won't see this color difference from the interstate.

Between Avon and Alexandria, you are driving over moraines and minor outwash deposited on the eastern edge of the Des Moines lobe. Near Melrose during the construction of I-94 in the mid-1960s, bones of an extinct bison, *Bison occidentalis*, were unearthed from a small peat bog. They were dated at more than 7,000 years old using the radiocarbon method.

Alexandria is built upon glacial outwash of the Des Moines lobe. The nearby lakes are kettle lakes, formed when blocks of ice buried beneath glacial sediment melted.

Kensington Runestone

In downtown Alexandria is a 28-foot-tall statue of a Viking. He is standing there because the Kensington Runestone was found near the village of that name, about 15 miles southwest of Alexandria. It is a flat piece of metagraywacke with dimensions of 31 inches by 16 inches by 5.5 inches and weighs 202 pounds. It is on display in the Runestone Museum in downtown Alexandria, and a giant replica of the stone can be seen a mile to the east, where Business US 52 and Sixth Avenue merge.

In 1898, Olof Ohman, a Swedish immigrant farmer, discovered this large flat stone entwined by tree roots while clearing land near Kensington. The stone had carvings on it that proved to be letters, or runes, of a Norse alphabet. While long declared a fake by runologists, it is now being reinvestigated, with

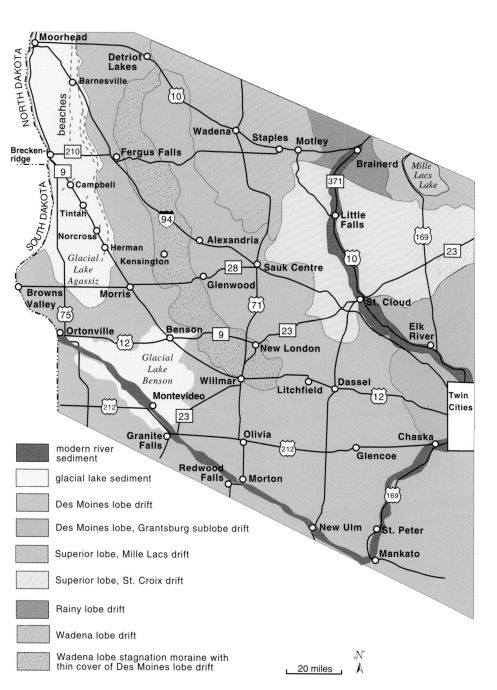

modern river sediment

glacial lake sediment

Des Moines lobe drift

Des Moines lobe, Grantsburg sublobe drift

Superior lobe, Mille Lacs drift

Superior lobe, St. Croix drift

Rainy lobe drift

Wadena lobe drift

Wadena lobe stagnation moraine with thin cover of Des Moines lobe drift

20 miles

N

Glacial geology of central Minnesota. —Modified from Hobbs and Goebel, 1982

Bones of Bison occidentalis, *an extinct bison, are on display at the University of Minnesota Duluth.*

an emphasis on geological as well as rune data. Did Vikings beat Christopher Columbus to the New World?

Alexandria Moraine

Between the Garfield exit northwest of Alexandria to the Dalton exit south of Fergus Falls, I-94 is on the high-relief Alexandria moraine, one of the most prominent large-scale glacial features in Minnesota. It was deposited by the Wadena lobe about 24,000 years ago and modified by the Des Moines lobe, which overrode the region and moved southward down both the east and west sides of the moraine only 14,000 years ago. Notice the abundance of lakes and swamps in the topographic lows. These depressions are all the result of the melting of pieces of glacial ice that were buried by glacial drift before they melted.

The Glacial Ridge Trail Scenic Byway is a 245-mile-long road route with several loops that takes you on a tour of the Alexandria moraine. It begins in Alexandria and heads south on MN 29 and includes some of the state's most rugged and beautiful glacial terrain, including Glacial Lakes State Park.

The western edge of the Alexandria moraine forms a continental divide between waters that flow west to the Red River of the North and hence to Hudson Bay, and waters that flow eastward to the Mississippi River and hence to the Gulf of Mexico. The interstate crosses the divide about 8 miles southwest of Fergus Falls at the junction with US 59.

Kames at Glacial Lakes State Park.

Fergus Falls to Moorhead

Fergus Falls is located on a north-south strip of Des Moines drift about 10 miles wide that was deposited to the west of the Alexandria moraine. The highway trends obliquely across this till for a distance of about 30 miles. This terrain is topographically more subdued than the Alexandria moraine and has fewer lakes.

Between a point just north of the Rothsay exit (which you can take to view a 13-foot-tall prairie chicken) and the Minnesota–North Dakota border, the terrain is flat; this is the lakebed of Glacial Lake Agassiz. Beaches that formed along the east shore of this huge lake are very subtle north-south trending ridges that cross the interstate at a low angle. Try to spot them at about milepost 33, between mileposts 29 and 28, and near the Barnesville exit between mileposts 25 and 24. These slight topographic highs are a little more obvious when traveling from west to east.

The Red River of the North, which flows north toward Hudson Bay, separates the cities of Moorhead, Minnesota, from Fargo, North Dakota. The Hjemkomst Center in Moorhead houses a replica of a Viking boat built near Moorhead and actually sailed to Norway.

US 2
Grand Rapids—East Grand Forks
182 miles

Along US 2 between Grand Rapids and East Grand Forks, glacial deposits blanket the area to a depth of 200 to 400 feet, and in places even thicker. There is only one place where you can see a small rock outcrop. Between mileposts 180 and 181, a few miles west of Grand Rapids, is the Pokegama Dam Recreation Area on the Mississippi River. On the far side of the dam, part of the riverbank is a small exposure of the Pokegama Quartzite, about 1,900 million years old, deposited in an ancient ocean. The Pokegama underlies the economically important Biwabik Iron Formation.

Grand Rapids is considered the western end of the Mesabi Iron Range, and there are old high-grade iron ore pits a few miles to the west and northeast. Part of the city is located on end moraine of the St. Louis sublobe, and part is on outwash plain. The flat area between Grand Rapids and Cohasset is on glacial outwash. Between Cohasset and Deer River, US 2 crosses ground moraine of the St. Louis sublobe. Deer River, Ball Club, and Bena are all located on flat land, outwash of the Des Moines lobe. Watch for the bridge over the Mississippi River, still very small, just west of Ball Club.

Bena, named for the Ojibwe word for ruffed grouse, is on the south shore of Lake Winnibigoshish. It is the fourth largest lake completely within Minnesota, but its size has been increased by a dam at the east end of the lake that impounds the Mississippi River. Its long name, commonly shortened to "Winni" in the vernacular, means "a body of dirty water." This shallow lake has a sandy lakebed easily stirred up by waves, making the water dirty. The lake is located on a broad area of sandy glacial outwash.

Leech Lake, Minnesota's third largest, is a few miles off the highway just south of Bena. The end moraine of the Wadena lobe forms a natural dam along

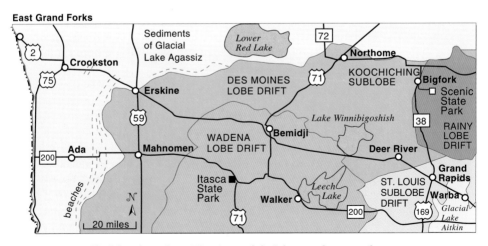

Glacial geology along US 2. Areas of glacial outwash are not shown.
—Modified from Hobbs and Goebel, 1982

*The Pokegama Quartzite on the bank of the Mississippi
River at the Pokegama Dam Recreation Area.*

its eastern, southern, and western shores. On the south side of Leech Lake at a park at Whipholt, a historical marker commemorates an 1898 battle between the U.S. Infantry and the victorious Ojibwe, the last battle of the Indian Wars. The marker is embedded in a long stone wall of trimmed glacial erratics that consist mostly of granites but also include black basalts and gabbros that probably were not found in the local glacial till.

Between Bena and Bagley, a distance of about 60 miles, US 2 crosses over flat areas of St. Louis sublobe glacial outwash interrupted by higher relief areas, especially just east of Bemidji. All of these higher areas are older Wadena lobe ground moraine. Note the large gravel pit operations in the moraine east of Bemidji between mileposts 122 and 123, and also at milepost 126.

Lake Bemidji

Bemidji is built on a flat outwash plain, and Lake Bemidji, like many other lakes in the area, is a kettle lake formed where glacial ice was buried by glacial sediment and eventually melted, forming a depression. The Ojibwe called the lake *Bemidjigumaug,* meaning "cross water," or "the lake which the river flows directly across." The Mississippi enters the southern end of the lake and exits on the east side, and the current where the river crosses the lake is noticeable. The lake is also home to a unique filamentous green algae species, *Cladophora aegagropila,* which grows in spherical shapes on the lakebed. There are only a few other places where this unique lake ball species is known to grow, including a lake in Japan and a lake in Iceland. A short hike in Lake Bemidji State Park, at

This roadcut, Wadena lobe till exposed during 1996 highway construction on US 2 at milepost 121 near Bemidji, is now grassed over. The boulder at the upper left is Archean gneiss, and the boulder at the upper right is Archean granite.

the northeast end of Lake Bemidji, will bring you to Rocky Point, a bluff composed of end moraine of the St. Louis sublobe.

Solway to East Grand Forks

The area between Solway and Shevlin is ground moraine of the Wadena lobe. The presence of boulders in nearby pastures shows that this is unsorted material, glacial till, deposited by glacial ice.

Between milepost 79, west of Bagley, and Fosston, at about milepost 67, US 2 passes over hummocky stagnation moraine deposited along the eastern edge of the Des Moines lobe. Notice the numerous small lakes, ponds, and swamps, as near Lengby. These are kettle lakes, formed over spots where buried ice melted as the glacier stagnated and stopped moving.

Between Fosston and about milepost 57, located between McIntosh and Erskine, US 2 is on a gently rolling area of ground moraine of the Des Moines lobe. McIntosh is situated on the west bank of an old drainage channel formed by glacial meltwater flowing into Glacial Lake Agassiz, which was situated just to the north. Erskine is located just west of a small area of stagnation moraine deposited by the Des Moines lobe.

The entire distance between Erskine and East Grand Forks is on the flat bed of Glacial Lake Agassiz, which formed on previously deposited ground moraine of the Des Moines lobe. Waves in the lake reworked some of the moraine material

Bouldery pasture in Wadena lobe glacial till along US 2 between Solway and Shevlin.

Black soil overlies a thin layer of fine-grained lakebed sediments of Glacial Lake Agassiz and two glacial tills in a bank of the Clearwater River at Red Lake Falls.

into its lakebed. Over the eastern portion of the lakebed, where the water was shallower and wave and current energy was higher, there is sand and gravel. The fine-grained lake sediment on top of the till is thin, so farmers frequently encounter boulders and add them to the boulder piles you can see in the flat fields. Farther west the lakebed is dominantly silt and fine sand, and nearer the North Dakota border, where the water was deeper and the lake energy still lower, it is clay and clayey silt. Mentor is situated on an old beach, and there are big gravel pits between mileposts 45 and 46 where beach sediment and the underlying till are being removed.

If you want to get a look at the glacial till underlying the fine-grained sediment of Glacial Lake Agassiz, take MN 32 north from Marcoux to Red Lake Falls, a distance of 9 miles. From the bridge over the Clearwater River, you can see a high riverbank composed of the till. If you want a short hike to get a better look, go to Riverside Park in Red Lake Falls and walk upstream to other exposures along the river.

US 10
Twin Cities—Moorhead
231 miles
See map on page 197

Between the Twin Cities and St. Cloud, US 10 is on terraces of the Mississippi River, with glacial drift of the Grantsburg sublobe of the Des Moines lobe located on both sides of the river valley. In Elk River, near the intersection with US 169, look for the flat terraces formed by the downcutting Mississippi River before it formed its present channel. A geological marker at a rest area just west of this intersection describes the glacial deposits of the region. Just south of St. Cloud is a large gravel pit on the floodplain of the Mississippi.

Near St. Cloud, look for granite exposures and granite quarries. The first quarries were developed in 1868 to obtain granite for construction of the Minnesota State Reformatory. A 22-foot-high granite wall forms the perimeter of the reformatory, just west of US 10 on the southeast side of St. Cloud 2 miles south of the intersection with MN 23.

The granites were intruded into the bowels of the Penokean Mountain range, a fold-and-thrust belt that formed about 1,850 million years ago from Minnesota to the Upper Peninsula of Michigan. Many of the granites of the St. Cloud area have dates ranging from 1,780 to about 1,730 million years, so they postdate the actual mountain building. Because granites crystallize slowly at depth but here are now exposed at Earth's surface, several miles of rock above the granite must have been eroded away. Some formal names for the various granites quarried here are the Reformatory, Rockville, and St. Cloud Red.

Between St. Cloud and Little Falls, drift of the St. Croix advance of the Superior lobe is present on both sides of the highway. Between Sauk Rapids and Sartell, the valley of the Mississippi River narrows so that there is hardly any floodplain. The glacial deposits are thin here, and the bedrock is near the surface.

Between mileposts 169 and 170, about 1 mile north of Sartell, there is a small roadcut on the east side of the road that contains a mixture of fine-grained gray diorite and coarse pink granite that is 1,780 million years old. Although the rocks in this outcrop have many different colors and textures, they all crystallized from magma at about the same time. This is a good place to stop and see the granite because the shoulder of the road is wide.

In Little Falls there is a dam across the Mississippi River built on the outcrops of the Little Falls Formation, estimated to be 2,100 million years old. Biotite schist of this formation is exposed on the riverbank at a small city park near the east end of the dam.

The Little Falls Formation is also present in Blanchard Park, which is on the Mississippi River about 7 miles south of Little Falls. To get there, take County Road 231 to the west of US 10 for about 1 mile, then turn left on County Road 258 (Hilton Road) for about 0.5 mile, and then turn right on Garland Road and follow it about 0.3 mile to the park. On the south side of the railroad trestle at water level, the biotite schist contains dark staurolite crystals, some twinned in the form of a cross. This metamorphic mineral formed during the Penokean mountain building event. Prior to metamorphism, the rock was made of muddy and sandy sediments.

Between Little Falls and a point a few miles south of Motley, you are driving through hilly terrain formed by moraines of the St. Croix advances of the Superior lobe. About halfway between Little Falls and Randall, at a point about 5 miles north of Little Falls, the highway crosses an esker complex.

Want to see an exposure of sheared Early Proterozoic greenstone? If so, look at a railroad cut in Randall just east of the town's water tower. Notice the quartz veins and pods in the fragmented greenstone.

Greenstone in a railroad cut in Randall.

Motley is situated on glacial outwash. The long stretch of highway between Motley and Detroit Lakes mostly crosses Wadena lobe till and outwash with an age of about 28,000 to 24,000 years. Look for boulder piles lovingly accumulated by the farmers.

US 10 passes through the Wadena Drumlin Field, a fan-shaped array of about 1,200 large teardrop-shaped glacial hills formed beneath the Wadena lobe as it moved toward the south and southwest. Aldrich is located on a low drumlin, but otherwise they are not very visible.

To get a better look at the drumlins, take a 25-mile loop trip and end up back on US 10. Turn south at Staples onto MN 210, which passes over many drumlins between Staples and Hewitt, a real roller-coaster ride. At Hewitt, take US 71 north to Wadena and the junction with US 10. Notice the numerous rock piles along this route. See the road guide for **MN 210: Brainerd—Breckenridge** for a photo and description of the drumlins.

Just west of Wadena, US 10 passes over the Leaf River, which flows in an old glacial outwash channel that carried waters eastward from the melting Des Moines lobe. This channel cuts across the Wadena Drumlin Field. The Des Moines lobe moved into the area a few tens of miles to the west of Wadena about 14,000 years ago. Perham, Luce, and Frazee are located on glacial out-

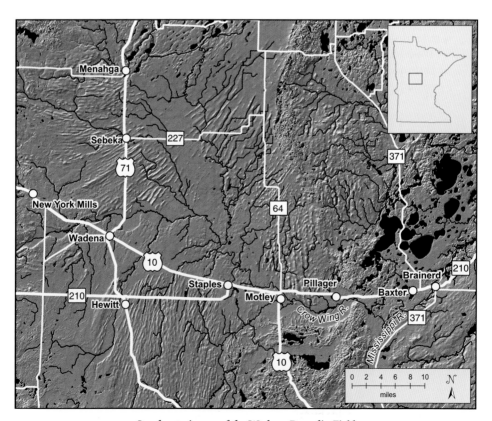

Landscape image of the Wadena Drumlin Field.

wash likely derived from the same melting ice. Between Frazee and Detroit Lakes, US 10 passes through a gap cut through the high Alexandria moraine by these eastward-flowing waters.

Along the highway in Detroit Lakes is a historical marker about the lakes of Minnesota, an appropriate topic here because there are dozens of lakes in all directions from Detroit Lakes. Most are kettle lakes formed at sites where blocks of ice were buried in either stagnation moraine or glacial outwash.

Between Detroit Lakes and Hawley, notice the irregular topography of lakes and swamps that formed on the stagnation moraine of the Des Moines lobe. Look for the large gravel pit operation near milepost 23, where some boulders are 3 feet in diameter.

Just west of Hawley are four prominent shoreline beaches of Glacial Lake Agassiz. They are barely perceptible because they are broad and have a low relief. Look for them at about milepost 20, between mileposts 18 and 19, between mileposts 16 and 17, and between mileposts 14 and 15. This last beach, the Campbell beach, is the youngest of the beaches.

Buffalo River State Park

You can see the Campbell beach, the youngest beach of Glacial Lake Agassiz, along the eastern edge of Buffalo River State Park. The park is also noteworthy because it partially contains the Bluestem Prairie Scientific and Natural Area, one of the finest and largest remaining prairie tracts in Minnesota.

US 12

Twin Cities—Ortonville

157 miles

See map on page 197

The land is forested between the Twin Cities and the vicinity of Litchfield, but between Litchfield and the Dakota border at Ortonville you are driving on prairie grasslands. Nearly all of the trees here have been planted by farmers.

US 12 between the Twin Cities and Ortonville crosses glacial deposits of the Des Moines lobe. Between the Twin Cities and Delano, the hilly terrain is end moraine. Between Delano and Atwater, it is stagnation moraine, as evidenced by the numerous lakes. Between Atwater and Willmar, the Des Moines lobe deposited a thin layer of till on top of the southern end of the prominent Alexandria moraine, made of till of the Wadena lobe. This moraine extends for 125 miles to the northwest. Between Willmar and DeGraff, the area is covered by ground moraine. Between DeGraff and a point 4 miles west of Danvers, a total distance of about 19 miles, you are driving on the flat lakebed of Glacial Lake Benson. This short-lived glacial lake was about 40 miles in diameter. It formed on ground moraine of the Des Moines lobe as this lobe was melting back to the north of the lake.

Between Danvers and Ortonville, most of the terrain is higher, gently rolling ground and stagnation moraine of the Des Moines lobe. Look for rock piles, gathered from the fields by farmers over the last century and a half, near mileposts 35 and 39.

Just east of Ortonville is a pull-off overlooking the wide valley of Glacial River Warren, which drained Glacial Lake Agassiz. The small Whetstone River of South Dakota built a delta of sand and silt across this ancient drainage channel, impounding Big Stone Lake. Paul Bunyan forgot one of his big granite anchors (a quarried stone block) at this pull-off. River terraces of Glacial River Warren are present here, but they have been much modified by human activity.

The Ortonville granite, exposed in a roadcut in town and in a nearby quarry, is 2,600 million years old.

US 59
Canadian Border—Erskine
87 miles
See map on page 217

The northernmost 87 miles of US 59, between the Canadian border and Erskine, are on the lakebed of Glacial Lake Agassiz. The McCauleyville beach, one of the last beaches to form on the eastern shore of this vast lake as it was diminishing in size in this northernmost Minnesota area about 8,000 years ago, passes through Lake Bronson State Park, the northwesternmost of Minnesota's seventy-one state parks. A dam was constructed at the point where the South Branch of the Two Rivers flowed across the beach ridge, thus forming Lake Bronson. The park is on the boundary between prairie on the west and aspen parkland on the east.

Karlstad is on the Campbell beach, the lowest major beach that formed on the eastern edge of Glacial Lake Agassiz when the lake level stabilized between about 11,000 and 9,400 years ago. See the road guide for **MN 11: International Falls—Karlstad** for more information on this ancient beach.

To see an impressive series of Glacial Lake Agassiz beaches, take County Road 6 west about 10 miles south of Karlstad. This county road crosses four beaches in the 11-mile drive to Florian, which is on the westernmost beach. The beaches are easiest to spot when driving eastward toward the beach rise. This same road crosses the Tamarac River about 2 miles east of Florian; just upstream from the bridge you can see a cut in glacial till that underlies the lakebeds.

South of Karlstad along US 59, look for white cobbles and pebbles in the dark soil of the fields. These were reworked from the underlying Des Moines lobe till by the waves and currents in Glacial Lake Agassiz. The white clasts are composed of limestone, picked up by the glacier in the Lake Winnipeg region. Occasional piles of boulders in the fields remind us that only a thin layer of the fine-grained glacial lake sediment was deposited on the underlying Des Moines lobe till.

US 59 crosses three beaches of Glacial Lake Agassiz between Newfolden and Thief River Falls. A few miles to the south of Newfolden are large gravel piles east of the highway, where gravel pits are mining a former beach. The beaches are subtle, for the elevation rise is only a few feet on each. Look for them between mileposts 372 and 373, at milepost 370, and at milepost 368. There is another with a farm on it between mileposts 365 and 366. They are much easier to spot when heading south than when heading north.

International Falls—Morton

348 miles

See maps on pages 197 and 217

Between International Falls and Mizpah, a distance of about 63 miles, US 71 is straight and flat, for this is the lakebed of Glacial Lake Agassiz. The terrain mainly consists of black spruce bogs on the lowest ground and aspen stands on slightly higher ground. The higher ground is likely beach complexes or glacial till reworked by waves and currents in the lake. The highway crosses the most prominent beach about 14 miles northeast of Mizpah or 17 miles southwest of Big Falls, near Gemmell. This slight topographic rise is best seen on aerial photographs, but even then the beach is subtle. Some of the highest ground has been cleared for agriculture.

There are only two rock outcrops on this stretch of US 71. At Big Falls, the Big Fork River has exposed migmatite composed of biotite schist and gray granite. These two rock types are Archean in age, about 2,700 million years old, and are among the westernmost exposures of Archean rock in northern Minnesota. The exposure just below the bridge is worth looking at. Park in the community park just west of the river in a stand of large white pines.

At Margie, there is a roadcut in biotite schist formed by metamorphism of thinly bedded sedimentary rocks; the bedding is still visible in the schist. At one time, the site of Margie probably stood above Glacial Lake Agassiz as a low island.

Migmatite of Archean age along the Big Fork River at Big Falls.

A close view of the migmatite along the Big Fork River shows light-colored granite mixed with darker biotite schist.

Close view of biotite schist of Archean age in a roadcut along US 71 at Margie. The original bedding of the preexisting sedimentary rock is still visible in the schist.

Between Mizpah and Bemidji, the topography is gently rolling ground and stagnation moraine deposited by the Des Moines lobe. You might notice some large boulders if you keep a sharp lookout, but as usual, farmers have removed the rocks from their fields. During highway construction, the large rocks may simply be moved to the side of the road.

In the vicinity of Northome, the highway passes over a hilly stagnation moraine of the Des Moines lobe. The glacial till that makes up the moraine is quite thick. Just west of Northome there are wide, high, sloping roadcuts in the moraine, now planted with grass.

At about the village of Hines, between Blackduck and Tenstrike, US 71 crosses the major drainage divide between waters flowing north to Hudson Bay and waters flowing south to the Mississippi and on to the Gulf of Mexico.

Lake Bemidji State Park, 5 miles north of Bemidji, covers 2.5 square miles of glacial outwash and moraine deposited by the Des Moines lobe. Several bogs and lakes within the park, as well as Lake Bemidji, are the result of buried ice blocks melting and thus forming depressions. Rocky Point on the shore of Lake Bemidji provides a spectacular viewpoint from atop a hill consisting of outwash overlying glacial till. There are also remnants of virgin pine forests within the park. The Ojibwe called the lake *Bemidjigumaug,* which means "cross water." The Mississippi River "crosses" the lake and generates a noticeable current, which the Native Americans utilized on this travel route.

US 71 crosses the entire extent of the Wadena lobe deposits between Bemidji and Long Prairie, a distance of about 100 miles. South of Long Prairie, this highway is on glacial deposits of the Des Moines lobe all the way to the Iowa border.

Between Bemidji and Itasca State Park, a distance of about 29 miles, you may spot boulders in pastures and in rockpiles, as between mileposts 295 and 298. Also watch for the many lakes, ponds, and swamps in this glacial terrain.

Itasca State Park and the Mississippi River

Itasca State Park, Minnesota's second largest at 54 square miles, is also the oldest. It was established in 1891 to protect the drainage basin around the source of the Mississippi River—Lake Itasca—and also to protect stands of virgin white and red (Norway) pines that are 100 to 300 years old.

The park contains 150 lakes more than 2 acres in size. (To help you visualize 2 acres, note that a square acre is 208.7 feet on a side.) Most of the park area is on the hilly end moraine of the Wadena lobe known as the Itasca moraine. Numerous small lakes and ponds formed where blocks of ice melted. To the north of the park the glacial drift is deeply dissected Wadena lobe ground moraine.

Based on the dating of a giant extinct bison, *Bison occidentalis,* at a kill site, we know that hunters were here 8,500 years ago. Analysis of pollen from sediment at the kill site shows that the area was then prairie rather than forest. The Dakota were here from about 3,000 to 350 years ago, and one cemetery is more than 500 years old. The Ojibwe were here from about 300 years ago to the present. During the New Deal days of the 1930s and early 1940s, the swampy mouth of the Mississippi at the north end of Lake Itasca was converted into a much-visited pleasant spot.

In 1832, Henry Rowe Schoolcraft identified Lake Itasca as the source of the Mississippi River. He was brought here by Ozawindib, his Ojibwe guide. The

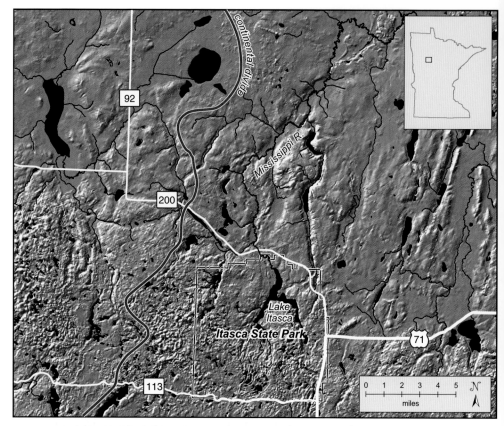

Landscape image of the area around Itasca State Park. The hilly end moraine of the Wadena lobe is in the southwestern part of the image, and the ground moraine of the same lobe is to the north. Also note the continental divide separating eastward drainage to the Mississippi and western drainage to the Red River of the North.

Ojibwe called the lake *Omushkos,* and the French called it *Lac la Biche,* but Schoolcraft renamed it utilizing portions of two Latin words—*veritas* (truth) and *caput* (head). Some disputed Lake Itasca as the source of the Mississippi, but Jacob Brower, the "father" of the park, emphatically stated in 1891, "The collection of lakes to the south should be considered the upper reaches of the watershed, but a true river is formed only where the river leaves Lake Itasca."

The Mississippi River, the fourth longest river in the world, had a total length of 2,552 miles in 1934, but it has since been shortened by about 200 miles due to channelization by the U.S. Army Corps of Engineers. About 696 miles or 27 percent of its length are in Minnesota. There are ten locks and dams on the river in Minnesota, enabling large boats and barges to navigate to a point 4.5 miles north of St. Anthony Falls in downtown Minneapolis. You can drive the Great River Road in Minnesota from Lake Itasca to the Iowa border.

If you want to canoe the entire Mississippi River from its source to the Gulf of Mexico, you may want to begin downstream of where the river passes under MN 200 in a culvert, less than one-quarter mile from Lake Itasca.

MN 200 crosses the continental divide about 6 to 7 miles west of the north entrance to Itasca State Park, somewhere between mileposts 76 and 78. From the drainage divide, waters flow north via the Red River of the North to Hudson Bay and south via the Mississippi to the Gulf of Mexico.

Park Rapids to Morton

Between Itasca State Park and Park Rapids, US 71 passes over outwash and end moraines of the Wadena lobe. The area between Park Rapids and Menahga is mostly glacial outwash. Between Menahga and Long Prairie, the highway crosses the Wadena Drumlin Field, which is a fan-shaped array of 1,200 drumlins formed beneath the Wadena glacial lobe. See the road guide for **US 10: Twin Cities—Moorhead** for more information on the drumlins.

Between Long Prairie and a point about 6 miles south of Belgrade, the highway crosses hilly moraines deposited beneath the Des Moines lobe and flatter areas of outwash. Between this point and Willmar, it crosses the southern end of the Alexandria moraine, which is comprised of Wadena lobe deposits overlain by a thin layer of Des Moines lobe drift. A major esker complex crosses US 71 just south of the junction with MN 9 near the entrance to Sibley State Park. Buildings in the park were built out of pink and gray granite from the St. Cloud area by the Veterans Conservation Corps in the mid-1930s. The park's classic knob-and-kettle topography contains several kettle lakes and Mt. Tom, a 1,375-foot-high knob.

In Menahga, glacial boulders make up the base of the statue of St. Urho, a fictitious Finnish saint who drove the grasshoppers out of Finnish vineyards with his pitchfork. There are no grasshoppers or vineyards in Finland today, but global warming could change that.

At Olivia in a rest area with a big corn cob is a large piece of pink gneiss from a quarry in Morton. Look for a weathered surface on one side with lines scratched by rock-studded ice flowing across it.

US 75
Canadian Border—Ortonville
272 miles
See maps on pages 217 and 197

US 75, which runs parallel to the entire western border of the state and follows the Red River of the North, was originally a Native American trail. It has been designated as the King of Trails Scenic Byway. The stretch of US 75 between Canada and Ortonville is almost entirely on the flat lakebed of Glacial Lake Agassiz, which existed between 11,700 and 9,400 years ago. The lake sediments between the Canadian border and Breckenridge are commonly fine-grained, consisting of clay and silt. In some areas, as in the vicinity of Angus, Shirley, and between Climax and Halstad, only a thin layer of lake sediments was deposited on Des Moines lobe glacial till reworked by lake waves and currents. Such lake-modified till is the main material over the southern portion of the lakebed, between Breckenridge and Graceville, which is due east of Browns Valley.

Rivers flowing westward into the Red River of the North have cut through the glacial lakebeds and into the underlying glacial till. At Crookston the Red Lake River has cut down several feet, at Hendrum the Wild Rice River has cut down several feet, and at Georgetown the Buffalo River has carved a fairly deep valley.

Crookston, Moorhead, and Breckenridge are partially built on the ancient lakebed and partially in the valleys of the Red Lake River, the Red River of the North, and Bois de Sioux River, respectively. Several villages, including Climax, Halstad, Georgetown, and Wolverton, are largely built on the floodplain of the Red River of the North.

Side Trip over Beaches of Glacial Lake Agassiz

Between Halstad and Hendrum, turn east on MN 200 and proceed to Ada to cross five beaches that at various times formed the eastern shore of Glacial Lake Agassiz. They are subtle topographic rises, very gentle ridges with a total relief of only about 5 feet. They are a bit more obvious when traveling from west to east rather than from east to west. The lowest beach is east of Ada between mileposts 26 and 27. The next is between mileposts 27 and 28, another is at milepost 28, another is at about milepost 31 just west of the junction of MN 200 and MN 32, and the highest one is at about milepost 35.

From Wheaton to Ortonville

Collis, on US 75 between Wheaton and Graceville, is situated on the southernmost part of the Herman beach, the highest and oldest beach of Glacial Lake Agassiz. Between Graceville and Ortonville, you are on stagnation moraine with a fair number of lakes. Just north of Clinton, you will cross the continental divide; from here waters flow north to Hudson Bay via the Red River of the North and south to the Gulf of Mexico via the Minnesota and Mississippi Rivers.

See the road guide for **US 75: Ortonville—Interstate 90**, in the chapter on southwestern Minnesota, for a discussion of Big Stone Lake.

MINNESOTA 9
Breckenridge—New London
110 miles
See map on page 197

Between Breckenridge and Morris, MN 9 crosses the four main beaches of Glacial Lake Agassiz at the places for which they were named. The towns of Campbell, Tintah, and Norcross were built on their namesake beaches. These three beaches are broad and the differences in elevation compared to the adjacent lakebed are minor. All are more obvious when driving toward the southeast rather than toward the northwest, but they are best observed on topographic maps. The oldest beach, the Herman beach, about 1 mile northwest of that town, is the most obvious, with a difference in elevation of about 10 feet higher than the lakebed to the northwest. It was formed by lake processes acting upon the topographically higher Des Moines lobe ground moraine on the eastern shoreline of Glacial Lake Agassiz. A point of interest along MN 9 on the Herman beach is a plaque describing the discovery of mammoth bones within the beach deposits.

Ground moraine, present just southeast of Herman, and stagnation moraine make up the gently rolling topography with abundant lakes all the way to a point about 10 miles southeast of Morris.

Between Hancock and Benson, and to a point 8 miles east of Benson, the flat terrain with very black soil is part of the lakebed of Glacial Lake Benson. The lake formed in front of the retreating Des Moines lobe and covered about 1,500 square miles to a depth of about 45 feet. During its short lifetime of about forty years, it did not have the time to develop prominent shorelines, as did Glacial Lake Agassiz. Instead, its presence is known by the flat topography of wave-worked moraine deposits and, in places, by the presence of glacial varves, which are thin coupled layers in lakebeds. A lighter-colored, silty to sandy layer is deposited during the summer when the lake is not frozen, and a thinner, dark, organic-rich layer is deposited during the winter when ice covers the lake. Some varves contain dropstones deposited from melting icebergs, indicating that the calving glacier existed on its northern margin. Glacial River Warren, which drained Glacial Lake Agassiz, was multichanneled where it crossed this flat area.

Between Benson and New London, you are on the high, hilly Alexandria moraine. Milepost 27 is at its western edge and New London is at its eastern edge. The moraine was formed by the Wadena lobe about 24,000 years ago and was overridden by the Des Moines lobe about 14,000 years ago. It is host to a myriad of kettle lakes, formed as blocks of ice, buried in glacial till, melted. Some other lakes simply occupy what are low areas on the moraine. Monson Lake State Park and Sibley State Park are located on the moraine. The Glacial Ridge Trail, a 245-mile-long Minnesota scenic byway, follows the moraine from Willmar to Alexandria or Sauk Centre via several signed loops, mostly on country roads.

For several miles north and west of New London, MN 9 is built either on or adjacent to a long ridge, an esker formed by deposition of fine- to coarse-grained sediment in an ice-walled river beneath the melting ice of the Des Moines lobe.

MINNESOTA 11
International Falls—Karlstad
170 miles

Minnesota 11 has been designated the Waters of the Dancing Sky Scenic Byway. From International Falls to Baudette and Lake of the Woods, it follows the Rainy River, and the wide river is clearly visible at many places. The entire length of MN 11 is on the bed of Glacial Lake Agassiz, so the big word for any trip on this highway is *flat!* All of this lakebed area is underlain by glacial tills, the latest of which was deposited by the Des Moines lobe about 14,000 years ago. There are a few exposures of rock along this highway despite a general

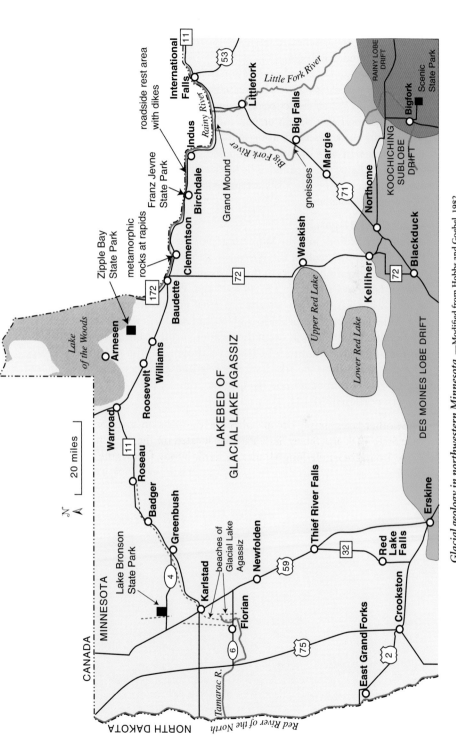

Glacial geology in northwestern Minnesota. —Modified from Hobbs and Goebel, 1982

cover of glacial sediments, but geologic bedrock maps of the region are largely based on geophysical measurements of gravity and magnetics, plus some mineral exploration drill holes.

More than one hundred exploration holes were drilled in the area between Lake of the Woods and Lower Red Lake by various companies in the late 1960s and 1970s in a search for copper and zinc deposits in the buried bedrock. They drilled where surface measurements indicated electromagnetic anomalies but found only thick layers of iron sulfide (worthless pyrite) or graphite. After expenditures of tens of millions of dollars, only traces of ore minerals were discovered. However, the hidden bedrock still has potential for metals, including gold, because ore deposits are present in the same types of rocks to the northeast in Canada.

Glacial Lake Agassiz

As the Des Moines lobe in Minnesota and the James lobe in North Dakota melted back at the end of the Wisconsin ice age, meltwaters were trapped between the retreating glaciers to the north and moraines to the south, forming Glacial Lake Agassiz about 11,700 years ago. Waves and currents in this lake leveled what was probably already low-relief ground moraine. Icebergs floating in the lake dropped pebbles, cobbles, and boulders when they melted, and fine-grained sediment was swept throughout, further contributing to a flat lake bottom. From time to time, the lake level dropped as the water found escape channels. Each time the lake level was relatively constant for a few hundred years, beaches formed around its margins. Some of these are visible along the western portion of MN 11.

The flat bed of Glacial Lake Agassiz. Note the light gray lake sediment beneath the dark peat.

The scattered pebbles in this thin-bedded mud and silt of Glacial Lake Agassiz are likely dropstones that fell to the lakebed from melting icebergs. Glacial varves, most clearly shown to the right of the hammerhead, are composed of light-colored layers deposited during summer and dark, organic-rich layers deposited during winter.

Rainy River

The Rainy River flows westward from Rainy Lake to Lake of the Woods, with its waters ultimately reaching Hudson Bay. The river was part of the voyageur route of the 1700s and traveled by Native Americans long before that. The river is also famous for its sturgeon, fish that can be as old as 100 years, weigh as much as 250 pounds, and be 6 to 8 feet long. Pollution of the river by wood product mills in International Falls and Fort Frances was bad in the 1970s and 1980s but has greatly improved. It is one of the largest rivers in Minnesota. The two biggest streams in the river's drainage basin are the Big Fork and the Little Fork Rivers. Minnesota 11 crosses both of them where they empty into the Rainy River.

Grand Mound

Twenty miles west of International Falls at the confluence of the Big Fork and Rainy Rivers is the location of the Grand Mound, the largest surviving prehistoric structure in the Upper Midwest. Built as a burial mound by Paleo-Indians between about 200 BC and 1400 AD, it is 115 feet in diameter and 28 feet high. However, it is closed to the public in deference to the fact that it is a burial site. Smaller mounds nearby have yielded burials of bundled bones, and there are more than twenty burial mounds over a distance of 90 miles along the Rainy River in both Minnesota and Ontario. They are part of the Laurel culture, a distinctive local Woodland culture.

Manitou Rapids and Sault Rapids Dikes

Between mileposts 164 and 165 is a short paved road leading toward the Rainy River. The 200-foot-wide Manitou Rapids mafic dike, which is responsible for the Manitou Rapids, is exposed near the farthest parking lot, where it forms a ridge a few feet high, and at the end of a path leading to the river. This dike is part of the 2,100-million-year-old Kenora-Kabetogama Dike Swarm. On both sides of the black dike, unfortunately very covered with lichen, are lighter-colored, tannish felsic volcanic rocks—the country rocks intruded by the dike.

Between mileposts 157 and 158 is the entrance to Franz Jevne State Park, which is located where the Sault Rapids Dike intersects the Rainy River. The dike is visible on the riverbank only at low water, but a concentration of its mostly black boulders makes the rapids. On the road into the park is a farm with an outcrop of the dike in the yard. Within the park, reachable on hiking trails, are other rock outcrops. The dike intruded greenstone, a metamorphosed mafic volcanic rock of Archean age.

Birchdale Granite

Between mileposts 155 and 157 are roadcuts in the Birchdale pluton, a small body of Archean pink granitic rock 3 to 4 miles in diameter.

Rapid River at Clementson

About 20 miles west of Birchdale and 9 miles east of Baudette is a bridge over the Rapid River at rapids formed by a bedrock exposure. There are parking areas on both sides of the river, but the western side, at Clementson, allows better

The Manitou Rapids Dike on the Ontario side of the Rainy River, viewed from the Minnesota side.

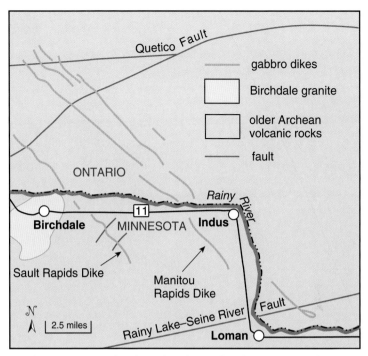

The Manitou Rapids Dike and Sault Rapids Dike are just two of many 2,100-million-year-old mafic dikes in northern Minnesota. —Modified from Ojakangas, Meineke, and Listerud, 1977

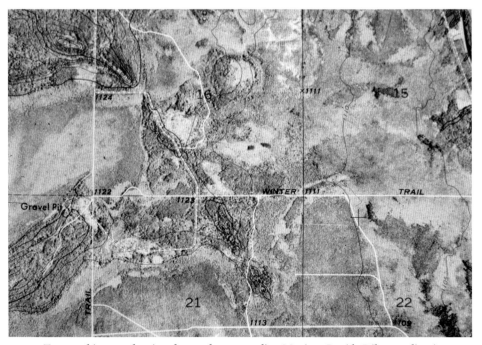

Topographic map showing the northwest-trending Manitou Rapids Dike standing in relief above the low and swampy terrain of the bed of Glacial Lake Agassiz. —From U.S. Geological Survey 7.5-minute Loman Quadrangle

The Rapid River at Clementson flows over metagraywacke and slate of Archean age.

Close-up of metagraywacke and slate (black) beds at rapids on the Rapid River at Clementson.

access to the rocks. The outcrop is composed of slate (metamorphosed mudstone) and metagraywacke (metamorphosed graywacke sandstone), with the original bedding still visible. The beds vary in thickness from 2 inches to 4 feet. Grading, in which the sizes of the grains decrease upward within an individual bed, is visible on some beds, with coarse sand grading upward into silt and clay. The graded beds formed when the sediment settled out of turbidity currents, swirling water capable of carrying mud, silt, sand, and even pebbles. These may have moved down the steep slope at the margin of the continent, or perhaps down the submerged flanks of volcanoes, into deeper water where they slowed. Upon slowing, the bigger and heavier grains settled first and the smaller grains last. The beds were tilted during Algoman mountain building an estimated 2,700 million years ago.

Zippel Bay State Park

From Baudette, MN 172 leads north 20 miles to Zippel Bay State Park, on a bay of Lake of the Woods. One of the remnants of Glacial Lake Agassiz, Lake of the Woods covers 1,485 square miles, with more than half of that in Ontario. It has 65,000 miles of shoreline and 14,000 islands. The northern tip of the lake in Ontario is 80 miles away from Zippel Bay State Park. The lake is as deep as 150 feet. Older, higher shorelines within the park, as much as 30 feet above the present lake surface of 1,060 feet, indicate the lake was once deeper, presumably when this area was part of Glacial Lake Agassiz. Rocks within the park include amphibolite gneiss and granite. There is an exposure of a mafic dike on the sandbar at the entrance to Zippel Bay.

The flat peninsula northwest of Zippel Bay contains numerous low-lying outcrops of pink and gray granite and amphibolitic gneiss. Near the junction of County Roads 11 and 17 north of Roosevelt, there are active granite quarries where the rock is crushed and used for roads and concrete. An outcrop on the north side of County Road 17 about 7.5 miles north of Roosevelt contains ten 3- to 10-inch-thick basalt dikes cutting gray granite.

At Arnesen, at the end of County Road 17 about 12 miles north of Roosevelt, is a northwesterly trending mafic dike at least 125 feet thick that protrudes into the lake at Rocky Point. The dike cuts across gray granite. If you inspect this well-exposed dike, you will see two sets of glacial striations. One set trends more southerly, with an azimuth of 210 degrees, and the other easterly, with an azimuth of 70 degrees. This indicates that two different glacial lobes moving in two different directions abraded this outcrop. Determining which one is the latest by looking at the striations is a bit difficult because they are somewhat weathered. However, the east-west striations are likely the youngest because the Des Moines lobe moved eastward in this part of Minnesota and was the most recent advance here.

The Northwest Angle

The Northwest Angle, the small piece of Minnesota separated from the rest of the state by Lake of the Woods, can be reached by road only by first driving into Canada. This 132-square-mile area is the northernmost piece of land in the forty-eight contiguous states, and the only part north of the forty-ninth parallel, which forms the international boundary from here to the West Coast.

The story of how it became part of Minnesota began with Benjamin Franklin and John Adams at the Treaty of Paris in 1783, which ended the Revolutionary War. According to that treaty, the international boundary between the United States and Canada was to extend due west from the northwestern corner of Lake of the Woods to the Mississippi River, which was then thought to extend into Canada. The Anglo-American Convention of 1818, which resolved the War of 1812, drew the boundary due south from the northwestern corner of the lake to the forty-ninth parallel. The border was eventually finalized in 1842 by the Webster-Ashburton Treaty. Much of the Northwest Angle is flat, swampy lakebed of Glacial Lake Agassiz. The bedrock is mostly granite and pegmatite, with minor pillowed greenstone at one locality. Two wide, long, northwest-trending mafic dikes, part of the Kenora-Kabetogama Dike Swarm, are also present.

Beaches of Glacial Lake Agassiz

Minnesota 11 and the parallel railroad are situated on a beach ridge for the entire 40-mile distance between Roseau and Karlstad. The beach ridge rises 20 to 30 feet above the lakebed on the northwest and is about one-quarter mile wide. Sand and gravel pits are abundant on the ridge and provide good locations for cemeteries, as at Badger. This is the Campbell beach, which has an elevation of 981 feet at Campbell about 180 miles to the south, but is at about 1,060 feet in this area. The underlying crust, which had been depressed by the

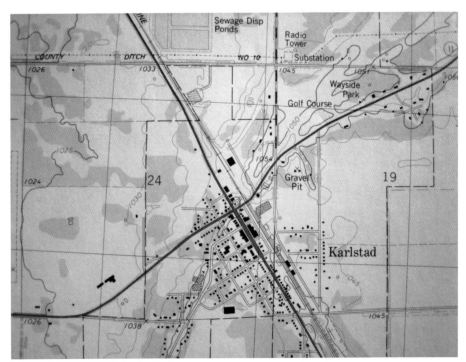

The U.S. Geological Survey 7.5-minute Karlstad Quadrangle map shows the prominent northeast-trending beach at Karlstad. MN 11 is on the beach ridge northeast of Karlstad.

thick glacial ice, rose more in the north than in the south, tilting the beaches. In northernmost Minnesota and adjacent Canada, where the glacial ice was thicker and survived longer than in west-central Minnesota, Earth's surface was more depressed. The Campbell beach probably existed between 11,000 and 9,500 years ago.

Gravel in the Campbell beach is largely composed of rounded white limestone fragments reworked from the underlying glacial drift. The Des Moines lobe picked up the fragments from limestone bedrock in the Lake Winnipeg area to the north in Manitoba.

A long gravel pit on the Campbell beach of Glacial Lake Agassiz just northeast of Badger, along MN 11 at milepost 60. A thickness of about 4 feet of beach gravel is being removed from beneath a thin layer of black soil.

MINNESOTA 23
St. Cloud—Granite Falls
95 miles
See map on page 197

For several miles west of St. Cloud, "The Granite City," there are a few roadcuts, quarries, and crushed rock operations in granite near MN 23. The first quarries opened in 1868 to get material for the St. Cloud Reformatory and its 22-foot-high granite perimeter wall. There have been as many as one hundred quarries, but only four are still in operation, one in St Cloud. There are several individual bodies of granite in east-central Minnesota, many of which have formal or informal names, such as the Reformatory, Rockville, Richmond, St. Cloud Red, Isle, Watab, Warman, Pierz, Foley, Ann Lake, and Freedhem granites. Collectively these individual granite plutons form a semicontinuous mass that has come to be known as the East-Central Minnesota Batholith. The ages of these granites cluster around 1,775 million years, but range in age from about 1,800 to 1,750 million years. The granite is slightly younger than the 1,875- to 1,835-million-year-old Penokean mountain building event that is most evident in rocks along the south side of Lake Superior.

One place where you can see old quarries up close is Stearns County Quarry Park in the village of Waite Park, which borders St. Cloud's west side. To get there, turn south off MN 23 onto Tenth Avenue South and turn west (right) onto Seventh Street. You are now on County Road 137. Follow it for 0.7 mile to the park entrance.

Another inactive quarry—the "Rockville Beige" quarry in the Rockville granite—is on the north side of old MN 23 (now County Road 82) in Rockville, west of new MN 23, which bypasses Rockville on its south side. The active "Rockville White" quarry is on the south side of the new highway. The massive granite rock is cut into "loaves" that can be 25 feet high, 20 feet wide, and 150 feet long! These are then cut into "small blocks" only 5.5 feet by 5.5 feet by 10.5 feet long, which weigh 28 tons and can be transported on flatbed trucks. Granite with too many joints or cracks is not as valuable and is used for crushed rock.

Look for some very large granite boulders on the south side of MN 23 just east of Rockville by a big gravel pit. At first glance, they may look like glacial boulders. However, they are core-stones, remnants of a granite outcrop deeply weathered along joints. The weathering penetrates all sides of a block of jointed granite, and the corners weather fastest, producing the rounded shapes. This weathering may have occurred during Cretaceous time, about 100 million years ago.

Between Rockville and Cold Spring you will see the high-relief end moraine of the St. Croix advance of the Superior lobe. This is near the westernmost limit of this ice advance.

Watch for the roadcuts in dark grayish green granite near the bridge over the Sauk River in Cold Spring, where there are also quarries. If you turn south on County Road 49 in Cold Spring and drive about 0.2 mile, you will see outcrops of pink to green Richmond granite on both sides of the road.

Between Richmond and Hawick, the broadly rolling farmland is on either flatter areas of outwash, as at Paynesville, or on gently undulating stagnation

Core-stones in weathered granite at a gravel pit near Rockville.
—Terry Boerboom photo

moraine deposited by the Des Moines lobe 14,000 years ago. Notice the abundance of lakes, typical of areas where glacial ice stopped moving and stagnated.

Between New London and Willmar, a distance of 15 miles, the markedly more hilly topography is stagnation moraine deposited by the Wadena lobe about 24,000 years ago and overridden by the Des Moines lobe about 14,000 years ago. Here, MN 23 crosses the southeastern end of the prominent 140-mile-long Alexandria moraine, with its abundance of kettle lakes. Each lake formed where a block of glacial ice, buried by glacial debris, later melted out. Sibley State Park and Monson Lake State Park, both west of New London off MN 9, make use of some of the lakes. A 20-mile-long, east-west-trending esker parallels MN 9.

Between Willmar and Alexandria located some 50 miles to the north, you can drive the Glacial Ridge Trail, a 245-mile-long route with several loops on small county roads. The topography is changeable, with appreciable relief and an abundance of kettle lakes and swampy low areas.

Just south of Willmar near the intersection of MN 23 and US 71 is a large gravel pit in ground moraine of the Des Moines lobe. Most of the distance between Willmar and Granite Falls is this gently undulating ground moraine, which makes excellent farmland. Look for the abundant rock piles, which verify that you are driving over bouldery glacial moraine. A short stretch of flat area between Clara City and Maynard is part of the lakebed of Glacial Lake Benson, a lake older than Glacial Lake Agassiz. We know this because Glacial River Warren, which drained Glacial Lake Agassiz, cut across and through this older lakebed.

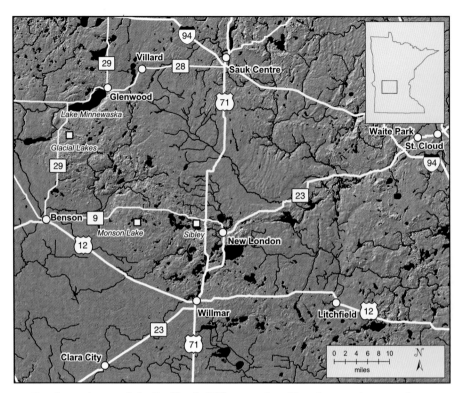

Landscape image of the St. Cloud--Willmar region. Note the prominent northwest-trending Alexandria moraine, with its many lakes, which extends from Willmar to the northwest corner of the image. The flat area southwest of US 12 between Benson and Willmar is the lakebed of Glacial Lake Benson and Des Moines lobe ground moraine.

For the bedrock geology of the Granite Falls area, see the road guide for **Minnesota 23: Granite Falls—Interstate 90**, in the chapter on southwestern Minnesota.

MINNESOTA 28
Sauk Centre—Browns Valley
95 miles
See map on page 197

Between Sauk Centre and Westport, MN 28 crosses Des Moines lobe stagnation moraine and ground moraine with moderate relief. Between Westport and a point about 1 mile east of Glenwood, the terrain is quite flat—you are on a glacial outwash plain with several lakes.

Glenwood and Starbuck are located on the prominent Alexandria moraine, deposited about 24,000 years ago by the Wadena lobe. The 7-mile-long Lake Minnewaska, one of Minnesota's 10,000 lakes, lies between the two towns.

A park on the lake in Glenwood has an interesting stone wall built of glacial boulders carried to this area from northern Minnesota by the Wadena lobe. A roadside rest area high above Glenwood on MN 55 provides a good view of the large lake and also has a long stone wall made of cut glacial boulders. The many lakes of this knob-and-kettle topography formed in the drift of the Des Moines lobe, which mantles the older Wadena lobe drift. The low spots—kettles—formed where large pieces of glacial ice were buried, and the high spots are kames—somewhat conical hills that formed where sediment was deposited in openings on the surface of stagnant ice. Lake Minnewaska formed over a large topographic low, perhaps where the buried ice was thicker and therefore lasted longer, or perhaps where a large tunnel valley existed beneath the glacial ice as it was melting.

Glacial Lakes State Park, 5 miles south of Starbuck just east of MN 29, is on the Alexandria moraine. It is an ideal place to see numerous glacial depositional features, including kames, kettles, and eskers. It also contains an esker complex made of several eskers, each formed by a debris-laden stream flowing in an ice tunnel at the base of the melting glacier. However, they are difficult to delineate from the ground.

Most of the 56 miles between Cyrus and Browns Valley is either ground moraine or stagnation moraine of the Des Moines lobe. Two miles east of Morris, MN 28 crosses the 1-mile-wide valley of the Pomme de Terre River. The wide valley was cut by southward-flowing glacial meltwaters that were more voluminous than the modern river. The cluster of lakes at Graceville formed on stagnation moraine of the Des Moines lobe.

Aerial view of kames in prairie land of Glacial Lakes State Park. —David F. Reid photo

Chokio and Barry both sit on a continental divide; waters from here flow north to Hudson Bay via the Red River of the North and south to the Gulf of Mexico via the Mississippi and Minnesota Rivers. Between Beardsley and Browns Valley, the land surface slopes gently westward toward the lakes and rivers on the Minnesota–South Dakota border. The surface of Lake Traverse, on the north side of the divide, is 9 feet higher than Big Stone Lake, a few miles to the south. The divide has an elevation of 980 feet at the border. The long, narrow Big Stone Lake is a result of the damming of the Minnesota River by a delta of the Whetstone River, which enters the Minnesota River Valley from South Dakota.

Look for three river terraces visible along MN 28 southeast of Browns Valley. They are best expressed between mileposts 4 and 5. The highway is on the middle terrace. You may also be able to distinguish them across the valley on the South Dakota side. These broad, somewhat flat and elongate terraces were cut into the glacial deposits of the Des Moines lobe by Glacial River Warren, the predecessor of the Minnesota River. They were cut in succession, from highest to lowest, as the river eroded a deeper valley.

Glacial River Warren, which was as much as 5 miles wide and 300 feet deep, formed when Glacial Lake Agassiz overflowed its southernmost point at Browns Valley several times between about 11,700 and 9,400 years ago. When the glacier retreated much farther north, lower outlets to Lake Superior in Ontario were uncovered and this southern outlet of Glacial Lake Agassiz was thus abandoned.

A boulder-strewn terrace of Glacial River Warren.

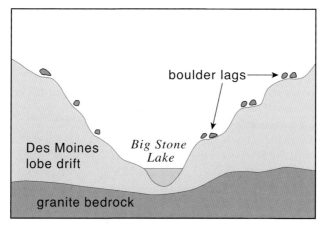

Generalized cross section, with vertical exaggeration, of erosional terraces formed by Glacial River Warren. Boulders that were too big for the river to carry remained behind on the floodplain, which became a terrace as the river cut down farther into the glacial drift.

The lowest terrace, at an elevation of 1,046 feet, is littered with granite boulders that were in the glacial till. Some are 10 feet in diameter—too large to be removed by the river—and were left behind on the channel floor. This lowest terrace can be traced for another 20 miles downstream to the southeast, to a point 6 miles north of Ortonville. Also on the ancient river bottom are exposures of 2,600-million-year-old granitic rock that were abraded by the high-velocity and high-volume floodwaters in the river as Glacial Lake Agassiz was being drained.

Before dropping down to Browns Valley, look westward, and on a clear day you may see the eastern escarpment of the topographically high, flat-topped Coteau des Prairies, about 12 miles away in South Dakota. The eastward-facing slope rises about 700 feet above the land surface to the east. The Coteau was a topographic high during the last ice advance, splitting the southward-moving ice sheet into the James lobe on its western side in the Dakotas and the Des Moines lobe on its eastern side in Minnesota and Iowa. The Coteau appears to be a high area of bedrock covered by an erosional remnant of older (pre-Wisconsin) glacial drift.

Browns Valley is the site of Minnesota's most famous Paleo-Indian burial. Browns Valley Man, one of the few confirmed Paleo-Indian skeletons in the Americas, was uncovered in 1933 in a municipal gravel pit on the southern edge of town. Besides a skull and other bones in this burial site, there were several beautiful projectile points made of chalcedony, a variety of quartz. This adult male was evidently buried in gravels at the southern outlet of Glacial Lake Agassiz. A radiocarbon-14 date on bone fragments shows that he lived about 9,000 years ago, about 400 years after Glacial Lake Agassiz drained. These remains are now at the Science Museum of Minnesota.

MINNESOTA 72
Blackduck—Baudette
75 miles
See map on page 217

Flat and mostly straight is a short description of MN 72, for the northern 55 miles or so is on the bed of Glacial Lake Agassiz. The northernmost 20 miles, in Lake of the Woods County, passes over farmland on higher parts of the lakebed underlain by glacial till that was reworked by waves and currents. The southern 20 miles of MN 72, between Blackduck and Kelliher, is on ground moraine deposited by the Des Moines lobe about 12,000 years ago. In general, the glacial drift is relatively thin, and there are a few bedrock exposures along some of the rivers crossed by the highway.

Lower Red Lake and Upper Red Lake, two of Minnesota's largest lakes, are remnants of Glacial Lake Agassiz, which came into existence approximately 11,700 years ago as the glacial ice was retreating northward. The two lakes are separated by a small bit of Des Moines lobe stagnation moraine. Near Waskish, where you can get a glimpse of Upper Red Lake, you will see cultivated wild rice paddies with low earthen dams around them to keep in the water. Hybridization research performed at the University of Minnesota produced this farmed wild rice. Native wild rice, a staple food of the Native Americans for centuries, ripens a bit at a time, from the top of the stalk downward. To harvest it requires several trips through the lakes and rivers by canoe to knock off the few ripe grains. Grains of rice on the hybrid stalks all ripen at the same time, permitting harvesting by large combines.

Bog vegetation between mileposts 48 and 49 on MN 72. Notice the dark peat in the ditch. The water reflects a high water table.

Big Bog State Recreation Area, between Upper Red Lake and the Tamarac River, is located on an old sand beach formed during a higher stand of the lake. Nine miles north of Waskish is a northern portion of this recreation area, located 0.5 mile west of MN 72; look for the gravel road between mileposts 45 and 46. The Big Bog is a classic patterned peatland 50 miles long in an east-west direction and 12 miles wide, covering 500 square miles, the largest peat bog in the Lower 48. The peat probably began forming about 3,000 years ago as the low-lying remnants of Glacial Lake Agassiz became overgrown with vegetation. The average thickness of the peat is 10 feet.

MINNESOTA 210
Brainerd—Breckenridge
119 miles
See map on page 197

Between Brainerd and Breckenridge, MN 210 passes over glacial drift that in general is 200 to 400 feet thick, so don't expect to see any bedrock! Brainerd was built on terraces of the Mississippi River. In the vicinity of Brainerd, Baxter, and Pillager, the highway traverses an area of glacial outwash plain and some flatter remnants of the southern part of the lakebed of short-lived Glacial Lake Brainerd. It covered 150 square miles for about 100 years as the Rainy lobe melted back to the east. This flat terrain contains kettle lakes, formed where blocks of ice from the retreating glacier were buried by meltwater sediments. A network of rivers flowing west from the melting Rainy lobe deposited valuable sand and gravel of the outwash plain. Note the big gravel operations between mileposts 128 and 129 and between mileposts 130 and 132. Another big pit is on the north side of the highway about 4 miles east of Pillager, at milepost 113. The piles of large boulders indicate that there were high water velocities in the meltwater streams.

Pillager is on a low-relief terrain of glacial outwash, with high hills of Rainy lobe end moraine nearby to the north and south. This topographic low, called the Pillager Gap, was eroded by a westward-flowing river of meltwater from the Rainy lobe to the east, but the Des Moines lobe moved in and blocked that drainage. The modern Crow Wing River flows eastward through this gap. Motley is located on the same outwash deposits that Pillager is built upon.

Wadena Drumlin Field
Between Pillager and Motley, mileposts 102 to 105, the highway crosses over a number of drumlins, southwest-trending streamlined hills sculpted in ground moraine beneath the Wadena lobe. However, they are so large—as much as 2 miles long, one-quarter to one-half mile wide, and several tens of feet high—that the teardrop-shape of an ideal drumlin will not be obvious from the road.

Between Staples and Hewitt, notice the many drumlins that are visible from the highway. These drumlins are part of the Wadena Drumlin Field, which covers a large area in Wadena, Otter Tail, Todd, and Cass Counties. There are about 1,200 drumlins in all, forming a fan-shaped array trending to the south and the west. They are the oldest glacial features in the northern

Minnesota 210 crosses drumlins between Staples and Hewitt.

two-thirds of Minnesota, probably formed 23,000 to 18,000 years ago, before the advance of the Des Moines lobe 14,000 years ago. They are composed of pale yellow, limestone-rich sandy till derived in part from Precambrian rocks of the Canadian Shield and in part from Paleozoic rocks in Manitoba.

Henning to Battle Lake

For 5 miles on either side of Henning, you are driving over glacial moraine of the Wadena lobe. Look for the boulder piles in the fields, gathered by the farmers to make the land more suitable to cultivation. Vining is near the middle of a 6-mile stretch of MN 210 that crosses uneven stagnation moraine formed when the Des Moines lobe stopped moving southward and melted in place. Battle Lake and Clitherall are located on a pitted outwash plain, a flat area that includes numerous kettle lakes.

Alexandria Moraine and Inspiration Peak

Between Battle Lake and Fergus Falls, a distance of about 15 miles, MN 210 crosses the hilly Alexandria moraine, one of the most prominent moraines in Minnesota, standing as much as 700 feet above the Red River Valley to the west. The moraine was deposited by the Wadena lobe sometime about 24,000 years ago, when it stopped moving and stagnated. It is composed of the same pale yellow, limestone-rich, sandy till that forms the Wadena drumlins to the east. On top of this prominent topographic feature is a cap of olive brown silty till (3 to 30 feet thick) deposited by the Des Moines lobe about 14,000 years ago. The 120-mile-long, generally north-trending moraine is home to a good proportion of Minnesota's 10,000 lakes, most of which are kettle lakes.

Large dolostone boulder and a smaller granite boulder 1 mile south of Battle Lake just east of MN 78 on North Clitherall Lake Road. Although placed here by human activity, they were very likely from the Des Moines lobe till that blankets the area. The dolostone was probably transported to this vicinity from Manitoba by the glacier.

For a more intimate look at the hills and lakes of the Alexandria moraine, drive 10 miles south on MN 78 from Battle Lake. Turn east on County Road 38 and drive for 6 miles to a Minnesota wayside rest named Inspiration Peak. Look at the array of large granitic and gneissic boulders along the edge of the parking lot, all glacial erratics from northern Minnesota and Ontario. Walk up a steep paved path through a dense oak forest to the top of this hill, the highest point in central Minnesota at 1,750 feet above sea level. You will have climbed about 200 vertical feet to a point 400 feet above prairies to the west and forested hilly country with numerous scattered lakes to the east. Inspiration Peak is a glacial kame, a conical hill formed by sediment-laden meltwater

This gravel pit at milepost 44 on MN 210 exposes a bedded glacial deposit that contains some white carbonate clasts. Note the well-developed organic-rich prairie soil at the top.

flowing downward at a specific spot within a melting glacier. For more detail on this interesting spot, see Constance Jefferson Sansome's excellent book entitled *Minnesota Underfoot*.

Fergus Falls to Breckenridge

Fergus Falls is located on a stagnation moraine of the Des Moines lobe. This moraine extends 8 miles westward to a grain-loading facility on the railroad siding at French. West of here is the flat lakebed of Glacial Lake Agassiz, which existed between 11,700 and 9,400 years ago. Two miles west of French, between mileposts 18 and 19, a beach of Glacial Lake Agassiz trends perpendicular to the highway. The difference in elevation is very subtle and is most easily seen when driving eastward. Another subtle beach is present about 1 to 2 miles east of Foxhome. Waves and currents in the lake reworked and leveled the glacial drift deposited by the Des Moines lobe. This flat land with nearly 10,000-year-old prairie soil makes excellent farmland.

Though this countryside looks flatter than a pancake, there is a very slight dip toward the west. At Breckenridge, the west-flowing Otter Tail River joins the north-flowing Bois de Sioux River and together they become the northward-flowing Red River of the North, which is the longest northward-flowing river in the United States and ends in Lake Winnipeg in Canada. Headwaters Park in Breckenridge is on the river.

MINNESOTA 371
Brainerd—Little Falls
30 miles
See map on page 197

North of Brainerd in an area of about 200 square miles are dozens of kettle lakes on a highly pitted glacial outwash plain and the lakebed of Glacial Lake Brainerd. The lakes formed where ice of the melting glacier was buried by meltwater sediments. Depressions formed as this buried ice melted, and they later filled with water. The Paul Bunyan Scenic Byway is a 54-mile double-circle route through these lakes north of Brainerd. You can access the loop from MN 371 near Pine River.

Glacial Lake Brainerd existed for only about 100 years about 15,000 years ago. As the Rainy lobe melted back to the northeast, meltwater ponded between the ice and the moraine to the west. The water eventually escaped southward, helping carve the modern Mississippi River Valley.

About 2 miles south of the intersection with MN 210 at Brainerd, MN 371 crosses the Mississippi River. Watch for the green Great River Road highway markers between Brainerd and Little Falls, depicting this segment of MN 371 as part of the road that follows the Mississippi along its 2,350-mile-long course from Lake Itasca in northern Minnesota to the Gulf of Mexico.

Crow Wing State Park, on the Mississippi River 9 miles south of Brainerd, is located where the Crow Wing River enters the Mississippi River. The Dakota and Ojibwe fought a major battle here in 1768. The confluence was the home of several great Ojibwe chiefs and later was the site of the town of Crow Wing, a fur trading and logging settlement. For one hundred years this town was the northernmost settlement of Europeans on the Mississippi River. The Red River Oxcart Trail, which connected St. Paul to the Canadian frontier, crossed the Mississippi River at this point. In 1868, the Ojibwe were relocated to the White Earth Reservation about 100 miles to the northwest, and in 1871 the Northern Pacific Railroad bridged the Mississippi River several miles upstream, where Brainerd was established.

Between Crow Wing State Park and Little Falls, MN 371 is built on flat terraces of the Mississippi River. The higher topography on both sides of the river valley is moraine of the St. Croix advance of the Superior lobe.

A glacial esker, a snakelike deposit of a river that flowed beneath the melting Rainy lobe glacier, is visible just to the east of MN 371. Between Fort Ripley and Camp Ripley, drive east on County Road 48 for 0.7 mile, then north on County Road 282 for about 1 mile. A geological marker at the Ripley Esker Scientific and Natural Area describes how this esker was formed. A 0.75-mile-long portion of the nearly 7-mile-long esker is protected. Many eskers have been mined away for their sand and gravel.

The high hill east of MN 371 just north of Little Falls is composed of Superior lobe ground and end moraine. The dam across the Mississippi in Little Falls was built on a waterfall formed by the river cascading over an exposure of the 2,100-million-year-old Little Falls Formation. The biotite schist is exposed on the riverbank in a small city park near the east end of the dam. Originally muddy and sandy sedimentary rock, it was metamorphosed during the Penokean mountain building event.

The Ripley esker at Ripley Esker Scientific and Natural Area. —Howard Mooers photo

SOUTHWESTERN MINNESOTA
Quartzites and Old Rocks

The gently undulating prairie of southwestern Minnesota disguises some interesting geologic stories. At 3,500 million years old—that's 3.5 billion—the
gneisses exposed in the Minnesota River Valley are some of the oldest rocks in
the world. Much younger, but still pre-dating plant life, the 1,700-million-year-
old Sioux Quartzite surfaces at Pipestone National Monument, Blue Mounds
State Park, and Jeffers Petroglyphs. Much younger bedrock (Cretaceous), less
than 100 million years old and containing abundant evidence of plant and animal life, is also present but rarely exposed. Elsewhere, glacial deposits blanket
the bedrock. Remnants of tallgrass prairie, some of the last in Minnesota, sur-
vive where the glacial deposits have not been plowed.

GLACIAL GEOLOGY

In the southeastern corner of Minnesota is the topographically prominent
Coteau des Prairies, French for "highland of the prairies." This plateau, which
stretches from the northeastern corner of South Dakota south into southwestern Minnesota and northwestern Iowa, is as high as 2,000 feet above sea level,
1,000 feet higher than the Minnesota River. The Coteau divided the southerly
moving glacial ice of Wisconsin age into two lobes: the Des Moines lobe flowed
on its eastern side in Minnesota and Iowa and the James lobe on its western side
in the Dakotas. The combined presence of the high Coteau and a topographic
low in the bedrock of the Minnesota River Valley caused the Des Moines lobe
to assume a southeasterly direction. A portion of the Coteau about 20 miles
wide and 80 miles long in a north-south direction in the southwesternmost
corner of Minnesota escaped glaciation during the Wisconsin epoch. While the
southern part of the Coteau has a partial bedrock core of quartzite, most of it
is composed of thick glacial drift older than the late Wisconsin drift, perhaps
more than 300,000 years old.

   This erosional remnant of older glacial deposits hints at the volume of glacial
material that must have existed elsewhere in Minnesota before it was eroded.
Where is this material now? Part of it was recycled into the glacial drift of the
Des Moines lobe. However, another part of it is likely in the Gulf of Mexico,
where the Mississippi River deposits much of its sediment load.

   Two prominent southeast-trending ridges in southeastern Minnesota are
glacial moraines that formed along the western edge of the Des Moines lobe
about 14,000 years ago. The Bemis moraine, the westernmost and highest of

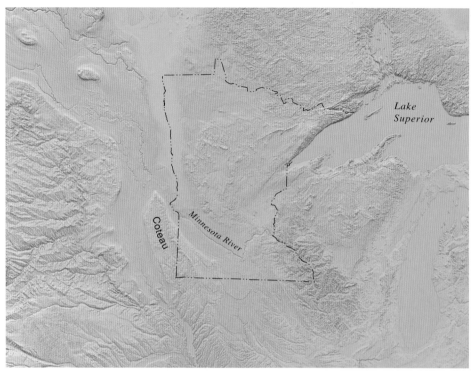

Digital elevation model of the Coteau des Prairies, a high plateau on the eastern edge of South Dakota. —NASA image

Cliff of Sioux Quartzite at Blue Mounds State Park in southwestern Minnesota.

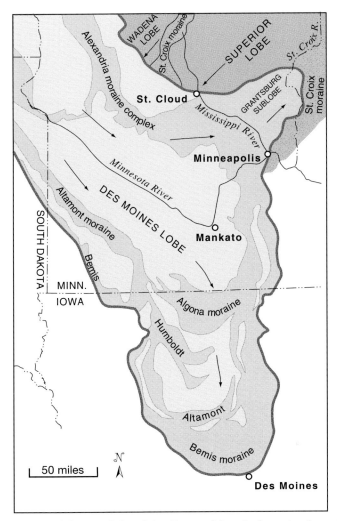

The Des Moines lobe extended south into Iowa and deposited moraines in southern Minnesota, northern Iowa, and eastern South Dakota, as well as in northern Minnesota. Note that the Des Moines lobe came down a lowland, now occupied by the Minnesota River, and a part of it moved northeastward up the Minneapolis lowland as the Grantsburg sublobe. —After Wright and others, 1973

the two, constitutes a major drainage divide. From this divide, streams flow southwestward into the Missouri River and northeastward into the Mississippi River via the Minnesota River. At the town of Lake Benton, the moraine consists of 200 feet of Bemis till on top of 400 to 600 feet of older glacial drift. At 800 feet, this is one of the thickest accumulations of glacial deposits in Minnesota. This wind-swept topographic prominence on the treeless prairie is also known as Buffalo Ridge. Hundreds of wind turbines along its crest generate electricity.

Aerial photograph of the Altamont moraine in South Dakota a few miles west of the Minnesota border. —J. P. Gilbertson photo

The slightly younger Altamont stagnation moraine to the east of the Bemis is an inner moraine of the Des Moines lobe. It is a few hundred feet lower in elevation than the Bemis. Hundreds of lakes on the moraine fill depressions that formed when ice blocks buried in the till later melted. The ice became buried when the Des Moines lobe stopped moving and stagnated.

The Minnesota River starts at Big Stone Lake at Browns Valley and flows 330 miles across southern Minnesota to its confluence with the Mississippi River in the Twin Cities. This moderate-sized river flows in a valley as much as 5 miles wide, cut by Glacial River Warren mainly between about 11,700 and 9,400 years ago when part of Glacial Lake Agassiz catastrophically emptied. The Minnesota River is called an underfit river because it occupies a big valley that the modern river could not have eroded.

For the past 9,000 years or so, tributaries have been cutting down to the level established by Glacial River Warren, filling the Minnesota River Valley with sediment that the modern river is not capable of removing. Deltas have formed at tributary mouths, backing the Minnesota River up into lakes, such as Big Stone Lake at the Whetstone River, Marsh Lake at the Pomme de Terre River, and Lac qui Parle at the Lac qui Parle River. Waterfalls have formed near the mouths of most tributaries, as suggested by the town name of Redwood Falls along the Minnesota River.

BEDROCK GEOLOGY

Southwestern Minnesota features two main areas of bedrock. Exposures of 3,500-million-year-old Archean gneisses are present along a portion of the Minnesota River Valley. These are among the oldest rocks in the world—in the

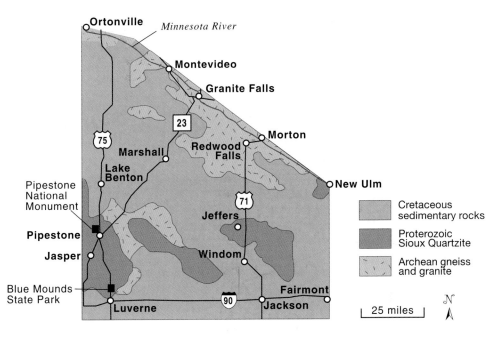

Bedrock geology of southwestern Minnesota. —After Morey, 1993

1960s when radiometric age dating of rocks came into use, they were considered *the* oldest rocks. Volcanic rocks in Quebec now hold the record at 4,280 million years.

The other main area of bedrock consists of exposures of Sioux Quartzite, notably at Pipestone National Monument, in and near Jasper, at Blue Mounds State Park, and near Jeffers. However, it is best exposed along the Sioux River at Sioux Falls, South Dakota, 15 miles across the border. This rock formation, about 1,700 million years old, may be as thick as 5,000 feet. It consists of quartz sand that must have been eroded from older basement rocks to the north during a long period of weathering. Virtually all other minerals were removed from the sand, largely by weathering and abrasion by wind and water. Cross-bedding in the formation shows that currents in braided, sand-rich streams generally flowed to the south. Thin, muddy beds deposited by low-velocity water formed the red pipestone beds that Native Americans quarried hundreds of years ago, and still quarry, at what is now Pipestone National Monument. Archean gneisses and granites immediately beneath the Sioux Quartzite were weathered to a clay-rich residuum, or saprolite, as thick as 100 feet in places, before the sand was deposited.

The study of samples from water wells and holes drilled during mineral exploration has allowed geologists of the Minnesota Geological Survey to interpret some additional geological features and history. The topographic relief on the bedrock surface of the Sioux Quartzite and older Precambrian rocks was as much as 1,100 feet above sea level about 100 million years ago when the Cretaceous sea advanced into Minnesota from the west. Thus the highest Sioux exposures stood as islands, part of the Sioux Ridge.

We know this because the resistant quartzite knobs sheltered Cretaceous marine deposits from erosion by the Pleistocene glaciers. Although Cretaceous sedimentary rocks, mostly shales, are not naturally exposed in southwestern Minnesota, they exist beneath glacial deposits and are as thick as 600 feet between the quartzite hills. Fossil clams, fish scales, and shark teeth indicate that most of the shale was deposited in the sea. In more easterly exposures in clay pits, as near New Ulm, the shale contains fossils of tree leaves and brackish to freshwater invertebrates, indicating proximity to the eastern shoreline of the Cretaceous inland sea. The fine-grained, generally muddy nature of the Cretaceous sedimentary rocks indicates that the continental landmass to the east was generally low. Chemical alteration of the Morton Gneiss and other feldspar-rich bedrock formations to a clay-rich residuum more than 100 feet thick in some places indicates that an extended period of wet, warm climatic conditions existed prior to the deposition of the Cretaceous rocks. The western shore of this Cretaceous sea was near the young, rising Rocky Mountains.

Road Guides in Southwestern Minnesota

South Dakota Border—Fairmont
102 miles

In the southwestern part of Minnesota, I-90 overlies glacial sediment a few hundred feet thick and as thick as 500 feet in places. Except for the far western stretch of I-90, which was not covered by Wisconsin-age ice sheets, the slightly undulating topography along I-90 is how it looked after the Des Moines lobe deposited the glacial sediment about 14,000 to 12,000 years ago (except for the present-day vegetation).

Between the South Dakota border and Magnolia, a distance of about 18 miles, look to both the north and south for great scenic views over gently undulating prairie topography that is now excellent agricultural land. Why is this topography even more subdued than glaciated areas farther east? There are two main reasons. This southwesternmost portion of Minnesota is underlain by old pre-Wisconsin glacial sediment. Also, much of this area was covered with a few feet of glacial loess, windblown clay and silt derived from the Des Moines ice lobe as it was melting just to the east of this area during late Wisconsin time.

The soils in the fields are black to very dark brown even though the glacial sediment and loess are light colored. Plants of the tallgrass prairie have been growing and dying since the last of the glaciers melted away, enriching the soil with dark-colored organic matter. Before this region was settled, prairie grasses (some as tall as 8 feet) and associated flowering plants extended as far as you could see without anything rising above them as today's trees, electric poles, TV and radio towers, and elevated highway overpasses do.

You can take a 50-mile loop trip from I-90 to see some of southwestern Minnesota's more interesting geology. Only 28 miles north of I-90 on MN 23 is Pipestone National Monument, where Native Americans have been quarrying pipestone for their pipes and other ceremonial pieces for hundreds of years. See the road guide for **MN 23: Granite Falls—Interstate 90** for details and photos. Between I-90 and the town of Pipestone, you will drive through Jasper, which like Pipestone has many old buildings made of pink Sioux Quartzite. You can return to I-90 from Pipestone via US 75 and visit Blue Mounds State Park, located about 8 miles north of I-90 and Luverne. This park includes a spectacular 90-foot-high cliff of Sioux Quartzite, as well as original prairie vegetation because the thin soil overlying the hard bedrock has never been plowed. See the road guide for **US 75: Ortonville—Interstate 90** for more details.

Luverne is located in the 2- to 3-mile-wide river valley now hosting the Rock River. Notice that the modern stream is very small in comparison to the wide river valley. About 14,000 years ago, a much larger river flowed southward from here, draining the melting ice of the Des Moines lobe, situated about 15 miles to the east.

For about 4 miles on either side of the Adrian exit at milepost 26, you are driving over glacial sediments of late Wisconsin age that are probably somewhat

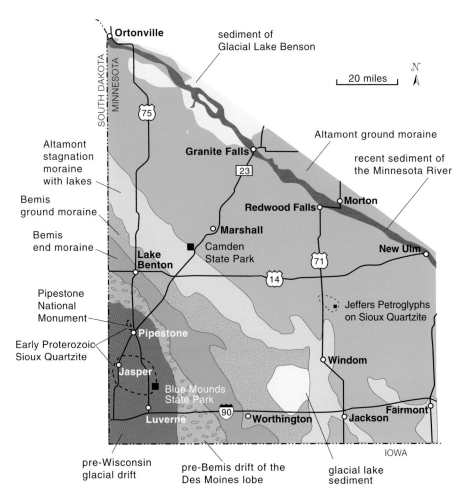

Glacial geology in southeastern Minnesota, also showing areas of Sioux Quartzite.
—Partly after Patterson and others, 1995; also from Hobbs and Goebel, 1982

older than those of the late Wisconsin Bemis moraine deposited by the Des Moines lobe. This till has been covered by windblown fine sediment, called loess. The loess is quite thin, and you can see boulders from the till protruding up through the loess in the fields near the Adrian exit. Stones faceted by wind abrasion (ventifacts) have been found in this area.

Between about mileposts 30 and 64 (the Lakefield exit), you are driving on the Bemis moraine, unsorted till deposited as an end moraine on the western side of the Des Moines lobe, and also on Bemis ground moraine, till deposited beneath the ice. The Bemis moraine in this area is topographically less prominent than 50 miles to the north, where it is a high feature called Buffalo Ridge. While lower here along Interstate 90, the moraine still forms a major regional divide. Streams on the north side flow northeastward to the Minnesota River and hence to the Mississippi, and streams on the south side flow southwestward to the Missouri River. Between Worthington and Jackson, you are driving just south of and parallel to this drainage divide that here has an east-west trend. Note wind turbines at milepost 54.

A small, unnamed, very short-lived glacial lake about 12 miles in diameter existed north of I-90 near the Lakefield exit. It formed in front of the melting Des Moines lobe where outwash streams were temporarily dammed. Heron Lake and South Heron Lake are the largest present-day lakes on this ancient lakebed. MN 60 crosses the very flat lakebed between Brewster and Wilder.

Just west of Jackson, you will cross the West Fork of the Des Moines River. Note the relief along this actively downcutting river, for which the Des Moines lobe was named.

The gently rolling topography between exit 64 at Lakefield and exit 102 at Fairmont, my rather arbitrary boundary between the southwestern and southeastern regions, is the Altamont stagnation and ground moraine of the Des Moines lobe. The stagnation moraine accumulated in a 10- to 20-mile-wide zone along the edge of the melting ice lobe. In southwestern Minnesota, it contains hundreds of lakes formed in irregularities on the surface of the glacial sediment.

About 15 miles northwest of Fairmont and 6 miles north of I-90 is the small town of Trimont, located on the hilly Altamont stagnation moraine of the Des Moines lobe. The hilly terrain hosts the Trimont Area Wind Farm.

US 14
New Ulm—South Dakota Border
102 miles
See map on page 246

Bedrock is exposed on the east side of New Ulm on the south side of US 14 just west of the junction with County Road 37. This conglomerate, part of the base of the Sioux Quartzite, formed on top of the Archean gneiss. It represents a billion years of weathering of the ancient gneiss and incorporation of pieces of the gneiss into the quartzite. An outcrop of granite gneiss is nearby.

Between New Ulm and the South Dakota border, US 14 crosses glacial till deposited by the Des Moines lobe. Notice that the many streams crossed by the highway are all flowing toward the northeast, down the regional slope of the topography. Many are tributaries of the Cottonwood River, which flows southeast before turning and flowing northeast into the Minnesota River.

Between New Ulm and a point a few miles west of Tracy, a distance of about 60 miles, the highway crosses ground moraine, along with glacial outwash sediments. Between Tracy and Florence, the highway crosses stagnation moraine. The thickness of the underlying glacial deposits increases from less than 200 feet at Tracy to 450 feet at Florence. Lakes are present on the stagnation moraine filling depressions where buried glacial ice melted.

The glacial deposits increase in thickness from 450 feet at Florence to 800 feet at Lake Benton. Part of this thickness increase is due to the 200-foot-thick

Bemis moraine, which forms the prominent topographic high known as Buffalo Ridge. However, the Bemis moraine sits atop 600 feet of older till, together making up one of the thickest glacial sections in Minnesota. One of the thickest sections of Cretaceous sedimentary rocks in southwestern Minnesota, 500 feet, underlies the same area. Therefore, you would have to drill down 1,300 feet to reach hard crystalline bedrock.

US 71
Morton—Jackson
70 miles
See map on page 246

Between Morton and Jackson, most of US 71 crosses Altamont ground moraine of the Des Moines lobe. Near Windom and Jackson, the highway crosses higher-relief stagnation moraine.

Morton is on the Minnesota River. You can see the 3,500-million-year-old Morton Gneiss in many exposures and roadcuts on the north side of town, including some by the high school and near a quarry on the east edge of town just off MN 19. The rock was quarried in Morton for building stone. A new roadcut at the entrance to a gas station northeast of the junction of US 71 and MN 19 in Morton is an excellent exposure.

A roadcut in Morton Gneiss at the entrance to a gas station and inn at the junction of US 71 and MN 19 at the north edge of Morton. Geologists do not know what the rock was prior to metamorphism, but the black inclusions were probably basalt.

Redwood Falls in Alexander Ramsey Park. Note the hard, relatively unweathered Morton Gneiss on the left and the weathered Morton Gneiss on the right (the saprolite), directly above relatively unweathered Morton Gneiss.

Redwood Falls, just 7 miles west of Morton, is home to a waterfall of the same name on the Redwood River, which flows through town. The waterfall is in Alexander Ramsey Park, which has nice exposures of the weathered residuum (saprolite) of Morton Gneiss. The gneissic texture is preserved, but the original minerals are nearly completely altered to clays, mostly kaolin. These exposures were the basis of Sam S. Goldich's basic research in the 1930s that led to the Goldich stability series, which describes the order in which minerals break down.

The weathering residuum forms as acidic waters move through fractures in the rock, weathering it. Intersecting fractures create blocks in the rock, and the blocks become rounded because there is increased water flow and weathering at the block corners. Many of the giant boulders found at the land surface or in the glacial deposits of this region were created by this process. The weathering here occurred before late Cretaceous time, 100 to 80 million years ago. The climate during the weathering had to have been warm and wet to cause such deep and thorough alteration of the original gneiss.

US 71 passes by the Jeffers Petroglyphs, operated by the Minnesota Historical Society, where there are about two thousand rock carvings. A conservative estimate of the age of the oldest is 7,000 years, based on comparisons with other petroglyph localities. Native Americans carved figures of animals, thunderbirds, and human forms into the very hard, pink to red, glacially striated Sioux Quartzite, which is about 1,700 million years old. Turn east on County Road 10, which is 29 miles south of Redwood Falls and 39 miles north of Jackson. Drive east for 3 miles to County Road 2 and then drive south for 1 mile. Look for the signs. Bring your camera, especially if you are there in the morning or evening when the lighting accentuates the relief on the carvings. You can walk on winding paths through the prairie to outcrops of quartzite.

Near the Jeffers Petroglyphs is Red Rock Dells, a Cottonwood County Park with a gorge exposing the Sioux Quartzite. It is 1 mile north of County Road 10 along Mound Creek.

Rock carvings on the 1,700-million-year-old Sioux Quartzite at Jeffers Petroglyphs.
—Courtesy of Minnesota Historical Society

Low-lying red Sioux Quartzite at the Jeffers Petroglyphs.

Ortonville—Interstate 90
123 miles
See map on page 246

US 75, known as the King of Trails Scenic Byway, extends from the Minnesota-Manitoba border to the southwestern corner of the state. The Minnesota portion was originally an Indian trail that passed through what is now Pipestone National Monument.

Big Stone Lake
Ortonville is located at the lower end of Big Stone Lake. Big Stone Lake State Park provides access to the lake at three places. The southernmost part, the Meadowbrook Area, can be reached by driving northwest out of Ortonville on MN 7 for a few miles. MN 7, part of the Minnesota River Valley Scenic Byway, follows the shore of Big Stone Lake and river terraces carved by Glacial River Warren. The terraces are further described in the road guide for **MN 28: Sauk Centre—Browns Valley** in the chapter on northwestern and central Minnesota. In many places, the lakeshore is a mass of large boulders, concentrated by Glacial River Warren as it eroded the existing glacial till, removing the finer sediments and leaving behind the boulders. If you look closely, you will also spot many large granitic boulders in the hillsides above MN 7.

Big Stone Lake formed when the Minnesota River backed up behind a delta-like barrier of sand and silt deposited by the Whetstone River, which flows east out of South Dakota and into the Minnesota River.

Notice how wide the Minnesota River Valley is compared to the size of the modern river. The large valley was carved by rushing floodwaters of Glacial River Warren, which drained Glacial Lake Agassiz between 11,700 and 10,900 years ago, and then again for awhile about 9,400 years ago. The great volume of fast-moving water cut through the unconsolidated glacial drift and soft Cretaceous sedimentary rock, exposing the underlying hard bedrock of granite and gneiss. In places, the river bluffs are 200 feet high. The Ortonville granite, about 2,600 million years old, is quarried on the old riverbed east of town. The pink, medium-grained granite contains coarse-grained pegmatite dikes.

At the Big Stone County Museum just south of Ortonville, a vantage point provides a view of the broad valley of Glacial River Warren. You can also see Paul Bunyan's 110-ton boat anchor (a quarried block of granite)!

Big Stone National Wildlife Refuge
A few miles east of Ortonville, between mileposts 133 and 134, is an entrance to the Big Stone National Wildlife Refuge. The refuge is on the riverbed of Glacial River Warren, now the floodplain of the modern Minnesota River. You can drive on a 5-mile-long paved road through part of the 1,700 acres of tallgrass prairie, 4,000 acres of wetlands, and 100 acres of granite outcrops that were abraded to smooth surfaces by Glacial River Warren. Except for some shallow potholes, the hard rock was not deeply eroded. The granite outcrops support prickly pear and ball cacti.

This granite outcrop is on the riverbed of Glacial River Warren.

Odessa to Lake Benton

Minnesota 75 crosses the 4-mile-wide valley of Glacial River Warren, now occupied by the comparatively small Minnesota River, just south of Odessa. Note the broad erosional terraces, farms, and granite quarries on the valley floor. Between the river valley and Bellingham, the highway crosses about 5 miles of the western edge of the lakebed of Glacial Lake Benson, which existed for about fifty years based on glacial varves. It formed in front of the retreating Des Moines lobe and drained when the water breached a moraine on its southern side. It was a fair-sized lake, roughly 40 miles in diameter.

Between Bellingham and a point about 4 miles north of Canby, the terrain is the gently rolling surface of Altamont ground moraine, including the area around Madison, the "Lutefisk Capital of the U.S.A." The cod used for the lutefisk has no relationship whatsoever to Glacial Lake Benson. It comes from Norway, as did the Norwegians settlers, who farmed the rich prairie soil that developed over the last 10,000 years.

In the vicinity of Canby, the countryside is quite flat because it is part of an old glacial outwash channel. Between about 6 miles south of Canby and 6 miles south of Ivanhoe near the intersection with County Road 15, US 75 crosses the hilly terrain of the Altamont stagnation moraine of the Des Moines lobe. The moraine includes hills, lakes, and swamps. At milepost 83 is the deep valley of the Yellow Medicine River, which flows northeastward to the Minnesota River south of Granite Falls.

Look for occasional piles of boulders, including white carbonate boulders derived from Manitoba, gathered by farmers as they prepared their fields. The till certainly contained more boulders than the rare rock piles would indicate. Farmers typically toss the boulders into unfarmable low spots that get overgrown with brush and trees, so the rocks are now out of sight. As my farmer father-in-law, Ted Luoma, used to say, "The first crop is rocks." With frost action bringing more rocks to the surface every year, there are also later crops of rocks.

The 7-mile-long, narrow Lake Benton formed in a tunnel valley, a drainage channel of a fast-moving river beneath the ice. The confined water was under high pressure, so it deeply eroded the preexisting glacial deposits. Hole-in-the-Mountain Prairie, south of the town of Lake Benton, is a preserved site of rare original prairie in the gap where the subglacial stream flowed out from under the ice.

Buffalo Ridge and Wind Energy

The town of Lake Benton is located on Buffalo Ridge, the narrow but high Bemis end moraine that formed on the southwest side of the Des Moines lobe. It is located on the eastern edge of the Coteau des Prairies. Near Lake Benton, the glacial tills are 800 feet thick, making this one of the thickest glacial deposits in the state.

The Bemis moraine extends for 300 miles in a northwest-southeast direction from South Dakota, across southwestern Minnesota, and more than halfway across Iowa to Des Moines. This topographic high is a drainage divide between waters flowing west to the Missouri River and east to the Mississippi River, although all end up in the Gulf of Mexico. The end moraine is only 2 miles

Wind turbines on Buffalo Ridge, an end moraine of the Des Moines lobe.

wide at Lake Benton and 7 miles wide at the Iowa border but is a 50-mile-wide complex at Des Moines.

The Heritage and Wind Power Learning Center is located in Lake Benton, which is proud of the title of the "Original Wind Power Capital of the Midwest." More than four hundred wind turbines had been erected on Buffalo Ridge near Lake Benton as of 2006. Another large project is located to the south at Storm Lake, Iowa, also on Buffalo Ridge. The topographically high ridge on the treeless prairie is an ideal place to harness the wind for generating electricity. The turbines need winds of 8 to 65 miles per hour to be effective. Leasing wind turbine sites to the electric companies for wind farms has become a new royalty-paying "crop" for farmers and ranchers. And they can continue to utilize the land for their usual crops or for grazing. Each turbine takes up only one-eighth of an acre and produces enough nonpolluting energy for a few hundred homes. Electricity generated by other means, such as fossil fuel plants, solar panels, and hydroelectric dams, is also essential because the winds do not always blow.

South of Lake Benton to Luverne

From about 4 miles south of Lake Benton to about 5 miles north of Pipestone, US 75 crosses glacial sediment older than the Bemis moraine but still likely of Wisconsin age. It is covered by windblown loess—clay and silt—and by outwash deposits.

From Pipestone south to Luverne, and on into Iowa, the glacial sediment is pre-Wisconsin in age, meaning older than about 75,000 years. It may be hundreds of thousands of years old, far beyond the reach of carbon-14 dating, so its age is uncertain. The topography over this drift is somewhat subdued, perhaps because the topography of the original deposit was fairly gentle, or erosion may have leveled it and a cover of windblown loess may have further evened the surface.

Pipestone National Monument

See the road guide for **MN 23: Granite Falls—Interstate 90.**

Sioux Quartzite

Between mileposts 14 and 22, look for numerous low outcrops of white to pink Sioux Quartzite in the fields adjacent to the highway. This rock is about 1,700 million years old and is part of the largest area of exposed quartzite of this age in the Lake Superior region. Several smaller areas of exposed quartzite are present in Wisconsin; the largest is the Baraboo Quartzite. The maximum thickness of the Sioux Quartzite has been estimated at 5,000 feet, but no drill holes penetrate the formation to give a true thickness. Most of this quartz sand was deposited by southward-flowing river systems on a surface without vegetation, as land plants had not yet evolved. In adjacent South Dakota, there is evidence that the sand in the upper third of the Sioux Quartzite was deposited in the tidal zone of a shallow sea. The same is true for the Baraboo Quartzite.

Cross-bedding in the rock sequence provides evidence of the direction in which the currents that deposited the sand were flowing. Whereas the vast majority of more than 1,200 cross-bedding measurements and 240 asymmetrical ripples in Minnesota and adjacent South Dakota indicate current flow toward the south, some dip to the north. At some localities in South Dakota, northward-dipping cross-beds lie immediately above southward-dipping cross-beds. Rivers usually flow in only one direction, so it is unlikely that rivers formed these cross-beds in South Dakota. A more likely explanation is that they were formed by incoming and outgoing tides along a seashore.

How was the age of deposition determined? Tiny grains of zircon, deposited with the quartz sand and likely derived from the same crystalline rock, have been dated by radiometric methods. The youngest zircon found in these quartzites is 1,712 million years old. Therefore, the quartz sands that are now quartzite must have been deposited after those zircons were eroded out of their original igneous source. So, 1,700 million years is an approximate maximum age, a best guess, of the oldest age for deposition of the quartzite.

Where did all that quartz sand come from? In Early Proterozoic time, the Penokean Mountains were formed along a zone from east-central Minnesota across northern Wisconsin and into Michigan. Weathering and erosion of these mountains produced a lot of sand composed of quartz. Many other minerals break down into clay, which is carried away by water, but quartz is a common mineral that resists chemical breakdown. After burial, cementation by quartz precipitated out of groundwater transformed the quartz sand into a very hard rock. Low-grade metamorphism between 1,630 and 1,465 million years ago further solidified it into quartzite.

Cross-bedded Sioux Quartzite.

Blue Mounds State Park

Blue Mounds State Park is east of US 75 a few miles north of Luverne. A spectacular high hill of Sioux Quartzite, which early settlers heading west saw as a blue mound, rises above the prairie. The eastern edge of the mound is a 90-foot-high vertical cliff. Look for old building-stone quarries in the park, dating from the late 1800s.

The park is a 1,500-acre remnant of tallgrass prairie. The very thin soil and abundant outcrops on the quartzite hill saved it from being plowed, although it was grazed. Prickly pear cactus grows on some quartzite exposures. From a safe, elevated stand, you can see a herd of American bison in their natural prairie habitat.

An unusual man-made line of quartzite rocks—1,250 feet long and aligned in an east-west direction—is present near the interpretive center. On the first day of spring and the first day of fall, sunrises and sunsets are in perfect alignment with the stone line. Who made this line is unknown. One thing is sure—some people did a lot of hard work and it took some time!

Other interesting phenomena in the park are a few highly polished quartzite outcrops. Some people have thought that the polish is due to buffalo rubbing against the rock. However, it is more likely that most of the polish, and some pitting, is due to wind abrasion by silt shortly after glaciation. Still another explanation is manganese and iron oxides precipitated from groundwater brought up by capillary action. Some highly polished surfaces are on loose pieces of quartzite at ground level, within reach of the capillary action. Maybe all three occurred.

The cliff of Sioux Quartzite at Blue Mounds State Park
looked like a blue mound to settlers heading west.

MINNESOTA 23
Granite Falls—Interstate 90
103 miles
See map on page 246

Just north of Granite Falls is a pull-off on MN 23 at a point of interest that provides a lesson in why you shouldn't believe everything you read. The sign states that mountains here in the past were 4 miles high. They were more likely half that high. It also states that 1-mile-high glaciers melted, forming Glacial Lake Agassiz to the north of here. The glaciers were much thinner in Minnesota, and perhaps only several hundred feet near here. The other information on the sign is accurate.

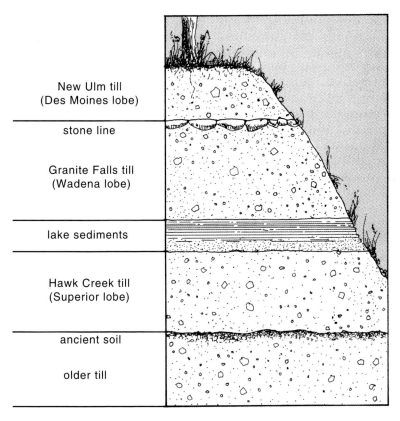

New Ulm till
(Des Moines lobe)

stone line

Granite Falls till
(Wadena lobe)

lake sediments

Hawk Creek till
(Superior lobe)

ancient soil

older till

Four glacial tills were once visible in the Granite Falls area before the encroachment of vegetation. This exposure was 30 feet high. The yellowish brown New Ulm till, deposited by the Des Moines lobe, contains abundant gray shale and carbonate fragments from the Dakotas and the Winnipeg area. The yellow to yellowish brown Granite Falls till, deposited by the Wadena lobe, lacks shale but contains abundant carbonates from either the Winnipeg or Hudson Bay area and granite from northern Minnesota and Ontario. The reddish Hawk Creek till, deposited by the Superior lobe, contains a variety of fragments from the Lake Superior region. The older tan till at the bottom contains material similar to the Granite Falls till. —After Ojakangas and Matsch, 1982.

The sloping highway roadcuts where MN 23 drops down into the Minnesota River Valley on the east side of the valley indicate that the glacial deposits are quite thick, about 200 feet. Vegetation has now covered the banks, but before the vegetation took over, the deposits were studied and found to contain four different glacial tills of different compositions and ages. An ancient soil separates the lower two, fine-grained lake sediments separate the middle two, and a layer of glacially striated large stones constituting a boulder pavement separates the upper two.

When catastrophic floods raged down Glacial River Warren, they carved through the glacial sediment, Cretaceous rocks, and the weathered surface on the gneiss, exposing the hard bedrock. Within the Granite Falls area, some gneisses have been dated at 3,500 million years. Pink granitic gneiss is interlayered with dark gray gneiss. Because the original textures have been obliterated by the recrystallization of minerals, only the chemistry of the rocks remains as a clue to the original rock type, but it is not definitive. The gneiss could have been metagraywacke, volcanic rock, or granitic rock before it was metamorphosed. These exposures give geologists only a tantalizing glimpse of the bigger picture, most of which is obscured by glacial sediments. Other rocks exposed farther to the north and south of Granite Falls have ages of "only" 2,700 million years.

A good place to stop is at the north roadcut closest to the MN 23 bridge over the Minnesota River on its east side. If you have a very discerning eye, you should spot a few remnants of smooth-sided potholes carved into the gneiss by high-velocity waters and swirling rocks carried by Glacial River Warren. As you cross the river, note the outcrops in the river valley, exposed by Glacial River Warren. The high roadcut on the west side of the Minnesota River opposite the Yellow Medicine County Museum also has a pothole at the top of the cut.

View across the Minnesota River Valley with the river in the foreground and lakes farther back. Glacial River Warren carved this wide valley.

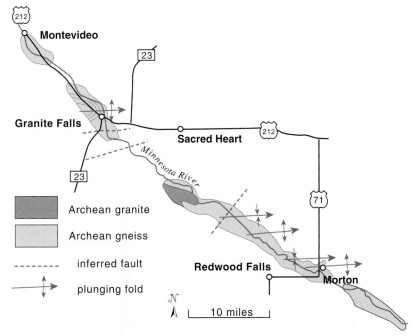

Generalized geology of 3,500-million-year-old gneisses in the vicinity of Granite Falls along the Minnesota River. —Modified from Grant, 1972

You may be wondering where the waterfall is at Granite Falls. It was on the Minnesota River, but a dam has been built over it.

Upper Sioux Agency State Park

Upper Sioux Agency State Park is 8 miles southeast of Granite Falls on MN 67. The meandering Yellow Medicine River empties into the Minnesota River within the park boundaries. Cuts along the Yellow Medicine River expose thick glacial tills, sediments deposited over a time interval of perhaps more than 1 million years. Also in the park is the site of the Upper Sioux Agency that was destroyed in the 1862 Dakota uprising.

The bank of the Yellow Medicine River in Upper Sioux Agency State Park may expose more than 1 million years of glacial sediment.
—Carrie Jennings photo, Minnesota Geological Survey

Side Trip to Montevideo

US 212 between Granite Falls and Montevideo parallels the Minnesota River as it flows across the flat lakebed of Glacial Lake Benson. Note the abraded rock exposures on the river bottom, waste rock piles from quarries, minor exposures of glacial till in some roadcuts, and tilled fields on the floodplain. You can stop and examine the ancient granitic gneiss in roadcuts just southeast of Montevideo.

Granitic outcrop on the Minnesota River floodplain about 2 miles northwest of Granite Falls along US 212.

Granitic gneiss near Montevideo on US 212 about 1.6 miles northwest of the bridge over the Minnesota River.

From Granite Falls to Florence

South of Granite Falls, MN 23 generally crosses over drift of the Des Moines lobe. Notice the gently rolling topography of the ground moraine between Granite Falls and Marshall. A few miles south of Marshall, between mileposts 66 and 68, look for large gravel pits in the till. Also look for big boulder piles. Before farmers piled these rocks while clearing their fields, they were scattered throughout the unsorted glacial till.

Between Lynd and Florence, MN 23 crosses the Altamont stagnation moraine, marking the western edge of the shrinking Des Moines lobe. Look for glacial boulders and an abundance of lakes on the hillier topography.

Camden State Park

The entrance to Camden State Park is 10 miles south of Marshall, near Lynd. The park is located on the Altamont stagnation moraine deposited on the southwestern side of the Des Moines lobe. The Redwood River meanders through the park and has cut down through more than 100 feet of glacial deposits, creating a rugged terrain. The river exposes older till of the Wadena lobe below the younger till of the Des Moines lobe. The streambed is full of large boulders that lagged behind as the smaller particles were carried away. Watch for the many springs along the riverbanks emerging from between the two till layers.

Windy Buffalo Ridge

Between Florence and Ruthton, the slightly higher topography denotes Bemis ground moraine deposited on the extreme western edge of the Des Moines lobe. Between Ruthton and Holland, a still higher, northwest-trending topographic high known as Buffalo Ridge is the stony Bemis end moraine. Its crest is the drainage divide between waters flowing northeastward to the Minnesota River and waters flowing southward to the Missouri River. The most impressive sight on this ridge, however, is the hundreds of towering, majestic three-bladed wind turbines. More and more are being built to harness the strong winds blowing over this treeless prairie. When I was field-checking for this road guide, it was so windy that the grasses and shrubs appeared to be growing at a 45-degree angle to the horizontal! The high elevation of the Bemis end moraine catches more wind than the lower areas of the prairie. The production of electricity from this pollution-free, renewable source decreases the amount of polluting fossil fuels, especially coal, needed to generate power.

The Bemis moraine extends southeastward 200 miles to Des Moines, Iowa, and there are wind turbines in northern Iowa as well. This is likely a prelude to future massive wind-power development in the area and in the nearby windy prairie states of North Dakota, South Dakota, and Nebraska. Farmers can continue to use their land beneath the windmills for crops or grazing, and leasing land for this "crop" is much more valuable to farmers than conventional crops or pasture.

Holland is located on the 4-mile-wide valley of the Rock River, which flows south into Iowa. Notice how small the present river is compared to its valley, which was initially formed by large amounts of meltwater flowing from a nearby glacier. The modern stream occupying the valley is called an underfit stream.

Pipestone National Monument

Pipestone National Monument, 1.5 miles north of the town of Pipestone, is known as the source of pipestone, valued for at least four hundred years by numerous Native American tribes. They carved pipes from the soft, red, clay-rich rock found here. The pipestone was originally deposited as mud about 1,700 million years ago. The primary layer used for pipestone is a layer of mud several inches thick between beds of quartz sand. The sand has since been cemented into the very hard pink Sioux Quartzite, which was deposited by streams long before there was any vegetation on the land. The heat and pressure of burial has altered the mud to pipestone. The pipestone has been named catlinite in honor of artist and historian George Catlin, who in 1836 described the pipestone quarries and the Native Americans who dug the stone.

Walk the 0.75-mile-long Circle Tour that starts at the visitor center. You will see the quarries, both rock types, a waterfall, and native prairie plants. Many of the rock surfaces are faceted and polished by northwest winds. Pipestone's downtown Historic District includes twenty buildings that are on the National Register of Historic Places, each built of the local quartzite between 1880 and 1900. See a more detailed description of the Sioux Quartzite in the road guide for **US 75:Ortonville—Interstate 90**.

Along the road into the monument are large granite boulders called the Three Maidens. Seven pieces, including three large ones, were once part of a single large boulder since fractured by frost action. The Native Americans

Cross-bedded Sioux Quartzite on a trail at Pipestone National Monument.

realized that the rock was not local in origin and gave it special spiritual significance. The granite boulder, very unlike the surrounding quartzite, was transported here by glaciers from granite near Millbank, South Dakota, or the Ortonville area, about 90 miles to the north.

Pipe made of pipestone quarried at Pipestone National Monument.
—Pipestone National Monument photo

Quarry in Sioux Quartzite at Pipestone National Monument. The dark red layer at water level is the pipestone.

Split Rock Creek State Park

Split Rock Creek State Park is located about midway between Pipestone and Jasper. The dam that impounds the reservoir was constructed out of Sioux Quartzite in 1935 by the Works Progress Administration. Some native prairie in the park remains untouched by the plow. The name of the creek comes from a spot near Jasper, 3.5 miles to the south, where the creek flows through a gorge in the Sioux Quartzite.

Jasper

Rock County, the southwesternmost county in Minnesota, is aptly named, but Jasper is not. The pink to red Sioux Quartzite may slightly resemble this rock, but it is *not* jasper, a fine-grained, precipitated chert common in iron-formations. The town of Jasper hosts an active quarry in Sioux Quartzite. The factory makes lining blocks for industrial mills, as well as stone benches and cemetery monuments. If you want your tombstone to last a really long time, consider one made of this quartzite! Remember, this rock is composed completely of quartz, and quartz is the most durable common mineral, both physically and chemically. Jasper boasts that it is built of the same stone on which it stands, with more than a dozen buildings made of quartzite. Most are just off the highway on Wall Street.

MN 23 follows the crest of a low quartzite ridge south of Jasper. Look for low outcrops of Sioux Quartzite and scattered boulders of quartzite moved by glacial ice. The quartzite is found in till all the way south to Nebraska.

Old Glacial Till in Southwest Minnesota

Between a point a few miles northeast of Pipestone and the southwestern corner of Minnesota, the glacial deposits are pre-Wisconsin in age and may be more than 300,000 years old. These glacial sediments are denser than the younger deposits. They are difficult to recognize, partly because of a cover of a few feet of loess, windblown clayey and silty glacial sediment. At about milepost 4, a few miles north of the southern terminus of MN 23 at I-90, look toward the south at the great view of rolling farmland on this older, subdued glacial topography.

SOUTHEASTERN MINNESOTA
Marine Rocks and Fossils

Southeastern Minnesota is the happy home of marine sedimentary rocks, lots of which are exposed because there is little glacial cover at the eastern edge of the region. The southeastern corner of the state is part of the so-called Driftless Area, part of which may have escaped glaciation entirely during the Wisconsin glacial advance. You can see cliffs of sandstone and limestone along the Mississippi River Valley and caves and sinkholes in the uplands. Huge volumes of glacial meltwater carved the deep valley of the Mississippi River, and modern tributaries continue to dissect and erode the uplands as the streams work down to the level of the Mississippi.

GLACIAL GEOLOGY

Glacial drift of Wisconsin age covers much of southeastern Minnesota. In the northern portion, in and near the Twin Cities, the southernmost of the Superior lobe drift is present. In the western half of the region, the glacial cover was deposited by the Des Moines lobe, including the Altamont stagnation moraine with its abundant lakes. The total thickness of the glacial sediments, especially over buried river valleys, is as much as 500 feet in places.

The eastern half of the region was not covered by the glaciers of the Wisconsin advances of the last 70,000 years. It lacks lakes and is deeply dissected by numerous streams flowing eastward to the Mississippi. Older glacial deposits, known informally as the Gray Drift, are mostly pre-Illinoian in age and are present over more than 2,000 square miles of southeastern Minnesota and probably once covered more than 5,000 square miles. Another older deposit, known as old Red Drift from the Lake Superior region, is found in a small area. Drill holes show multiple older tills in places. These older glacial drifts are not very visible because they are either highly eroded or are covered by windblown loess, derived from wind erosion of drift to the west. The loess is tens of feet thick in places, as in Great River Bluffs State Park where I-90 meets the Mississippi River. This fine-grained, windblown sediment developed into a fertile soil, but it eroded when farmers in the mid-1800s cultivated sloping surfaces. The eroded sediment is as thick as 8 feet in some river valleys and covers the black, organic-rich soil that had formed prior to farming.

Glacial River Warren, the channel for Glacial Lake Agassiz floodwaters, flowed down the Minnesota River Valley to the Mississippi River Valley and then southward from the Twin Cities, eroding the deep valley you see today.

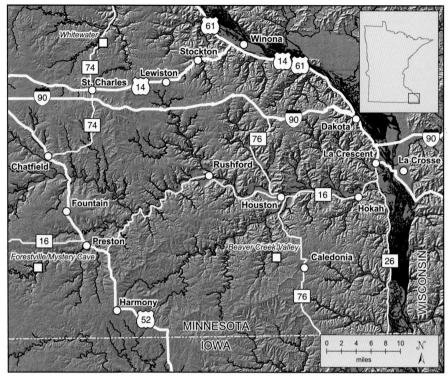

Landscape image of southeastern Minnesota, showing the deeply dissected area along the Mississippi River Valley.

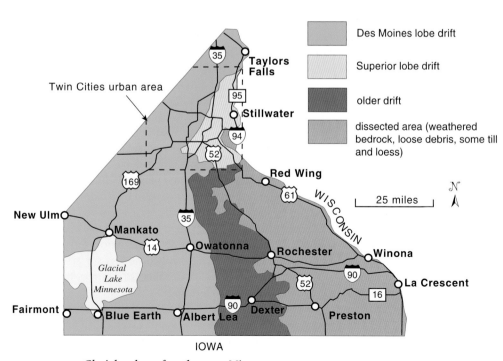

Glacial geology of southeastern Minnesota. —Modified from Hobbs and Goebel, 1982

The large meltwater river deposited outwash along its floodplain, and these old floodplains now stand as terraces above the modern river. The tributaries that flow into the deep valley were oversteepened, and erosion along them dissected the terrain. The Mississippi River, being much smaller than Glacial River Warren, is unable to carry away all the sediment carried in by the tributaries.

The easternmost 12-mile width of southeastern Minnesota is part of the Driftless Area, which also occupies a large part of adjacent southwestern Wisconsin. Glaciers of the Pleistocene ice ages of the last 1.8 million years did not ever cover this area. Higher topography to the north may have deflected the lobes of ice.

BEDROCK GEOLOGY

Paleozoic marine sedimentary rocks, which are more than 1,500 feet thick in some places, were deposited in this region between about 504 and 374 million years ago. Each rock unit is like a sheet—layers from a few feet to several hundred feet thick cover thousands of square miles. These rocks are essentially undeformed and unmetamorphosed, with the youngest rocks at the top and the oldest at the bottom. Most are either Late Cambrian or Ordovician, but some in the southernmost part of the region are Middle Devonian. Note that rocks of Silurian and Early Devonian age are missing, either because they were eroded or because no sediments were deposited during this time.

In the Paleozoic sea that covered southeastern Minnesota, several depositional environments were present. Sands were generally deposited along the shoreline or in offshore bars, depending on the water depth and the currents. Finer-grained silts and clay-sized particles were deposited farther offshore in quieter waters, but they were also present on tidal flats near the shoreline. Calcium carbonate was precipitated in warm, shallow seas. Depending upon ocean floor topography, such sites were on offshore platforms or even on nearshore tidal flats.

The Cambrian rocks are mostly quartz-rich sandstones, the end product of a very long period of weathering and erosion on the low-lying landmass to the north. Vascular terrestrial plants were not extensive until Silurian time, though microbial crusts likely covered the landscape in Cambrian time. Of lesser importance is shale, composed of clay minerals formed during weathering of the rocks to the north. Few carbonate rocks formed during Cambrian time, but the Ordovician and Devonian rocks are mainly carbonates—limestone or dolomite. The sandstones in Minnesota are poorly cemented and therefore are rather easily eroded. Where overlain by much more resistant limestone or dolomite, they are more likely to be preserved.

The carbonates were probably precipitated in shallow, warm water although some formed in cooler water. Limestone, usually gray, was commonly altered by magnesium-rich brines to buff-colored dolomite after deposition. The buff color is so distinctive that even while driving at high speeds down the highway, you can confidently call out the rock type. During this dolomitization process, the mineral and rock composition is changed from $CaCO_3$ to the mineral dolomite—$CaMg(CO_3)_2$. Technically, a rock composed of the mineral dolomite is a dolostone, but most geologists just call the rock dolomite. During dolomitization, fossils are commonly recrystallized and destroyed. However, fossils of marine organisms are present in the limestones, and some survived the dolomitization, confirming that the rocks were deposited in a sea and not a freshwater lake. The sea moved into southeastern Minnesota three main times, each time depositing a rock sequence. Erosional boundaries, or unconformities, separate sequences, so a sequence is by definition a stack of continuously deposited sediment. When the sea withdrew from an area, the sediments were exposed to erosion and the sequence ended. The first sequence, named the Sauk sequence, was deposited from Late Cambrian through Early Ordovician time, about 504 to 478 million years ago. The second, the Tippecanoe sequence, was deposited between 475 and 444 million years ago, during Middle to Late Ordovician time. The third, the Kaskaskia sequence, was deposited from about 385 to 368 million years ago, during Middle to Late Devonian time. There are also several other minor sea advances and retreats recorded in the rock record as unconformities.

The Cambrian and Ordovician rocks are best seen from US 61 along the Mississippi River. At the end of the last ice age, vast amounts of meltwater flowed down the valley, removing glacial deposits and exposing the bedrock along its course in both Minnesota and Wisconsin. You can also see the rocks along the St. Croix River to the north and at numerous other places in southeastern Minnesota, such as in Fillmore County just north of the Iowa border. The Devonian formations are visible mostly in rock quarries, where special permission is necessary to visit.

Though these Paleozoic rocks are essentially in their original, nearly horizontal depositional positions, there are regional differences in attitude that

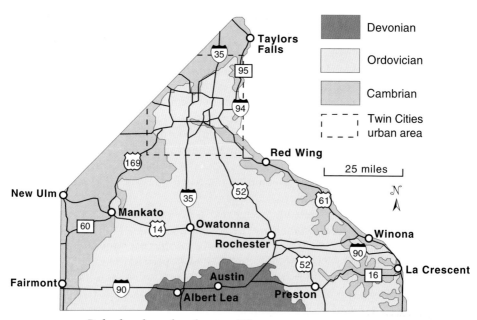

Bedrock geology of southeastern Minnesota. —Modified from Morey, 1993

TIME		ROCK UNITS		
era	period			
PALEOZOIC	DEVONIAN	Cedar Valley Group		
		Wapsipinicon Group		
	ORDOVICIAN	Maquoketa Formation		
		Galena Group	Dubuque Fm. Stewartville Fm. Prosser Fm. Cummingsville Fm. Decorah Shale	
		Platteville Formation		
		Glenwood Formation		
		St. Peter Sandstone		
		Prairie du Chien Group	Shakopee Formation	
			Oneota Dolomite	
	CAMBRIAN	Jordan Sandstone		
		St. Lawrence Formation		
		Tunnel City Group (formerly Franconia Formation)	Mazomanie Fm. Lone Rock Fm. Davis Fm.	
		Wonewoc Sandstone (formerly Ironton and Galesville Sandstones)		
		Eau Claire Formation		
		Mt. Simon Sandstone		
PRE-CAMBRIAN		Hinckley Sandstone		
		Fond du Lac Formation		
		crystalline basement rock		

Paleozoic rock column of Minnesota. Names in brown are new nomenclature proposed by Mossler (2008), in part to make the names compatible with those used in Wisconsin and Iowa. The Franconia Formation becomes the Tunnel City Group; the Ironton Sandstone and Galesville Sandstone become the Wonewoc Sandstone; the Shakopee Dolomite becomes the Shakopee Formation because it contains the New Richmond Sandstone; and the Decorah Shale and Dubuque Formation become part of the Galena Group. —From Lively, 1995, with updates in brown from Mossler, 2008

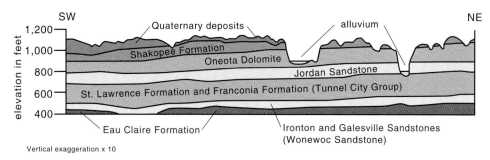

SW ... NE

elevation in feet

1,200 — Quaternary deposits ... alluvium

1,000 — Shakopee Formation

Oneota Dolomite

800 — Jordan Sandstone

600 — St. Lawrence Formation and Franconia Formation (Tunnel City Group)

400 —

Eau Claire Formation   Ironton and Galesville Sandstones
(Wonewoc Sandstone)

Vertical exaggeration x 10

Typical geologic cross section showing Paleozoic rocks over a distance of about 10 miles. Note the gentle dip down to the southwest. The vertical exaggeration is ten times, necessary to show the rock units as separate entities. —Modified from Mossler, 2001

are generally not discernible in individual exposures. The Paleozoic rocks were deposited in the Hollandale Embayment, a broad lowland that extended southward to the Ozark Basin in southern Missouri and the Illinois Basin in southern Illinois. It was repeatedly inundated by the shallow Paleozoic seas that advanced into this region from the south. This topographic low formed over the Midcontinent Rift of Middle Proterozoic age where it crosses southeastern Minnesota. Later, due to movements along the rift zone during Ordovician time, basins containing down-warped sedimentary rock layers developed within the embayment. The Twin Cities Basin is an important one, and another, the poorly defined Galena Basin, is on the Minnesota-Iowa border area south of Rochester. In places there are also minor upfolds—anticlines—and also faults with displacements of as much as several hundred feet.

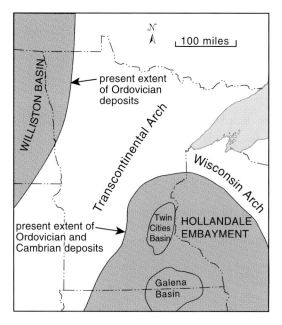

The Hollandale Embayment was a low area over the Midcontinent Rift that was inundated by shallow seas in Cambrian and Ordovician times. —After Webers, 1972

Why did the shallow and tropical Paleozoic seas move onto the continental interior and then retreat several times? Glaciation in Africa and South America during Ordovician time would have lowered the level of the sea worldwide, and when the glaciers melted, the sea would have risen and flooded lowlands like the Hollandale Embayment. Another important process that causes sea level rise and fall is related to activity where tectonic plates spread apart in ocean basins. During times of rapid spreading, the ocean floor along the spreading zone is being raised, therefore displacing a considerable volume of ocean water, which then creeps onto the continental landmasses. And during times of slow spreading, the water level lowers.

During Cambrian, Ordovician, and Devonian times, the equator was located at or near the middle of North America, and the continent was rotated about 90 degrees to the east compared to its present orientation. Thus the early Paleozoic equator extended from what is now the Gulf of Mexico to what is now Hudson Bay, and Minnesota was tropical.

Although some life existed in Precambrian time, the animals did not have hard parts, so fossils other than stromatolites are rare in Precambrian rocks. In Cambrian time, animals with shells evolved, and life in the seas was abundant and diverse. All of the invertebrate marine phyla that exist today were around then, including corals, and fossils of these organisms are abundant in Paleozoic rocks. Fossils are more easily preserved in limestone and shale than in sandstone because the latter is more porous and permeable—acidic water moving

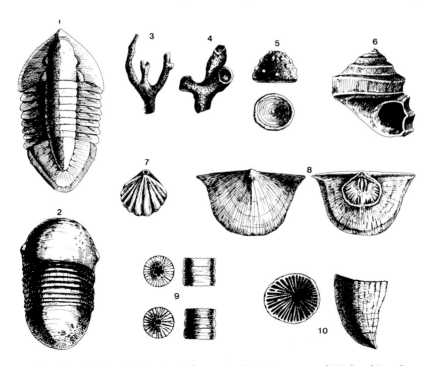

Ordovician fossils: trilobites (1, 2), bryozoans (3, 4, 5), gastropod (6), brachiopods (7, 8), crinoids (9), and horn coral (10). —From unpublished sketch by Don Wallace, Minnesota Geological Survey, 1960

through the sand dissolves the shells. Therefore, the Ordovician limestones and shales are the most fossiliferous rocks in Minnesota. Thin limestone beds within shale are especially productive. Though not as fossiliferous throughout, many Cambrian formations have individual beds littered with fragmentary trilobite fossils.

St. Peter Sandstone

The St. Peter Sandstone was deposited over much of the midcontinental United States during middle Ordovician time. In the Twin Cities Basin, near its northernmost extent, it averages 155 feet thick. The St. Peter Sandstone is not well cemented, so most exposures are overlain by the resistant limestone and dolomite of the Platteville Formation. These harder rocks protect the sandstone from erosion. The St. Peter was named for the St. Peter's River, an earlier name for the Minnesota River.

This formation is known the world over as the prime example of a quartz sandstone. Like Ivory Soap, it is "99.44 percent pure." Recall that quartz is the most resistant common mineral, physically and chemically, in Earth's crust. In order to derive a sandstone composed only of quartz, all of the other less-resistant minerals (feldspars, amphiboles, pyroxenes, micas, and others) must be eliminated by weathering and abrasion. This process is not easily accomplished, and there are very few if any comparable sands on modern beaches. The grains of sand in the St. Peter Sandstone are also well rounded, indicating much abrasion. It is generally thought that the sand must have gone through several cycles of erosion and deposition—in other words, it was recycled. It is likely that the older sandstones deposited during late Cambrian time were eroded, and the sands were reworked by wind on sand dunes on the as yet vegetationless land surface (vascular land plants didn't appear until Silurian time), and by water on the beaches.

Rivers don't round sand because there is always a water "cushion" between grains, so they don't hit each other hard enough and frequently enough to chip off corners. Sand dunes, on the other hand, are a good environment for rounding sand because there is no water cushion between grains. A beach environment is also effective, as the grains rub each other as the waves and currents drag them back and forth. In addition, grains remain on a beach for a long time and are subjected to the ebbs and flows of the tides, giving them a chance to become well rounded before they are finally buried.

The St. Peter is not 100 percent quartz because four other resistant minerals are also present in minute amounts: tourmaline, zircon, rutile, and garnet. Dating of zircon grains indicates that they were derived from Precambrian rocks ranging in age from 2,600 to 1,000 million years. Between those times and about 458 million years ago, when the St. Peter was deposited, there was plenty of time available for recycling. One researcher said the sand of the St. Peter may have been recycled a hundred times!

Deicke K-Bentonite

In Ordovician times, volcanoes in southeastern North America were erupting. Volcanic ash was deposited far and wide, including in Minnesota, in thin layers. These ash beds were later altered to a soft clay called bentonite. One of the

St. Peter Sandstone overlain by limestone of the Platteville Formation in St. Paul. —C. L. Matsch *photo*

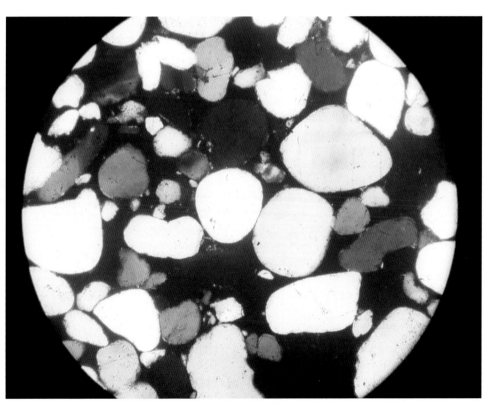

Photomicrograph of the St. Peter Sandstone. The larger, round quartz grains are about 0.5 millimeter in diameter.

The thin Deicke K-bentonite (in a roadcut at Sogn, Minnesota) was a layer of volcanic ash deposited 454 million years ago. The lens cap is on the bentonite layer. —John Mossler photo

best-known bentonites is the Deicke K-bentonite, which occurs in the lower-most part of the Decorah Shale. Geologists originally placed it near the top of the Platteville Formation but recent studies changed its placement. It is only a few inches thick, and it takes a specialist to find it. This ash bed, dated at 454 million years, is found over the entire Upper Mississippi River Valley, an area of about a million square miles. The total volume of ash is about 240 cubic miles, four hundred times more than the ash produced by the 1980 eruption of Mt. St. Helens. This enormous ashfall affected the animals living in the shallow Ordovician sea. Sloan, Middleton, and Webers (2005) studied fossils above and below the bed and found that 215 of 262 species were wiped out in the area of the ashfall. The ash would have transformed the clear, warm ocean habitat into a sea of choking, muddy water. Later, animals from adjacent regions slowly repopulated the depleted region.

Sinkholes and Caves

The dissected area of southeastern Minnesota, with its largely carbonate bed-rock, is the home of innumerable sinkholes and caves. Fillmore County, for example, probably has 10,000 sinkholes and hundreds of caves. They commonly occur in clusters, so small areas may have many and other, larger areas may have only a few. Farther west, where 50 feet or more of glacial drift covers the carbonate bedrock, sinkholes at the surface are uncommon, but the underlying carbonate still has cavities. The sinkholes range from a few feet to 100 feet in

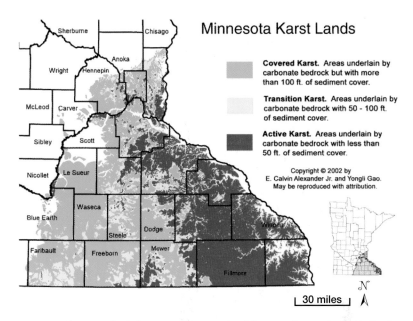

Minnesota Karst Lands

Covered Karst. Areas underlain by carbonate bedrock but with more than 100 ft. of sediment cover.

Transition Karst. Areas underlain by carbonate bedrock with 50 - 100 ft. of sediment cover.

Active Karst. Areas underlain by carbonate bedrock with less than 50 ft. of sediment cover.

Copyright © 2002 by
E. Calvin Alexander Jr. and Yongli Gao.
May be reproduced with attribution.

30 miles

Areas on the map shaded green, yellow, and red have carbonate bedrock. In the areas of green, the bedrock is covered with more than 100 feet of sediment so karst topography is not actively forming. In areas of red, the bedrock has less than 50 feet of sediment cover so karst is developing. Dakota, Rice, Goodhue, Wabasha, Dodge, Olmstead, Winona, Mower, Fillmore, and Houston Counties have extensive areas of karst landscape. —From Alexander and Gao, 2002

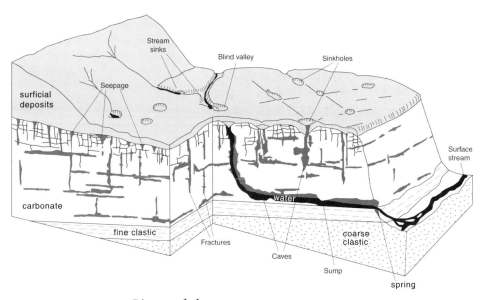

Diagram of a karst area. —Modified from Lively, 1995

diameter. The sinkholes that you see are formed by the collapse of overlying soil and sediment into the bedrock sinkholes underneath, which you usually can't see. Most are cone-shaped, caused by the angle of repose of the sediment, but some can be steep-sided if the underlying carbonate bedrock has collapsed into a subterranean cavity. The sinkholes are normally much wider than the underlying bedrock holes. New sinkholes continue to form.

Regions with sinkholes are called karst topography, named after a region in Yugoslavia. The karst develops where carbonate is dissolved by acidic water. Rainwater is slightly acidic because carbon dioxide (CO_2) in the air and soil dissolves in the water, producing carbonic acid (H_2CO_3). If the groundwater becomes saturated with calcium and bicarbonate (HCO_3^-) ions, calcium carbonate ($CaCO_3$) will be precipitated in cave networks, forming stalactites and stalagmites. Which are which? Stalactites hang from the ceiling of a cave, and stalagmites grow up from the floor of a cave. The following phrase will help you remember which is which: when the *mites* crawl up, the *tights* come down.

Although there are hundreds of caves in southeastern Minnesota, only two, both in Fillmore County, are open to the public. One is in Forestville/Mystery Cave State Park, and the other is Niagara Cave, a commercial cave near Harmony. For further information on the caves, see the road guide for **US 52: Twin Cities—Iowa Border**

Trees mark a sinkhole in a field west of Utica.

Road Guides in Southeastern Minnesota

Twin Cities

The metropolitan area of the Twin Cities of Minneapolis and St. Paul, and that of the surrounding suburbs, has a glacial topography with glacial deposits as thick as 400 feet. Where the Mississippi and Minnesota Rivers have cut down through the glacial cover, essentially horizontal Ordovician marine rocks about 475 to 450 million years old are exposed.

The Twin Cities metropolitan area contains several hundred lakes, and there are twenty-two within the boundaries of Minneapolis. All occupy depressions in glacial deposits. Most are kettle lakes formed where pieces of glacial ice were buried by glacial debris and later melted. Chains of lakes formed over buried bedrock valleys that were filled with ice and glacial sediment during the last glaciation.

The Twin Cities Basin in the Hollandale Embayment was a site of deposition of sediment during Early and Middle Ordovician time. Quartz sand and clay came from the weathered uplands to the east and to the west. Two Ordovician formations—the St. Peter Sandstone and the Platteville Formation—are visible in some roadcuts but are best exposed along the banks of the Mississippi River. The white, soft, 160-foot-thick St. Peter Sandstone is a poorly cemented

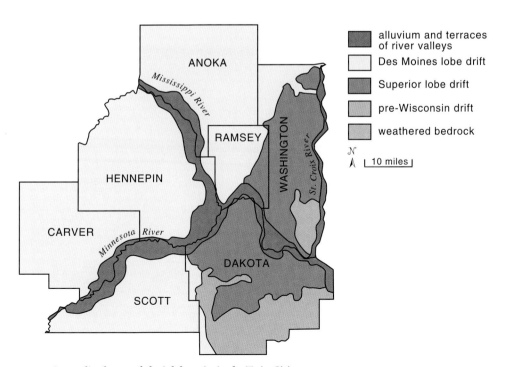

Generalized map of glacial deposits in the Twin Cities. —Modified from Hobbs and Goebel, 1982

pure quartz sandstone. The gray, hard, 30-foot-thick Platteville Formation is dominantly dolomitic limestone. Between these two units is the soft Glenwood Formation, a grayish green shaley rock that is very thin in places and rarely well exposed. The overlying Platteville is harder than the other two formations and thus protects them from erosion. Above the Platteville is the poorly exposed Decorah Shale. If you drive on Shepard Road along the north side of the Mississippi River in St. Paul, you can observe long, natural riverbanks of St. Peter Sandstone overlain by the Platteville Formation.

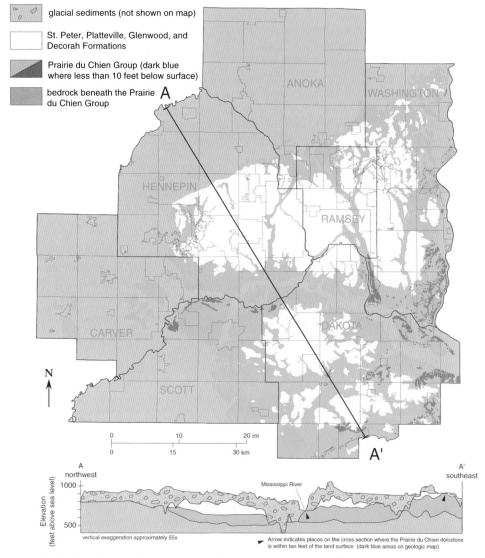

Bedrock geology and cross section of the Twin Cities metropolitan area. On the cross section, note the deep valleys carved into the Paleozoic bedrock by preglacial rivers and now filled with glacial sediment. The Prairie du Chien Group is not exposed in the Twin Cities but is close to the surface in places. —From Southwick and others, 2000

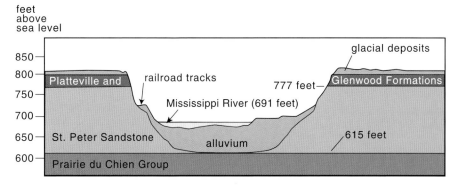

feet
above
sea level

Generalized cross section of the geology of the Twin Cities area along the Mississippi River near Fort Snelling. —After Schwartz and Thiel, 1954

ST. PAUL SITES

Lilydale Regional Park

The best place to see the Decorah Shale is in Lilydale Regional Park across the Mississippi River from downtown St. Paul. The park is the site of the former Twin City Brick and Tile Company quarry and clay pit. To get there from downtown St. Paul, take the Wabasha Street bridge across the Mississippi, proceed a short distance to Fillmore Avenue and turn right. This becomes Water Street; follow it for 1.5 miles to the park. You can collect fossils from the Decorah Shale in the park. On the way to the park, Water Street passes under another high bridge, beneath which the St. Peter Sandstone and the Platteville Formation can be observed at close range.

Crosby Farm Regional Park

You can see the St. Peter Sandstone and overlying Platteville Formation at Crosby Farm Regional Park along the Mississippi River in St. Paul. To get there, turn toward the river from Shepard Road south of I-35E. A bonus here is a man-made cave cut into the soft St. Peter Sandstone, but it is gated off for safety reasons. The caves provided cool places for food storage.

Summit Avenue

The best-exposed and most easily accessible exposure of the Paleozoic rock formations in the Twin Cities area is at the west end of Summit Avenue at East River Road (Mississippi River Boulevard) in St. Paul. As you walk on the steep paths down toward the Mississippi River, you will see 20 feet of the soft Decorah Shale, about 28 feet of the resistant carbonates of the Platteville Formation, and 18 feet of the uppermost St. Peter Sandstone. Look carefully; you may find fossils. The 4-inch-thick Deicke K-bentonite, altered volcanic ash, is present in the Decorah Shale about 2 feet above the top of the Platteville, but it will be hard to find because of slumping. The Deicke probably formed from ash spewed out from a volcano in Tennessee. The ash is 454 million years old and caused a major regional extinction of various forms of marine life.

St. Peter Sandstone and the overlying Platteville Formation in Crosby Farm Regional Park. Note the gated, man-made cave.

The Platteville Formation and the underlying Glenwood Formation and St. Peter Sandstone are exposed at the west end of Summit Avenue.

Indian Mounds Park

At Indian Mounds Park, east of downtown St. Paul at the top of the river bluff, are six large Paleo-Indian burial mounds, dating back to somewhere between 600 and 1,500 years before the present. They may be related to the Hopewellian culture in the Ohio River Valley, which existed there about 400 AD

MINNEAPOLIS SITES

Minnehaha Falls

Minnehaha Falls, off Minnehaha Avenue in Minneapolis, was memorialized by Henry Wadsworth Longfellow in his 1855 epic poem "The Song of Hiawatha." The 53-foot-high waterfall along Minnehaha Creek upstream from its confluence with the Mississippi is upheld by the resistant limestone of the Platteville Formation. The soft St. Peter Sandstone has been eroded away below the falls, resulting in the valley of Minnehaha Creek. The waterfall continues to retreat upstream as blocks of Platteville collapse because of erosion of the soft underlying sandstone. The name Minnehaha is derived from the Dakota language; *mini* means "water," and *haha* means "waterfall."

As you walk down the stairways to view the falls from the bottom, note the man-made rock walls. Most of the rocks are gray limestone slabs of the Platteville

Minnehaha Falls on Minnehaha Creek flows over the resistant Platteville Formation.

Formation, but some are made of buff-colored dolomite. Notice how badly the Platteville has weathered after a century or so of exposure. The dolomite slabs were put in to replace crumbling Platteville slabs. At one spot, the wall is a natural outcrop of the Platteville. A rock wall at the upper viewing point on the north side of the falls is made of rounded glacial erratics of Precambrian igneous and metamorphic rocks.

St. Anthony Falls

St. Anthony Falls, located upstream of the Stone Arch Bridge, is where the city of Minneapolis began. The Ojibwe called it *ka-kah bi-kah,* meaning "split rock," named for the large pieces of limestone of the Platteville Formation that broke off as the underlying St. Peter Sandstone was eroded. St. Anthony Falls is the only waterfall on the entire Mississippi River, and it isn't what it used to be. When Glacial River Warren, the ancestor of the Minnesota River, was draining Glacial Lake Agassiz about 10,000 years ago, the great torrent of floodwaters reached a point about 6 miles downstream from the site of Fort Snelling where it proceeded to excavate an old drift-filled bedrock valley dating back to a previous interglacial interval. A waterfall formed at this point after the drift was removed and the resistant Platteville Formation was exposed in the bedrock valley. The falls migrated upstream to Fort Snelling, where the postglacial Mississippi River entered Glacial River Warren. The St. Anthony waterfall has since migrated up the Mississippi from Fort Snelling about 8 miles at a rate of about 2.5 feet per year.

As the underlying soft St. Peter Sandstone was continually eroded away, the limestone of the Platteville Formation collapsed. Whereas it was a waterfall about 75 feet high where it began, by the time it reached its present location

St. Anthony Falls on the Mississippi River in Minneapolis as viewed from the Stone Arch Bridge.

in Minneapolis by the year 1850, at what is now St. Anthony Falls, it was only about 40 feet high. The change in height is a function of the gentle southward dip of the Platteville Formation and the infilling of the river valley by sediment-laden tributaries. The modern river cannot carry all the sediment away, so the base level of the river has been rising.

Settlers dammed the river at St. Anthony Falls and used the waterpower for sixteen sawmills and eventually twenty-seven flour mills. From 1880 to 1930, Minneapolis was the "Flour Milling Capital of the World," grinding wheat from the bonanza farms of the Red River Valley of the North on the Minnesota–North Dakota border. This waterpower and the mills were a major factor in the growth of Minnesota.

To prevent the further upstream retreat of the waterfall, a long concrete spillway was built in 1956. Today hydroelectric power is generated here.

Fort Snelling

Fort Snelling was completed in 1825 on a high bluff at the confluence of the Mississippi and Minnesota Rivers in order to control river traffic, and especially to stop the British fur trade. There are interpretive programs in the visitor center operated by the Minnesota Historical Society, and you can hike throughout the fort area. The type locality for the St. Peter Sandstone is below the fort in the park. A type locality is the specific place where a rock unit was first defined and it is usually a good place to see the full thickness of the rock. A rock gets its name from its type locality, and the Minnesota River used to be called St. Peter's River.

Pillsbury Hall, University of Minnesota

Though it may seem odd that Pillsbury Hall is listed as a geologic site here, there are several good reasons to visit it. This architectural gem was built in 1889 using Late Proterozoic rocks quarried in northern Minnesota. It was soot-covered for a century, but cleaning in the mid-1980s revealed a most beautiful building. Two colors of rocks were used in its construction. The dark red sandstone came from the Fond du Lac Formation at the west end of Duluth. The buff-colored sandstone came from quarries in the Hinckley Sandstone, in what is now Banning State Park, near Sandstone, Minnesota. These are the two youngest Precambrian rocks in Minnesota, deposited somewhere between about 1,000 and 500 million years ago. The building artistry includes arches, columns, and stone carvings of gargoyles, flowers, and other items. It has a clay tile roof, and copper eaves protect the rock construction.

An equally important reason to visit is to see a classic, 5.5-foot-diameter core of pillowed greenstone of Archean age residing in front of the building. The core is from a mine shaft at Ely. The greenstone was originally basalt that cooled from lava extruded beneath water. Pillows form when the outside of the flowing lava is quickly cooled by contact with water.

Pillsbury Hall, on the National Registry of Historic Buildings and the second oldest building on campus, was originally built as the science hall and named after John Pillsbury, who made a large donation for its construction. It seems appropriate that the department of geology and geophysics is housed in one of the oldest buildings on campus.

A pillowed greenstone core of Archean age rests in front of Pillsbury Hall on the University of Minnesota campus. Pillsbury Hall is built of buff Hinckley Sandstone and red sandstone of the Fond du Lac Formation, both of Late Proterozoic age.

INTERSTATE 35
Twin Cities—Iowa Border
107 miles

I-35W, between its northern junction with I-35E north of the Twin Cities near Forest Lake and its southern junction with I-35E in Burnsville south of the Twin Cities, runs through Minneapolis and several suburbs over hilly Des Moines lobe end moraine and flatter glacial outwash deposits. Part of the hilly terrain is influenced by the older St. Croix moraine of the Superior lobe, which underlies the Des Moines lobe sediments. All the high, grassed-over sloping banks of I-35 are cuts in glacial deposits.

The Mississippi River flows across the Des Moines end moraine in Minneapolis, and the Minnesota River has cut through stagnation moraine of the Des Moines lobe south of Minneapolis. Between the Minnesota River and the junction with I-35E, I-35W crosses St. Croix end moraine deposited by the Superior lobe. I-35E between the junction with I-35W just south of Forest Lake and the point in St. Paul where it crosses the Mississippi River is located on Des

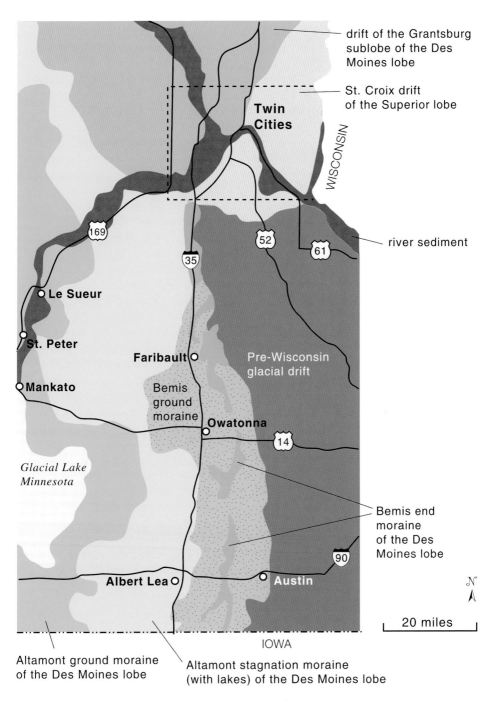

drift of the Grantsburg
sublobe of the Des
Moines lobe

St. Croix drift
of the Superior lobe

Twin
Cities

WISCONSIN

169

52

61

river sediment

35

Le Sueur

St. Peter

Faribault

Mankato

Bemis
ground
moraine

Pre-Wisconsin
glacial drift

Owatonna

14

*Glacial Lake
Minnesota*

Bemis end
moraine
of the Des
Moines lobe

90

Albert Lea

Austin

N

20 miles

IOWA

Altamont ground moraine
of the Des Moines lobe

Altamont stagnation moraine
(with lakes) of the Des Moines lobe

Glacial geology along I-35 between the Twin Cities and the Iowa border.
—Modified from Hobbs and Goebel, 1982

Moines lobe ground moraine of low relief, on hilly end moraine, and on quite flat outwash deposits. Some very flat areas are old lakebeds. I-35E south of the Mississippi River is mostly located on hilly St. Croix moraine, the southernmost deposit of the Superior lobe during the last glaciation.

I-35 between the Twin Cities and the Iowa border is an essentially straight north-south route that for much of the way runs along the crest of the hilly Bemis end moraine, which was deposited along the eastern edge of the Des Moines lobe as it moved southward. The moraine is thick, as you can see by the hilly topography, with the lows occupied by lakes, ponds, and swamps. Where the land surface is lower, the highway is on either ground moraine or stagnation moraine. Between the point where I-35W and I-35E join in Burnsville and Faribault about 30 miles to the south, I-35 is almost completely on the end moraine. Just south of the I-35W/I-35E junction, a high hill developed into a downhill ski area is probably composed of Des Moines lobe till on top of Superior lobe till. The Des Moines moraines are not nearly as bouldery as moraines of northern Minnesota, so you will have a hard time spotting big rocks.

Paleozoic sedimentary rocks are visible in scattered outcrops and roadcuts a few miles to the east and west of I-35, but not a single exposure can be seen from I-35. Also, pre-Wisconsin glacial deposits, older than 75,000 years, occur all along the east side of the Des Moines moraine, 2 to 20 miles east of I-35.

You will see excellent agricultural land all along I-35 between the Twin Cities and the Iowa border. Why is it so good? There are several reasons. Clay is an essential ingredient of a good soil because plants get minerals from clay. There is a good deal of clay in the glacial till and the loess to begin with, and weathering produces even more. Glacial deposits contain a lot of finely ground rock, called rock flour. The moving ice sheet, with its embedded rocks, acts like a massive sheet of sandpaper on the bedrock, generating rock flour. Air and water, the agents of weathering, can easily attack this abundance of fine-grained particles, producing clay. Though clay forms slowly in this northern climate, the nutrients essential for a good soil remain in the clays because there is only moderate rainfall. Another factor in the generation of these good soils is that southern Minnesota became prairie after the glaciers melted about 12,000 years ago. Southeastern Minnesota is now in the transition zone—partly prairie and partly deciduous forest—but prairie soils developed before the trees invaded. Decomposition of prairie vegetation, mostly grasses, over thousands of years has generated a thick, organic- and nutrient-rich, loose black soil. The boundary between forests to the north and upland prairie to the south is south of the Twin Cities.

Cannon River

I-35 crosses the northeastward-flowing Cannon River at Faribault. Southwest of Faribault, the river follows what may have been a meltwater channel—a tunnel valley—beneath the Des Moines lobe. The river passes through several elongate lakes—really wide spots in the river—including Sakatah Lake in Sakatah Lake State Park. The park entrance is on MN 60, 1 mile east of Waterville.

Between Faribault and Northfield to the northeast, the Cannon River flows in a narrower, bedrock-walled valley cut into the Paleozoic formations. The source of the water that did this considerable down-cutting may have been the northeastward-flowing drainage from Glacial Lake Minnesota, which was located south of Mankato. Later, as the ice retreated farther north, this lake drained northward into the Minnesota River. That short-lived lake in its largest dimensions was about 50 by 30 miles.

Faribault to Iowa

I-35 between Faribault and exit 32, about 10 miles south of Owatonna, is on gently rolling Bemis ground moraine, excellent farmland. Between exit 32 and the Iowa border, I-35 is on Altamont stagnation moraine. This stagnation moraine was deposited where the Des Moines lobe stopped in its tracks between 14,000 and 12,000 years ago. The glacier melted, and the sediment in the glacial ice was deposited. Some parts of this stagnation moraine are quite flat, allowing for big agricultural fields. Much of it is gently rolling. Some broad areas have an irregular topography with a myriad of lakes and ponds.

The lakes at Albert Lea are situated on a narrow glacial outwash plain of fine sediment deposited by meltwaters that flowed off the front of the melting Des Moines lobe. I-35 at the Iowa border is on a patch of quite hilly ground moraine.

INTERSTATE 90
Fairmont—La Crosse, Wisconsin
177 miles

Between Fairmont and Albert Lea, you are generally driving over stagnation moraine and ground moraine of the Des Moines lobe. This was mostly upland tallgrass prairie prior to the settlers' plows. Between Albert Lea and the Mississippi River on the Minnesota-Wisconsin border, there are only minor prairie openings in the deciduous forests.

Fairmont is situated on a north-south-trending topographic low, an old glacial channel cut into the tills of the Des Moines lobe. It is 30 to 40 feet deep, up to 1 mile wide, and 25 miles long. There is no meltwater sand and gravel at the surface along this valley, and it's not continuous. One has to conclude that it is a tunnel valley formed beneath an ice sheet, or perhaps a valley left over from a previous Des Moines advance before the last advance partly filled it with till. Look on the north side of the highway for the numerous small lakes that occupy the channel.

The flat area at Blue Earth is the floor of Glacial Lake Minnesota. Its northern extremity is at Mankato. The total thickness of the annual layers, or varves, in the lakebed sediments indicates that the lake had a short life span from decades to a few centuries. The lake formed at the end of the last Wisconsin glaciation.

The northward-flowing Blue Earth River, which passes through the town of Blue Earth, bisects the old lakebed on its course to Mankato, where it empties into the Minnesota River. Exposed along the banks of the Blue Earth River in places near Mankato is the bluish green clay of the Blue Earth Siltstone, a 3- to 6-foot-thick bed in the lower part of the Oneota Dolomite.

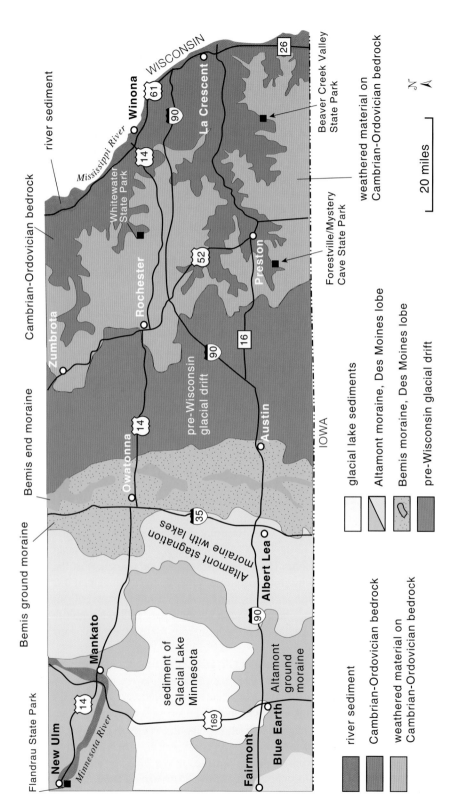

Glacial geology along I-90 between Fairmont and La Crosse, Wisconsin. —Modified from Hobbs and Goebel, 1982

river sediment

Cambrian-Ordovician bedrock

weathered material on Cambrian-Ordovician bedrock

	glacial lake sediments
	Altamont moraine, Des Moines lobe
	Bemis moraine, Des Moines lobe
	pre-Wisconsin glacial drift

20 miles

Flandrau State Park

New Ulm

Minnesota River

Mankato

Bemis ground moraine

Bemis end moraine

Cambrian-Ordovician bedrock

river sediment

Winona

Mississippi River

Whitewater State Park

Rochester

Zumbrota

Owatonna

sediment of Glacial Lake Minnesota

Altamont stagnation moraine with lakes

Albert Lea

Altamont ground moraine

Blue Earth

Fairmont

169

35

90

14

14

14

52

90

16

Austin

IOWA

pre-Wisconsin glacial drift

Preston

Forestville/Mystery Cave State Park

La Crescent

90

61

14

26

WISCONSIN

Beaver Creek Valley State Park

weathered material on Cambrian-Ordovician bedrock

N

Albert Lea, with its several lakes, is situated on stagnation moraine deposited along the east side of the Des Moines lobe as it was melting. Look for the large gravel pit in glacial drift on the south side of the highway west of the city.

Between Albert Lea and Austin, the topography is higher and hillier than to the west of Albert Lea. You are driving on ground and end moraine deposited along the easternmost margin of the Des Moines lobe. This moraine is the less-impressive counterpart of the topographically much higher Bemis moraine, known as Buffalo Ridge, which was deposited on the western side of the Des Moines lobe in southwestern Minnesota, 140 miles to the west.

Between Austin (Spam Town, home of Hormel's SPiced hAM) and the Rochester area, you are driving over gently rolling to hilly topography developed on old glacial till that is pre-Wisconsin in age, perhaps as old as 300,000 years. However, it is difficult to distinguish this older material from the Wisconsin drift.

Rochester Area to Mississippi River

Horizontal Paleozoic sedimentary rocks underlie the glacial drift along the entire route of I-90 in the southeastern region of Minnesota. The westernmost exposed bedrock along the highway is just east of exit 218, to Rochester. Look for dolomite of the Galena Group in a few roadcuts between exits 218 and 233.

Because most of I-90 in the southeastern region of Minnesota passes over carbonate rocks, limestone or dolomite sinkholes are relatively common. They form because carbonates can be dissolved by acidic rainwater and groundwater. Although they're usually difficult to spot from a moving vehicle, one sinkhole you can see is about 3 miles east of exit 233, to St. Charles. It is in the middle of a cultivated field on the south side of the highway, with trees growing in it.

Whitewater State Park can be accessed from exit 233 by heading north on MN 74 for about 10 miles. See the road guide for **US 14: Winona—New Ulm** for a description of the park, including 200-foot-high river bluffs.

Ordovician dolomite of the Prairie du Chien Group is exposed at the rest area near milepost 244, where I-90 crosses Rush Creek, a tributary of the Root River. A short trail here takes you to a scenic overview of the valley.

The high bluffs on the Minnesota and Wisconsin sides of the Mississippi River are present because the hard Ordovician dolomites of the Prairie du Chien Group resist erosion. Several softer sandstone formations of the Cambrian period are exposed beneath the dolomite; only the lowest sandstone formation, the Mt. Simon, is not exposed.

Watch for prominent large roadcuts in the white to yellow Cambrian Jordan Sandstone between milepost 267 and the intersection of I-90 with US 61 near the Mississippi River.

The village of Dresbach, accessed at exit 272, gave its name to the Dresbachian stage, a time-rock subdivision of the Cambrian period used by geologists all over North America until more fossiliferous sections of comparable age were found elsewhere and the term was superceded.

The valley of the Mississippi River is more than 2 miles wide in this area. Low-lying, sandy and muddy islands and wetlands occupy most of the valley floor. The channel meanders across the valley, so locks and dams are found on both the Minnesota and Wisconsin sides of the river. Lock and Dam No. 7 is in Minnesota just north of the I-90 bridge across the Mississippi.

US 14
Winona—New Ulm
158 miles
See map on page 288

The eastern portion of US 14, from Winona to Rochester, is in the dissected area of southeastern Minnesota, so there are only thin, relatively old glacial deposits above the Paleozoic rock exposures. About 6 miles west of Winona at the village of Stockton, there are high roadcuts in the Late Cambrian Jordan Sandstone. Iron oxides have stained it orangish yellow. If you look at it where it has *not* been sprayed with concrete to prevent erosion, you can tell it is a poorly cemented quartz sandstone. The numerous resistant concretions—harder parts of the rock—were cemented by groundwater after deposition. The harder, well-bedded Ordovician Oneota Dolomite is present above the Jordan here. The contact between these two formations is an unconformity that corresponds to the boundary between the Cambrian and Ordovician periods.

About 4 miles west of Stockton (2 miles east of Lewiston), US 14 is above the bluffs of the Mississippi River and its tributaries. The hard carbonates of the Prairie du Chien Group—the Oneota Dolomite and the Shakopee Formation—form the plateau at the top of the river bluffs. The beds look horizontal but actually dip toward the southwest at 15 feet per mile, or

The Jordan Sandstone, of Cambrian age, capped by the Oneota Dolomite (darker color) along US 14 near Stockton.

The Jordan Sandstone contains cross-beds and concretions (gray), which are well-cemented parts of the rock.

one-sixth of a degree. Therefore, if you are driving westward, you will be encountering successively younger Paleozoic rocks.

The carbonates are susceptible to dissolution by slightly acidic rainwater and groundwater, and numerous sinkholes have formed. They can be difficult to spot, but look for clumps of trees in the middle of fields. Between Lewiston and St. Charles, there are dozens of them, although farmers have filled many.

The plateau countryside between Lewiston on the east and nearly to Owatonna on the west was blanketed with several feet of windblown glacial loess (silt and clay) from the melting Des Moines lobe. This fine-grained material has weathered into an excellent agricultural soil.

Whitewater State Park

Whitewater State Park, about 7 miles north on MN 74 from St. Charles, has trails that lead from the meandering Whitewater River to the tops of the 200-foot-high bluffs. You will see the Cambrian Jordan Sandstone and the overlying cliffs of Ordovician Oneota Dolomite and the sandier dolomitic Shakopee Formation. Several springs issue forth from the contact zone between these latter two formations. On the Coyote Point Trail you can get a close look at the entrance to a cave in the Oneota Dolomite and can see fossil algal stromatolites, built up by sediment trapped on the sticky microbial layers. The geology of this park is described in a Minnesota Geological Survey booklet by Anthony C. Runkel. Also of interest in this park are buildings and bridges constructed out of native dolostone by the Civilian Conservation Corps and Works Progress Administration in the 1930s.

Rochester Area to New Ulm

Look for roadcuts of St. Peter Sandstone in the village of Dover east of Rochester. The sandstone is also exposed in Rochester in several places. You can also see roadcuts of white St. Peter Sandstone beneath the overlying Platteville Formation 2 to 3 miles west of the intersection of US 52 and US 14 in Rochester.

Between Rochester and Claremont, about 12 miles east of Owatonna, the gently rolling countryside is old Gray Drift, which is pre-Wisconsin in age. Between Claremont and Waseca (including Owatonna), the higher hilly terrain is on end and ground moraine of the Des Moines lobe. Between Waseca and Mankato you are crossing stagnation moraine of the Des Moines lobe, as indicted by the more numerous lakes. Just east of Mankato is the narrow, northern end of Glacial Lake Minnesota. Between Mankato and New Ulm, the highway is on the northern bank of the Minnesota River, either on terraces of Glacial River Warren or on ground moraine of the Des Moines lobe. Near New Ulm, the highway is on terraces in the Minnesota River Valley.

At Flandrau State Park, 2 miles south of US 14 at New Ulm, the Cottonwood River has cut deeply into glacial deposits, exposing some of the underlying Cretaceous sandstone. The sand was likely weathered from an upland of Precambrian rocks during Cretaceous time.

US 52
Twin Cities—Iowa Border
130 miles
See maps on pages 285 and 288

The northernmost portion of US 52 in the Twin Cities area overlies glacial deposits of the Superior lobe. From Hampton on south into Iowa, the highway is on highly eroded, older, pre-Wisconsin glacial deposits. The Red Drift near Hampton is thought to have been deposited by the Illinoian glacial advances. From just south of Hampton all the way to Iowa, the even older Gray Drift is thought to have been deposited by pre-Illinoian glacial advances; the till is best studied in drill holes.

This entire route is underlain by Ordovician marine sedimentary rocks about 450 million years old, but there are only a few good exposures visible from US 52. However, if you take short side trips off the highway, you can see a lot.

To see good roadcuts of the St. Peter Sandstone, Glenwood Formation, and Platteville Formation, take the Cannon Falls exit and drive 0.75 mile into the center of town on County Road 19. Turn right (south) on Fourth Street, which is County Road 24. Drive about 0.5 mile to the top of the hill and turn left onto County Road 25. The high yellow roadcut on the corner is the St. Peter Sandstone. It is overlain by the Glenwood Formation, which is comprised of several feet of blue, green, gray, and brown shale. The shale is overlain by the Platteville Formation, 16 feet of hard dolomite that breaks into large slabs.

About 4 miles south of Cannon Falls on US 52, between mileposts 92 and 93, there are long roadcuts in the Galena Group. Two carbonate rocks are included in this group, the Cummingsville Formation and the Prosser Formation. Many

St. Peter Sandstone at the junction of County Roads 24 and 25 in Cannon Falls. Swallows have excavated nest burrows in the soft rock.

Shale of the Glenwood Formation overlain by dolomite of the Platteville Formation in Cannon Falls near County Roads 24 and 25.

fossils have been collected from these beds in this area: brachiopods, bryozoa, echinoderms (including crinoids and cystoids), gastropods, corals, and various types of microfossils. About 450 million years ago, these creatures lived in a shallow tropical sea.

To see a good roadcut of the Glenwood, Platteville, and Decorah Formations requires another short side trip. Turn west on County Road 9 between mileposts 96 and 97. Drive 3.5 miles to the small village of Sogn and turn left (south) on County Road 14. Immediately after the turn is a long roadcut. The uppermost part of the St. Peter Sandstone (probably covered by slumps) near ditch level is overlain by 14 feet of the shaley Glenwood Formation, which in turn is overlain by 17 feet of hard carbonates of the Platteville Formation. Look for the Deicke K-bentonite, a 3-inch-thick shaley bed of altered volcanic ash between limestone beds in the lowest part of the Decorah Shale, about 3 to 4 feet above the top of the Platteville Formation. The ash bed will be eroded back to form a notch.

Between Cannon Falls and Rochester, you will see some small roadcuts in buff-colored dolomites of the Prairie du Chien Group at lower elevations where the highway crosses river valleys. White to yellow roadcuts are in the overlying St. Peter Sandstone. Buff-colored dolomites of the younger Galena Group are present at yet higher elevations, as between Cannon Falls and Zumbrota. Between Pine Island and Rochester, US 52 is at lower elevations and roadcuts are again down in the Prairie du Chien Group.

The St. Peter Sandstone is well-exposed in and near Rochester. Near the downtown area, you can see a big artificial cut in the sandstone in a parking lot at the intersection of Second Street Southwest and Eleventh Avenue Southwest.

A cut in St. Peter Sandstone in a parking lot in Rochester near the intersection of Second Street Southwest and Eleventh Avenue Southwest.

Large roadcuts at Golden Hill, a few miles south of the intersection with US 14 and south of the Zumbro River in the southern outskirts of Rochester, display the gray Decorah Shale overlain by the Cummingsville Formation, a buff-colored dolomite in the Galena Group. At the north end of the roadcut on the west side, limestone of the Platteville Formation is visible beneath the Decorah. Depending upon how recently highway crews have cleaned up rock debris that has fallen into the ditches, this roadcut can be a good place to stop and collect fossils. Likely to be the most productive are gray, thin slabs of limestone that are interbedded with shale in the Decorah, but loose fossils are also present.

The Golden Hill roadcut on US 52 a few miles south of the intersection with US 14 exposes gray Decorah Shale overlain by buff-colored dolomite of the Cummingsville Formation.

Fossils in Decorah Shale from the Golden Hill roadcut.

About 10 miles south of I-90 and 11.5 miles north of Chatfield is a quarry in the white to yellow St. Peter Sandstone used for fill material in construction projects.

Between Chatfield and Fountain, just north of the US 52 bridge over the Root River at 320th Street, there are high vertical roadcuts in dolomite of the Prairie du Chien Group. Here you can see that water has dissolved some carbonate along bedding planes, resulting in cavities. In places the beds are draped over domal structures that are stromatolites. They formed where carbonate minerals that precipitated out of the shallow, warm sea were trapped by sticky layers, or mats, of cyanobacteria (blue-green algae). The presence of currents helped form the stromatolites.

Roadcut in dolomite of the Prairie du Chien Group just north of the US 52 bridge over the Root River. The domed shapes with beds draped over them are stromatolites.

A quarry in horizontal St. Peter Sandstone north of Chatfield.

At Fountain, which is at a higher elevation than Chatfield to the north and Preston to the south, the dolomite roadcuts are in the Galena Group. This rock is somewhat younger than the Prairie du Chien Group, but still Late Ordovician in age, about 450 million years old. The big dolomite roadcuts just north and south of Preston are in the Prairie du Chien Group.

Caves and Sinkholes

Along US 52 south of Rochester, you are in the dissected area where carbonate bedrock (limestone and dolomite) is at the surface and thus is accessible to acidic rainwater. As the carbonate slowly dissolves, sinkholes form at the surface and caves form beneath it.

You can tour a cave in Forestville/Mystery Cave State Park, located 18 miles southwest of Preston off County Road 14. The cave is comprised of 13 miles of linear corridors dissolved in two rocks, the Dubuque and Stewartville Formations of the Galena Group. Radiometric dating indicates that some of the stalactites and stalagmites are as old as 160,000 years. There is even a lake in the cave. Mystery Cave was discovered in 1937 by a man walking along the South Branch of the Root River on a cold winter day. He saw steam rising from a hole in the ground, and the snow next to the hole had melted. The cave has a constant temperature of 48 degrees Fahrenheit year-round.

Niagara Cave, which you can also tour, is located just southwest of Harmony near the Iowa border on County Road 30, which is off County Road 139 heading south from Harmony. It was discovered in 1924 when a farmer missed three

Mystery Cave. —Deb Rose photo, Minnesota Department of Natural Resources

of his pigs. In his search, he found a sinkhole and sent some neighbor boys down by rope. At a depth of 75 feet, they found the pigs, alive, in a cave. This part of the cave system is now called the Reception Room and is where tours begin. The cave network is in three carbonate formation: the Dubuque, Stewartville, and Prosser Formations of the Galena Group.

There is an abundance of quarries, active and inactive, in the carbonate rocks of this area. A 6-foot-long cephalopod was found on the floor of an abandoned quarry near Mabel, which is 11 miles east of US 52 on MN 44.

Iron Ore

Would you believe that iron ore was mined in this area? From 1942 to 1968, 8 million tons of iron ore were produced from 125 separate properties, mostly south of Spring Valley, 8 to 16 miles west of MN 52, but some from a few miles west of Chatfield. The ore, as thick as 30 feet, was the iron oxide mineral goethite, possibly formed by the weathering of the iron carbonate mineral siderite, found in carbonate rocks mostly in the Spillville Formation, but some in the Stewartville Formation. This iron-rich zone was as thick as 30 feet in places.

However, siderite is not common in Minnesota and most carbonate rocks are low in iron. Another possibility is that weathering removed the iron from the overlying Cretaceous Windrow Formation, a sandstone/conglomerate rock that in places is heavily iron-cemented. The iron was then deposited in the Spillville and Stewartville Formations.

A large cephalopod found in dolostone in an abandoned quarry near Mabel, east of US 52.

St. Paul—La Crescent

115 miles

US 61 between St. Paul and La Crescent is part of the Great River Road, a national scenic byway that follows the Mississippi River from Lake Itasca to the Gulf of Mexico. Here in southeastern Minnesota, it connects a number of historical river towns that were established in the early to mid-1800s.

Between the junction of US 61 and I-494 and Hastings, the variable topography along US 61 is the result of deposition of end moraine and outwash of the Superior lobe at its farthest southern advance. Between Hastings and Red Wing, the highway overlies remnants of older pre-Wisconsin Gray Drift, but the remainder of the route is in the Driftless Area, a region that likely escaped glaciation altogether.

At Hastings, US 61 crosses the Mississippi. A short side trip in Hastings will take you to an overlook. Just south of the US 61 bridge over the Mississippi,

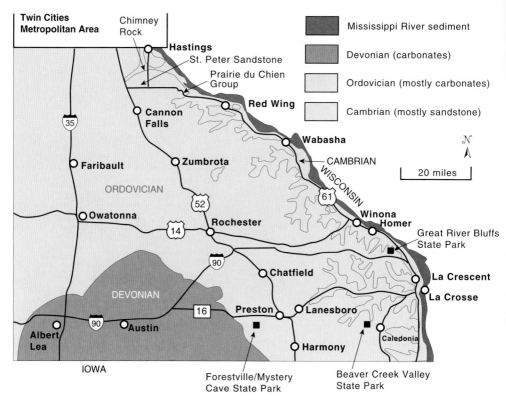

Geology along US 61 between St. Paul and La Crescent. —Modified from Morey, 1993

Legend:
- Mississippi River sediment
- Devonian (carbonates)
- Ordovician (mostly carbonates)
- Cambrian (mostly sandstone)

Twin Cities Metropolitan Area

Chimney Rock

Hastings
St. Peter Sandstone
Prairie du Chien Group

Red Wing

Cannon Falls

Wabasha

Faribault

CAMBRIAN

ORDOVICIAN

WISCONSIN

Zumbrota

20 miles

Owatonna

Winona
Homer

Rochester

Great River Bluffs State Park

Chatfield

La Crescent
La Crosse

DEVONIAN

Preston   Lanesboro

Albert Lea   Austin

Caledonia

Harmony

IOWA

Forestville/Mystery Cave State Park

Beaver Creek Valley State Park

The Oneota Dolomite and the underlying Jordan Sandstone in a bluff along the Mississippi River in Hastings, as viewed from the observation stand at Lock and Dam No. 2.

turn west on Third Street, immediately turn right onto Second Street, then turn left and follow the signs to Lock and Dam No. 2. From the observation stand, look at the high bluff across the river. The rusty yellow Cambrian Jordan Sandstone near river level is overlain by the buff to gray Ordovician Oneota Dolomite of the Prairie du Chien Group, which contains a rather large, domal reeflike structure, but it is difficult to spot because of vegetation. Deep gullies in the bluff are the result of erosion along fractures or minor faults. The Jordan Sandstone has been down-faulted here along a fault in the Hastings Fault Zone. The Jordan Sandstone is the main aquifer for Hastings.

At the south edge of Hastings immediately east of US 61 near a tall flour mill is a small city park on the south side of the Vermilion River. Here you can view a waterfall and gorge. The falls is held up by the resistant Oneota Dolomite of the Prairie du Chien Group.

Chimney Rock

A short side trip from US 61 will take you to Chimney Rock, a spirelike, 30-foot-high erosional remnant of the soft Ordovician St. Peter Sandstone capped by better-cemented beds of the same formation. About 6.5 miles south of Hastings, turn west on 220th Street and proceed 2 miles to Joan Avenue. Turn right (north) and drive for half a mile to a grove of trees on a hill; Chimney Rock

Chimney Rock is an erosional remnant of St. Peter Sandstone.

is barely visible in the trees on the left (west) side of the road. A few reddish beds accentuate the horizontal bedding. A mesa of about one-half square mile is situated in the woods just west of the spire. Delicate features like Chimney Rock indicate that you are in an area that escaped glaciation by the Wisconsin ice sheet between 75,000 and 14,000 years ago. Remnants of till are located just to the northwest and northeast of Chimney Rock. These remnants of the old Red Drift and the old Gray Drift, along with glacial erratics, indicate that earlier glaciation deposited drift across this area, but most of the drift was removed by erosion over the past few hundred thousand years. Chimney Rock is one of the last of many craggy erosional remnants that once existed in the area. Castle Rock, at the town of that name on County Road 86 northwest of Cannon Falls, is another one.

Hastings to Red Wing

Between Hastings and the intersection with MN 50 about 10 miles south of Hastings, US 61 crosses fairly flat glacial outwash deposited by meltwater flowing from the edges of the Superior and Des Moines lobes. Near this intersection, the hilly cultivated fields are older pre-Wisconsin glacial drift covered by windblown loess. The total lack of glacial erratics in the fields is a clue to the presence of the loess. This area is in the northwesternmost part of a region that was not glaciated during the last advance of the Wisconsin glaciers.

At the northwest corner of the intersection of US 61 and MN 50 is a sand quarry in the St. Peter Sandstone. Adjacent to the quarry on a small side road are roadcuts in the same rock. This soft sandstone was once a very widespread

St. Peter Sandstone near the intersection of US 61 and MN 50. Loose sand at the base of the cut is white. The rock face has been stained red by hematite, an iron oxide.

Roadcut in Oneota Dolomite along US 61 north of the Cannon River Valley.

formation, but it is easily eroded away. The remnant here survived erosion because the overlying limestone of the Platteville Formation provided a resistant cap. Look for large waste rock pieces of the limestone at the quarry.

Long roadcuts on the north side of the Cannon River Valley near milepost 100, 8 miles northwest of Red Wing, expose nearly horizontal beds of the Ordovician Oneota Dolomite of the Prairie du Chien Group. Some minor folding of some beds is most obvious in the roadcut between lanes as seen from the northbound lane. This folding may have occurred during deposition, or it may be related to a fault that cuts the Paleozoic rocks a few miles to the east.

Irregular solution zones along some bedding surfaces formed as acidic groundwater moving along the most permeable bedding planes dissolved the carbonate. Cavities in the dolomite formed when the original lime sediment was converted to dolomite by the replacement of some calcium with magnesium, and also by solution at later times. Numerous small cavities (vugs) are lined with calcite crystals. In other places, the cavities are sometimes lined with quartz crystals. Where weathering has been intense, as in the true Driftless Area, the dolomite has dissolved away, leaving behind quartz crusts.

Red Wing

High bluffs capped by resistant Oneota Dolomite of the Ordovician Prairie du Chien Group are visible all along US 61 between Red Wing and I-90 in the southeastern corner of the state. At road level are numerous roadcuts in the Cambrian sandstones that underlie the dolomite. All of these rock layers are horizontal or nearly so. The dolomite is named for the Wisconsin town of Prairie du Chien, on the Mississippi River 30 miles south of the southeastern corner of Minnesota.

Red Wing was a wheat-shipping port in the mid- to late 1800s, when steamboats plied the Mississippi River. On the south edge of the city is a long, high roadcut on the west side of Barn Bluff. This prominent hill, once an island created by an earlier course of the ancestral Mississippi, has survived because the hard, overlying Oneota Dolomite has inhibited erosion. If you feel ambitious, you can hike a trail to the top. The Red Wing Fault, a big normal fault, is visible at the western end of the bluff near the intersection of US 61 and MN 58. Here the yellow Jordan Sandstone, the uppermost Cambrian formation, has been dropped down about 125 feet so it is adjacent to the green, glauconitic sandstone of the underlying Franconia Formation (now part of the Tunnel City Group). Glauconite is a greenish clay mineral that forms on the seafloor. You can drive to Soldiers Memorial Park on the high bluff just south of the city for a spectacular view of Barn Bluff and features on the floodplain of the Mississippi. To get there, drive west on Seventh Street, just north of the Minnesota Correctional Facility, to the park entrance.

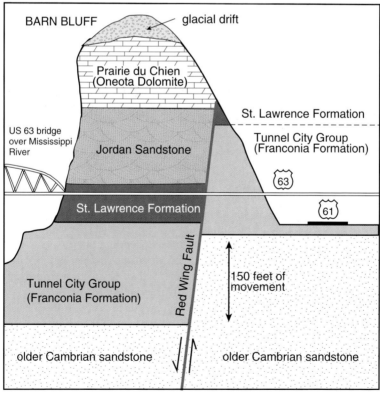

The Red Wing Fault, a normal fault, cuts the Paleozoic rocks at Barn Bluff in Red Wing. —Modified from Ojakangas and Matsch, 1982, after Sloan, 1967

Cambrian sandstones (Franconia Formation, now part of the Tunnel City Group, and the St. Lawrence Formation) at Barn Bluff in Red Wing along US 61. The darker rock at the base of the cut is a dark green glauconitic sandstone.

Lake Pepin and Wabasha Area

Lake Pepin, one of many lakes that formed along the sediment-choked Mississippi River Valley, began forming about 9,000 years ago when Wisconsin's Chippewa River built a delta of sand and gravel in the valley of the Mississippi River, constricting it. Between 11,700 and 9,400 years ago, the huge volumes of fast-flowing water in Glacial River Warren cut a deep channel through southeastern Minnesota and prevented the buildup of tributary deltas. The tributary streams were oversteepened by the deep river gorge, and they have since contributed large amounts of sediment to the much-smaller Mississippi River, which is not capable of carrying away all the sediment. The sediment in the delta deposited by the Chippewa River came from melting glacial ice to the northeast. Lake Pepin is 22 miles long, 1 to 5 miles wide, and 664 feet above sea level. It has 450-foot-high bluffs in Minnesota and Wisconsin. The lake once reached northward nearly to St. Paul and may have connected with Lake St. Croix in the lower St. Croix River Valley. Lake Pepin is over 45 feet deep just upstream of the sediment dam. About 250 feet of sediment overlie the bedrock here. Lake Pepin, traveled by early French explorers, appears on a 1703 map by De L'Isle, probably named in honor of King Pepin le Bref of the Franks, the father of Charlemagne the Great.

There are several pull-offs along the lakeshore from which you can view the lake and the bluffs. Frontenac State Park, located on what was an island in the ancestral Mississippi River Valley, is on a 400-foot-high bluff above Lake Pepin.

You can see dolomite of the Prairie du Chien Group in a roadcut on the road to the high part of the park.

The Cambrian Birkmose Member of the Franconia Formation (the Tunnel City Group in the 2008 nomenclature) is a minor dolomitic rock within the dominant sandstones. It is present in roadcuts at Reads Landing and Wabasha. Watch for a long roadcut of this thin-bedded dolomite on the north edge of Wabasha. It is very fossiliferous—a jumble of bits and pieces of fossils known to geologists as "fossil hash." The original calcium carbonate shells have been dissolved, leaving internal molds of brachiopods and other invertebrates. Also present are various miscellaneous trace fossils such as burrows and sedimentary structures formed by currents on the carbonate mud of the seafloor.

Between Wabasha and Kellogg is a roadcut in the Ironton and Galesville Sandstones of Cambrian age, now lumped together as the Wonewoc Sandstone in the 2008 nomenclature. At Minneiska there are roadcuts and a high bluff composed of Cambrian sandstones capped by the Oneota Dolomite.

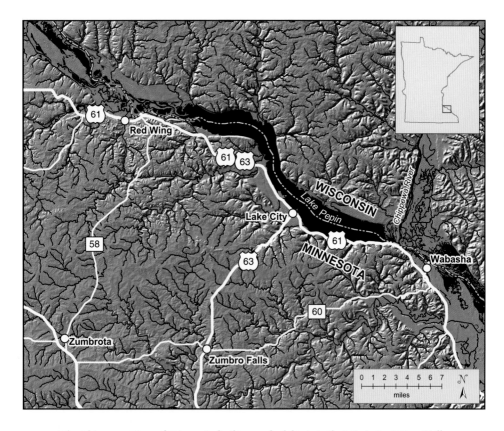

The Chippewa River of Wisconsin built a sandy delta into the Mississippi River Valley, impounding Lake Pepin. Note the highly dissected terrain on both sides of the river.

View to the south of bluffs capped by the Oneota Dolomite near John A. Latsch State Park.

John A. Latsch State Park

Look for three very prominent bluffs capped by the Oneota Dolomite near John A. Latsch State Park, about halfway between Wabasha and Winona. These bluffs were used by riverboat captains as landmarks in the mid-1800s. From south to north, they bear the names of Mt. Faith, Mt. Hope, and Mt. Charity. If you are really ambitious, you can hike up a deep ravine on Riverview Trail, which begins at the wayside. The view from the top is worth the difficult and strenuous hike.

Winona

Winona is in a spectacular setting best viewed from the lookout at Garvin Heights Park, more than 530 feet above the river and the city. Look for the scenic view turnoff sign along US 61 near the turnoff to Winona State University. Along the winding road to the park, you will be driving upward through a vertical thickness of about 500 feet of horizontal Cambrian sandstones beneath the resistant Oneota Dolomite of the Prairie du Chien Group. Look for the prominent soft, white to yellow beds of the Jordan Sandstone, the uppermost Cambrian rock formation. The rock walls of the scenic viewpoint are made of Oneota Dolomite.

From the viewpoint, you can see that Winona is built on an old, filled-in channel of the Mississippi River situated between a long island in the river valley and the main bluff along the river. Glacial River Warren, which transported a big sediment load as it flowed down the Mississippi River Valley, filled the channel with a gravel bar. The glacial river deposited sand and gravel in its floodplain, now terraces, and in giant sand and gravel bars, now islands in the modern valley. Winona is built on one of these islands, as is the nuclear waste storage site at Prairie Island, north of Red Wing. Much of the gravel appears to be eroded from Superior lobe glacial outwash originally deposited upstream in the Twin Cities Area.

As you drive through Winona, look for the prominent rock knob named Sugarloaf, a remnant of Oneota Dolomite left at the top of the bluff by an old quarrying operation. If you look closely, you can you spot the yellow Jordan Sandstone beneath the Oneota on Sugarloaf.

In the village of Homer at about milepost 20, a few miles south of Winona, is a long roadcut in the Jordan Sandstone. To see an excellent exposure, turn south in Homer on County 15 and drive 2.2 miles south of MN 61 to a 300-foot-long roadcut on the east side of the road. Look for several prominent beds of sandstone, each with internal cross-beds. Cross-beds dip toward the direction in which the depositing current was flowing.

Great River Bluffs State Park

Great River Bluffs State Park, located near the intersection of US 61 and I-90, is situated on top of the bluffs. The view from the park will give you a real feel

The cross-beds in the thickest, most prominent bed of Jordan Sandstone dip to the south (right) whereas those in the thinner overlying bed dip northward (left). Therefore, these sandstone beds must have been deposited in a place where successive currents flowed in opposite directions, such as a tidally influenced shallow sea. A very detailed study here indicated a tidal history in latest Cambrian time, about 490 million years ago. Furthermore, the regional paleogeographical data indicate the shoreline trended approximately east-west; thus tidal currents moving northward and shoreward (flood tides) and southward (ebb tides) fit the model.

for the power of erosion of the Mississippi River and its numerous tributaries. The excellent farmland on top of the bluffs owes its fertility to a layer of wind-blown loess derived from the sediment of the Des Moines lobe about 85 miles to the west. The park is in the Driftless Area, so no deposits of the Wisconsin glaciation, other than the wind-blown loess, are present.

La Crescent Area

Between I-90 and La Crescent are excellent roadcuts with long, parallel, horizontal beds in Cambrian sandstones. Such beds are indicative of shallow marine deposition, an environment in which individual beds can accumulate over a large area without interruption. La Crescent, which gets its fanciful name from the crescent-shaped bend of the Mississippi River here, is on three state scenic byways, Apple Blossom Scenic Drive, Historic Bluff Country Scenic Byway (MN 16), and the Great River Road. Apple Blossom Drive (County Road 29) is on the west side of town and winds up the bluff. There are excellent high roadcuts of yellow Jordan Sandstone overlain at the top by Oneota Dolomite. Bedding is clearly visible in the Jordan and displays some unique features. Some beds are highly burrowed by soft-bodied organisms, probably worms, but the overlying beds have no burrows. What probably happened is the worms were happily living in the soft sand, obtaining nutrients from between the sand grains. A storm developed and waves and currents buried this happy home under several inches of new sand, wiping out the inhabitants. Some time later, the area was again repopulated by worms, and life went on until the next episode of sedimentation.

Above the burrowed bed (at the tip of the pencil) is an unburrowed cross-bedded layer. This roadcut on Apple Blossom Scenic Drive is in the Jordan Sandstone of Cambrian age.

Near the top of the bluff, an inactive quarry in the Oneota Dolomite is an excellent place to view domal algal (microbial) stromatolites. Look for them in the roadcut at quarry floor level and on the upper level quarry floor. At the top of the bluff is a roadside park that provides a view of the Mississippi Valley.

Stromatolites on a bedding surface in the Oneota Dolomite in a quarry on the bluff above La Crescent.

US 169
Twin Cities—Blue Earth
116 miles
See maps on pages 285 and 288

For most of the distance between the Twin Cities and Mankato, US 169 passes over sediments deposited as terraces by Glacial River Warren when it was draining Glacial Lake Agassiz between about 11,700 and 9,400 years ago. In some places, such as south of Le Sueur, the road is on river sediments deposited more recently by the Minnesota River, which now meanders through the old river channel, a large wetlands area with abundant wildlife. Notice the higher topography both east and west of the river; this is glacial drift of the Des Moines lobe, deposited about 14,000 years ago.

The village of Jordan is the source of the name for the Jordan Sandstone, the uppermost Cambrian rock formation. It is not very well exposed near town, however. Just south of Jordan, notice the river terraces deposited by Glacial

River Warren. Between mileposts 62 and 64, north of the intersection with US 14 near the Minnesota River, watch for roadcuts of the Cambrian Jordan Sandstone. At this point, you are driving on a Glacial River Warren terrace. There are roadcuts in dolomite of the Prairie du Chien Group just south of the US 169 bridge over the Minnesota River, and there are quarries for dimension stone in the vicinity of Mankato.

Minneopa State Park

At Minneopa State Park, located 5 miles west of Mankato off MN 68, Minneopa Creek cascades over a double waterfall, with the lower falls 40 feet high. The presence of two waterfalls is the result of differential cementation of the Jordan Sandstone. Beds with more cement are harder and form the tops of the waterfalls. The falls have moved upstream about three-quarters of a mile in the last 10,000 years.

At Minneopa Falls, the creek cascades over two falls formed by resistant layers in the Jordan Sandstone.

The flat area in the park is a terrace of Glacial River Warren, which drained Glacial Lake Agassiz, located 160 miles to the northwest, between about 11,700 and 9,400 years ago. The large rounded boulders in this area were likely eroded out of the Des Moines ground moraine deposited in this area about 14,000 years ago. Some boulders have been split in half by the pressures generated by water freezing in cracks. A good view of the flat area with scattered boulders is from a vantage point at the Seppman Mill, built in 1864 as a flourmill.

This split boulder on a terrace of Glacial River Warren in Minneopa State Park was eroded out of glacial till.

Mankato to Blue Earth

Between Mankato and Blue Earth, US 169 crosses the very flat bed of Glacial Lake Minnesota, a short-lived glacial lake that formed in front of the retreating Des Moines lobe. The highway parallels the Blue Earth River, a tributary of the Minnesota River. The Dakota word *mankato* means "blue-green earth," (a reference to a bluish clay), the Dakota used for face paint. The bluish clay is a bed known as the Blue Earth Siltstone in the lower part of the Oneota Dolomite in a bank of the Blue Earth River about 3 miles upstream (south) from its confluence with the Minnesota River. In 1700, French explorer Pierre LeSueur thought that the clay might contain copper and shipped 2 tons of it back to France for testing. Result? Worthless.

MINNESOTA 16
La Crescent—Dexter
86 miles
See map on page 288

Minnesota 16, the aptly named Historic Bluff Country Scenic Byway, crosses the dissected area of southeastern Minnesota, a region that may not have been glaciated. The bedrock is right below the soil, which formed on windblown glacial loess derived from the Des Moines lobe sediments to the west. The resistant Ordovician dolomite, mostly the Prairie du Chien Group, forms the rugged topography. The highway follows the Root River between the Mississippi River and Preston. Note the excellent agricultural land on the valley floor, especially between La Crescent and Rushford. This is the floodplain of the river, with most of the alluvium derived from loess eroded from the uplands.

Beaver Creek Valley State Park
To reach Beaver Creek Valley State Park, drive south from Houston on MN 76 for 11 miles to the vicinity of Caledonia and then west on County Road 1. The topography of this park is very rugged, with a relief of 250 feet. The local base level was lowered as glacial meltwater downcut the Mississippi River Valley, probably over many glaciations, and thus the oversteepened tributaries cut deep valleys into the Ordovician Oneota Dolomite and underlying Cambrian Jordan Sandstone. Numerous springs issue forth from the valley walls because of the porosity of the Oneota Dolomite.

Rushford to Lanesboro
If you want to see an excellent exposure of the Cambrian Jordan Sandstone overlain by the Ordovician Oneota Dolomite, drive 2 miles west of Rushford on MN 30.

In the vicinity of Lanesboro, there are numerous roadcuts and outcrops of dolomite of the Prairie du Chien Group. All rocks of the Prairie du Chien Group are exposed along County Road 8 as the road climbs upward out of the valley toward Fountain. Drive north on Lanesboro's Main Street and turn west on the county road. The high roadcuts expose thick beds of gray Oneota Dolomite, the overlying New Richmond Member of white to yellow quartz sandstone, and finally the Willow River Member, a thin-bedded gray dolomite of the Shakopee Formation. In the Oneota Dolomite, look for chert layers and chert nodules, which formed as silica-bearing groundwater replaced carbonate after it was deposited but before it became hard rock. Look for low-angle cross-bedding, perhaps formed on a beach, in sandstone of the New Richmond Member.

Sinkholes and Forestville/Mystery Cave State Park
Carbonate bedrock is slightly soluble in rainwater and groundwater, which are somewhat acidic. Therefore, the dissected area is cave and sinkhole country. Look for isolated trees or clumps of trees in the fields—many are in sinkholes. There are thousands of sinkholes here in Fillmore County, especially between Preston and Spring Valley.

You can take an underground tour at Forestville/Mystery Cave State Park. About halfway between Preston and Spring Valley, drive south on County Road

A roadcut on County Road 8 west of Lanesboro in sandstone of the New Richmond Member of the Shakopee Formation.

A sinkhole adjacent to the north side of MN 16 between Preston and Spring Valley.

5 for 4 miles and follow the signs. The cave is in the Dubuque and Stewartville Formations, and there is some bedrock visible on the banks of the South Branch of the Root River near the cave. See the road guide for **US 52: Twin Cities—Iowa Border** for additional information on this cave.

MINNESOTA 95

Taylors Falls—Stillwater
27 miles

Although this part of MN 95, a portion of the St. Croix Scenic Byway, is located northeast of the Twin Cities, it is included in the Southeastern Minnesota chapter because it passes through the northernmost Paleozoic rocks deposited in the Twin Cities Basin. The route follows the St. Croix River, which has cut a deep valley through the early Paleozoic rocks, exposing 1,100-million-year-old lava flows of the Midcontinent Rift System. The St. Croix River was one of the first eight rivers protected by the federal Wild and Scenic Rivers Act of 1968.

Both Minnesota 95 in and near Taylors Falls and Taylors Falls itself are situated on an old terrace of the St. Croix River, high above the present river. This wide terrace shows that the St. Croix River was once a larger river than it is today. About 10,000 years ago it was the major river through which drained the waters of Glacial Lake Duluth, the ancestor of Lake Superior. The floodwaters escaped via the Portage outlet to the Moose Horn River and then through the Kettle River to the St. Croix in Minnesota, and via the Brule River outlet to the St. Croix River in Wisconsin. Today the Brule flows the opposite direction—into Lake Superior about 25 miles east of Duluth.

This great flow of water carved the broad valley of the St. Croix River, which in places is more than 300 feet deep. Vertical cliffs along the river are as high as 100 feet. You can see the prominent boundary between the highlands to the west and the valley at milepost 73 on MN 95 about 2 miles north of Taylors Falls. A scenic overlook from which to view the valley is located between mileposts 73 and 74.

Interstate State Park

Interstate State Park, so-named because Wisconsin's side of the river is also part of the park, is a must-see because of the spectacular scenery and geology. At the park entrance, on MN 95 at the south edge of Taylors Falls by the stoplight near the US 8 bridge over the St. Croix River, are outcrops of massive basalt. From the park's parking lot here at the south edge of town, you can walk a few hundred feet along well-marked paths.

The massive black rocks are 1,100-million-year-old basalt lava flows of the Chengwatana Volcanic Group, similar to what you can see on the North Shore of Lake Superior. They poured out on Earth's surface in the Midcontinent Rift when North America started to split apart in Middle Proterozoic time. There are ten separate lava flows on the Minnesota side of the river, each more than 10 feet thick. The tops of flows can be distinguished by the abundant gas bubbles that rose up through the lava before it cooled. The bubbles are filled with white quartz and some zeolites.

The basalt contains some vertical fractures, or joints, that formed as the lava cooled. The fast-moving water of the glacial river broke off large pieces of the basalt along these joints, forming the steep cliffs on both sides of the river. From the top of a high, water-polished basalt knob next to the river, you can see that the river makes a right-angle bend. Here the river turned as it eroded along a highly fractured zone in the basalt, in which the hard rock was broken into smaller pieces and was therefore more easily eroded. This narrow gorge is known as the Dalles of the St. Croix, utilizing the French word for a narrow, rock-sided river channel.

The most impressive features in the park are the huge, deep potholes. These vertical cylindrical depressions were cut into the hard basalt by the same surging floodwaters that cut the valley. There was probably a white-water rapids at this spot about 10,000 years ago, as the floodwaters encountered the hard basalt. Where pebbles, cobbles, and boulders were swirled around in eddies, they acted as tools and abraded the hard rock. Once a depression was started, the tools were trapped, destined to continue their work until the floodwaters subsided. There are more than eighty such potholes on this higher level, which is as much as 100 feet above the present river. Read the descriptive signs by many of the potholes to learn some more details. Whether these are indeed the world's largest potholes may be open to question, but they are certainly large and beautiful examples of this phenomenon. Interstate State Park in Wisconsin, just across the US 8 bridge, has similar features in basalt.

View looking downstream at basalt cliffs along the St. Croix River at Interstate State Park.

A giant pothole in Interstate State Park was eroded by glacial floodwaters 10,000 years ago. Litter is extremely difficult to remove.

Cambrian Rocks near Taylors Falls

The ocean invaded this part of the North American craton from the south about 504 million years ago, during Cambrian time. On US 8/MN 95 about one-half mile south of the US 8 bridge over the St. Croix River is a very large "Welcome to Minnesota" sign in the shape of the state. You can pull off the highway here and park. Walk across an old small-gauge railroad bed to a notch in the cliff that was cut by the St. Croix River; it is about 100 feet in front of the welcome sign. A path of sorts, formed by the feet of numerous geology students, leads to this notch. Here you will see a conglomerate made of large, rounded basalt boulders deposited along a shoreline about 504 million years ago, probably close to a basalt cliff. This is the oldest exposure of Cambrian rock visible in this area. It definitely was deposited next to a sea because tiny fossils of brachiopods, which are only found in marine waters, are embedded in the tan sand and silt between the boulders. These small shells have a composition similar to your fingernails, a chitinophosphatic material. This is a state park, so remember not to hammer on the outcrop.

The main office of Interstate State Park is located just south of Taylors Falls along US 8/MN 95 between mileposts 21 and 22. Behind the office building is a path that leads beneath MN 95 through a large culvert. The path continues to Curtain Falls; though nearly dry today, it must have been impressive when large amounts of glacial meltwater flowed down this valley. The rock that makes

This basalt-boulder conglomerate near Taylors Falls formed in Cambrian time when the early Paleozoic sea lapped against basalt cliffs.

Brachiopod fossils occur in the basalt-boulder conglomerate of Cambrian age at Taylors Falls.

up the waterfall is sandstone of the 500-million-year-old Franconia Formation (Lone Rock Formation of the Tunnel City Group in the 2008 proposed nomenclature). Its age has been determined by the trilobite fossils that it contains. The fossils are of rather poor quality, and it is illegal to remove them from a state park anyway. The soft sandstone is mostly yellowish to tan, with some reddish brown bands of iron-oxide—liesegang bands—deposited by groundwater. Bands of black manganese oxides are also present.

On a hill and curve on US 8/MN 95 about 3 miles south of Taylors Falls, there is a high roadcut in the Cambrian Franconia Formation (now the Lone Rock Formation of the Tunnel City Group). It is too dangerous to stop on this busy highway, but if you glance at this roadcut as you drive by, you will see prominent horizontal beds of tan sandstone. Cross-beds are visible within some beds.

Curtain Falls was carved in Cambrian sandstone by glacial meltwater. Today, the "falls" are nearly dry.

Roadcut along US 8/MN 95 south of Taylors Falls in the Cambrian Franconia Formation (Lone Rock Formation of the Tunnel City Group in the 2008 proposed nomenclature). It is dangerous to stop here.

Glacial Features between US 8 and Stillwater

Between mileposts 80 and 86, MN 95 crosses hilly end moraine deposited on the southeast side of the Grantsburg sublobe of the Des Moines lobe. The edge of a melting glacier is commonly a place where ice-deposited glacial till is in close proximity to meltwater stream deposits. You can view a big gravel pit in bedded meltwater sediments on the east side of MN 95 between mileposts 80 and 81. It contains white limestone cobbles, carried in the ice from limestone in Manitoba.

Between about mileposts 86 and 89, MN 95 passes over a small area of end moraine of Superior lobe ice. This end moraine is older than, and therefore underlies deposits of, the Grantsburg sublobe of the Des Moines lobe present to the north. In spring or fall when the fields are bare, you may be able to distinguish the slightly reddish soil of the Superior lobe from the brownish or tan soil of the Des Moines lobe moraine.

Between mileposts 97 and 101, MN 95 is situated on the end moraine of an advance of the Superior lobe. The topography is quite hilly here, best seen where the land has been cleared for farming.

Copas and Marine on St. Croix

The villages of Copas and Marine on St. Croix (Minnesota's first town, founded in 1838 as a lumber town) are built on terraces of the St. Croix River. The terraces were formed 10,000 years ago when the river was at its maximum flow with the floodwaters from Glacial Lake Duluth. Native Americans, both Dakota and Ojibwe, lived on these terraces. A total of twenty-seven Indian burial mounds were once present in the vicinity of Copas, but only two have survived. One can be seen in Copas, just south of the old schoolhouse, but it is overgrown with trees. A low oblong mound is visible in a field about 1 mile south of Copas just north of William O'Brien State Park. At the state park, you can see outcrops of white sandstone of the Cambrian Franconia Formation (Mazomanie Formation of the Tunnel City Group in the 2008 proposed nomenclature) along the river below the lower campground.

Stillwater Area

At about milepost 101, 2 miles north of Stillwater, you will see high roadcuts in late Cambrian and early Ordovician rocks. The dominant rock is white and yellow Jordan Sandstone of Cambrian age. At the top of the cut is buff Oneota Dolomite of Ordovician age, so the boundary between the two formations is also the boundary between geologic periods.

On MN 95 between mileposts 101 and 102, about 1.5 miles north of Stillwater on the first terrace above the river, is a Minnesota rest area. There is a steep vertical cliff below the rest area, but you can walk down a stairway to the river, thus getting a close look at the Cambrian Franconia Formation (the Mazomanie Formation in the 2008 proposed nomenclature). Look for fossil burrows in the thin-bedded sandstone. Close to this rest area is a geological marker describing the Late Cambrian Croixan Series, once the worldwide standard for rocks of this age.

Stillwater was built where the flowing water of the St. Croix River enters the still water of Lake St. Croix. The lake was one of many river lakes that formed

Cross-bedding in Jordan Sandstone in Stillwater.

as the modern river valleys filled with sediment. The enormous quantities of water draining Glacial Lake Agassiz and Glacial Lake Duluth carved the deep valleys of the St. Croix and the Mississippi. Tributaries were thus oversteepened and eroded a lot of sediment as they dissected the upland, and the modern rivers are not capable of carrying all the sediment away. The base level of the Mississippi River has been rising, and the St. Croix River does not carry enough sediment to rise with it—hence the formation of Lake St. Croix.

The old Stillwater Railroad Depot on the north edge of Stillwater, now a museum, is a good place to park and view both geology and history. The road-cuts across MN 95 from the depot are in the Jordan Sandstone of Cambrian age. A roadcut on the south side of a city street just opposite the depot displays abundant burrows made by soft-bodied marine worms about 490 million years ago. The burrows are concentrated in certain beds. After a layer of sand was deposited on the ocean floor, perhaps during a storm, animals that lived near the top of the sand reworked it, ingesting it for the nutrients and excreting it. Then another storm buried the burrowed layers in a new layer of sand, likely wiping out the inhabitants. This process was repeated time and time again. Look closely at the white sandstone on the north side of this street behind the fence. Here you will see excellent cross-bedding. Some of the cross-beds may be herringbone cross-beds, with one set deposited by tides moving in and the next set deposited by tides moving out.

Glossary

accretion. The addition of a volcanic island arc or microcontinent to a continent by convergent plate motion.

accretionary wedge. A triangular mass of sediment on the landward side of an oceanic trench composed of debris scraped off the upper surface of the subducting, or downgoing, plate.

actinolite. A greenish amphibole mineral that grows as needle or fibrous crystals in metamorphic schists and altered mafic and ultramafic igneous rocks.

aeromagnetic survey. A magnetic survey made with an airborne magnetometer.

agate. A variety of quartz, often with alternating bands of different colors.

alluvial fan. A relatively flat to gently dipping, fan-shaped wedge of loose rock material deposited by a stream, especially in semiarid regions, where streams flow out of mountains onto broad valleys or plains.

amphibole. A group of dark, iron- and magnesium-rich minerals commonly present in igneous and metamorphic rocks. Hornblende, the most common amphibole, crystallizes into black needles.

amphibolite. A medium- to coarse-grained metamorphic rock composed of hornblende and plagioclase.

amygdule. A vesicle in a volcanic rock that has been filled by minerals such as calcite, quartz, or zeolites.

anorthosite. A plutonic rock composed of more than 90 percent plagioclase feldspar.

anticline. A folded arch in layered rocks with the oldest rocks in the center.

arkose. A sandstone composed mainly of quartz and orthoclase feldspar, derived from weathering granite.

ash. Small shreds of lava that escape in the air during a volcanic eruption. Ash consolidates into tuff.

basalt. A black or very dark gray volcanic rock that consists mainly of microscopic crystals of plagioclase feldspar, pyroxene, and perhaps olivine.

basement. The fundamental rocks of the continental crust, mainly granite, schist, and gneiss.

batholith. A mass of coarsely granular igneous rock, generally granite, that is exposed over an area greater than about 40 square miles and consists of many plutons of differing composition.

bedrock. Solid rock exposed in place or that underlies unconsolidated superficial sediments.

biotite. Dark mica, a platy mineral. It is a minor but common mineral in igneous and metamorphic rocks.

boulder. A rock larger than 10 inches in diameter.

braided stream. A stream that divides into an interlacing network of small, shallow channels separated by channel bars; such a stream commonly deposits a lot of sediment, as it cannot carry its load out of the area.

breccia. A rock broken into angular to rounded fragments held together by a fine-grained matrix. Produced by any one of a variety of processes.

calcareous. Rock consisting of more than 50 percent calcium carbonate.

calcite. A mineral composed of calcium carbonate.

carbonate rock. A sedimentary rock composed of carbonate minerals such as calcite and dolomite.

chert. A sedimentary rock composed mainly of microscopic crystals of quartz, usually occurring as concretions in limestone; also common in iron-formation.

chlorite. A green, platy, micaceous mineral characteristic of low-grade metamorphic mafic rocks—rocks with iron and magnesium.

clast. A grain or fragment of a rock produced by disintegration of a larger rock mass. A **clastic rock** is composed of broken fragments derived from preexisting rocks.

clay. A sedimentary material composed of weathered minerals with grain sizes less than $\frac{1}{256}$ millimeter in diameter.

cleavage. A planar fabric in an unmetamorphosed or weakly metamorphosed, fine-grained rock.

coarse-grained. A relative term used to describe the size of constituents in a rock. Said of igneous rocks with minerals larger than 0.2 inch in diameter. Said of sedimentary rocks with particles larger than 0.08 inch in diameter.

cobble. A rock between 2.5 and 10 inches in diameter.

concretion. A hard mass of mineral matter, often spherical but sometimes disk-shaped or irregular, formed by precipitation around a nucleus within a sedimentary rock.

conglomerate. A coarse-grained sedimentary rock composed of pebbles, cobbles, or boulders set in a fine-grained matrix of silt or sand.

convergence. The process of two lithospheric plates moving toward each other, resulting in subduction and collision.

country rock. The rock that magma intrudes.

craton. A stable part of Earth's crust that has not been deformed for a prolonged period.

crescentic gouge. A crescentic mark caused by glacial plucking on a bedrock surface; it is concave toward the direction from which the ice moved, and the steep side of the gouge points up-ice.

cross-bed/cross-bedding. Inclined layers of sediment within a sedimentary bed, used to determine the direction toward which the current or wind was moving and transporting the sediment grains.

crust. The upper surface of the lithosphere. **Continental crust** consists mainly of granite, gneiss, and schist; **oceanic crust** consists of basalt.

crystalline. Said of a rock formed of interlocking mineral crystals, usually igneous or metamorphic.

debris flow. A jumbled mass of sediment and rock fragments moving downslope.

delta. A nearly flat accumulation of clay, sand, and gravel deposited in a lake or ocean at the mouth of a river.

diabase. An igneous rock with the composition of basalt but which cooled far enough beneath the surface to have visible crystals.

dike. A sheet of igneous rock that formed when molten magma filled a fracture in a solid rock.

diorite. A plutonic igneous rock intermediate in composition between granite and gabbro.

dip. The sloping angle of a planar surface in rocks such as a sedimentary bed or metamorphic foliation.

divergence. The process of two lithospheric plates moving away from each other (spreading) with volcanic activity along the mutual boundary.

dolomite. A sedimentary rock composed of the mineral dolomite, a calcium magnesium carbonate. Also called **dolostone**.

drainage basin. An area or region bounded by a drainage divide and occupied by a drainage system.

drift, glacial. All sediment deposited by a glacier, whether directly from the ice or from standing or flowing meltwater.

drumlin. A streamlined deposit of glacial till elongated in the direction of ice movement and having an elliptical profile.

end moraine. The ridge of till deposited at the farthest extent of a glacier, marking the cessation of glacial advance.

epidote. A typically pistachio green mineral formed in low-grade metamorphic rocks derived from alumina- and iron-bearing limy sediments. Also, an alteration mineral in mafic igneous rocks.

erratic, glacial. A block of rock transported by glacial ice and deposited at a distance from the bedrock outcrop from which it was derived.

esker. A long, narrow, commonly sinuous ridge deposited by a stream flowing in a tunnel beneath an ice sheet.

extrusive igneous rocks. Rocks that solidify from magma on the surface of the Earth (volcanic rocks).

fault. A fracture or zone of fractures in the Earth's crust along which blocks of rock on either side have shifted. A **normal fault** forms under extensional forces, and one side drops relative to the other side. A **reverse fault** forms under compressional forces, and one side is pushed up and over the other side. In a **strike-slip fault**, rocks on one side move sideways relative to rocks on the other side.

feldspar. The most abundant rock-forming mineral group, making up 60 percent of the Earth's crust and including calcium, sodium, or potassium with aluminum silicate. Includes plagioclase feldspars (albite and anorthite) and alkali feldspars (orthoclase and microcline).

felsic. An adjective used to describe an igneous rock composed of light-colored minerals, such as feldspar, quartz, and muscovite.

fine-grained. A relative term used to describe the size of constituents in a rock. Said of igneous rocks with minerals too small to see with the unaided eye. Said of sedimentary rocks with silt-size or smaller particles.

fold. A bend in a rock layer.

foliation. A textural term referring to planar arrangement of minerals or structures in any kind of rock.

foreland basin. An area adjacent to a mountain-building belt, toward which the rocks of the belt were thrust or folded over, and which subsides due to the weight of the adjacent stacked thrust sheets.

formation. A body of sedimentary, igneous, or metamorphic rock that can be recognized over a large area. It is the basic stratigraphic unit in geologic mapping. A formation may be part of a larger **group** and may be broken into **members**.

fossil. The remains of a plant or animal preserved in a rock. A **trace fossil** is a structure, such as a track or burrow, that is left by the activity of a plant or animal.

gabbro. A dark igneous rock consisting mainly of plagioclase and pyroxene in crystals large enough to see with a simple magnifier. Gabbro has the same composition as basalt but contains much larger mineral grains because it cooled at depth over a longer period of time.

garnet. A family of silicate minerals with widely varying chemical compositions. Garnets occur in metamorphic and igneous rocks and are usually reddish.

gneiss. A coarse-grained metamorphic rock with a streaky foliation due to parallel alignment of minerals, usually in bands of light- and dark-colored minerals.

graded bed. A sedimentary bed in which particle size progressively changes, usually from coarse at the base to fine at the top.

granite. An igneous rock composed mostly of orthoclase feldspar and quartz in grains large enough to see without using a magnifier. Most granites also contain mica or amphibole.

granodiorite. A group of coarse-grained plutonic rocks intermediate in composition between granite and diorite.

graywacke. A sedimentary rock made primarily of mud and sand, often deposited by turbidity currents.

greenstone. A dark green, altered or metamorphosed basalt or gabbro. The green comes from the minerals chlorite, actinolite, or epidote.

ground moraine. An extensive area of low-relief glacial till deposited beneath a moving glacier.

hematite. An iron oxide mineral.

hornblende. An iron and calcium silicate mineral of the amphibole group. It commonly crystallizes into blackish needles in igneous and metamorphic rocks.

ice front. The edge of a glacier.

ice sheet. A thick glacier covering a large region.

igneous rock. Rock that solidified from the cooling of molten magma.

Illinoian. The second-to-last major glaciation during Pleistocene time.

inclusion. A piece of rock from the surrounding bedrock contained within an igneous intrusion.

intrusive igneous rocks. Rocks that cool from magma beneath the surface of the Earth. The body of rock is called an **intrusion**.

iron-formation. A thinly bedded sedimentary rock containing more than 15 percent iron.

iron oxide. A group of minerals (including hematite, goethite, limonite, and magnetite) made of iron and oxygen.

joint. A planar fracture or crack in a rock.

kame. A variety of stratified landforms deposited by meltwater streams in contact with the ice of a glacier.

karst topography. A landscape formed by the dissolving of carbonate rock by acidic water and characterized by caves, sinkholes, and underground drainage.

kettle. A bowl-shaped depression or hole in glacial drift formed by burial of a block of ice by the drift. A depression forms when the ice melts.

lava. Molten rock erupted on the surface of the Earth. A **lava flow** is a layer of basalt cooled from a single outpouring of molten rock.

limestone. A sedimentary rock composed of calcium carbonate.

limonite. A hydrous iron oxide mineral.

lobe. Lobate portions of a major glacier, commonly moving independently and ahead of the main ice sheet.

longshore drift. Sand and other sediment moved along a shore by a current flowing near to and parallel to the shore.

mafic. An adjective used to describe a magma that contains more iron, magnesium, and calcium and less silica and sodium than a felsic magma; mafic rocks contain an abundance of dark minerals such as hornblende, biotite, and pyroxene.

magma. Molten rock within the Earth.

magnetite. A strongly magnetic iron oxide mineral.

mantle. The part of the Earth between the interior core and the outer crust.

marble. Metamorphosed limestone.

massive. Said of a rock that is relatively homogenous.

metamorphic rock. Rock derived from preexisting rock that changes mineralogically and texturally in response to changes in temperature and/or pressure, usually deep within the Earth.

metamorphism. Recrystallization of an existing rock. Metamorphism typically occurs at high temperatures and often high pressures.

metasedimentary rock. A sedimentary rock that has been metamorphosed.

metavolcanic rock. A volcanic rock that has been metamorphosed.

mica. A family of silicate minerals, including biotite and muscovite, that crystallize into thin flakes. Micas are common in many kinds of igneous and metamorphic rocks.

micaceous. Containing micas, such as muscovite, biotite, and chlorite.

microcline. A potassium-rich alkali feldspar, a common rock-forming mineral.

microcontinent. A small, isolated fragment of continental crust.

migmatite. A composite of metamorphic rock, commonly gneissic, mixed with igneous rock crystallized from magma melted out of or injected into the gneiss.

moraine. A landform made of glacial till. An **end moraine** is typically a ridge deposited at the edge of a moving glacier. **Ground moraine** is deposited beneath a moving glacier. **Stagnation moraine** is deposited when the ice stops moving and melts in place.

mountain building event. An event, usually at the margin of a tectonic plate, in which rocks are folded, thrust faulted, metamorphosed, and/or uplifted. Intrusive and extrusive igneous activity often accompanies it.

mudstone. A sedimentary rock composed of mud.

muscovite. A common, colorless to light brown mineral of the mica group. It is present in many igneous, metamorphic, and sedimentary rocks.

normal fault. A fault in which rocks on one side move down relative to rocks on the other side in response to extensional forces.

olivine. An iron and magnesium silicate mineral that typically forms glassy green crystals. A common mineral in gabbro, basalt, and peridotite.

orthoclase. A potassium-rich alkali feldspar, a common rock-forming mineral.

outwash. Sand and gravel deposited by meltwater from a receding glacier.

peat. An unconsolidated deposit of plant remains in a water-saturated environment such as a bog or fen.

pebble. A rock between ¹⁄₁₂ and 2.5 inches in diameter.

pegmatite. An igneous rock, generally granitic, composed of extremely large crystals.

peridotite. A coarse-grained ultramafic igneous rock consisting mainly of olivine. Earth's mantle consists mainly of peridotite.

phase. A term used for deposits that are the result of a minor glacial advance during a specific time.

phyllite. A metamorphic rock intermediate in grade (and grain size) between slate and schist. Very fine-grained mica typically imparts a lustrous sheen.

pillows. Globular structures in basalt formed during the extrusion of lava underwater.

pipestone. A pink to reddish clay-rich rock, carved by Indians into pipes; also known as **catlinite**.

plagioclase. A feldspar mineral rich in sodium and calcium. One of the most common rock-forming minerals in igneous and metamorphic rocks.

plate tectonics. A theory of global tectonics in which Earth's crust is divided into a number of plates that move horizontally relative to each other, with seismic and tectonic activity, commonly including volcanism, along the boundaries.

pluton. A large intrusion of igneous rock. The rock that is part of a pluton is called a **plutonic rock**.

pothole. A smooth, bowl-shaped or cylindrical hollow formed on a streambed by the grinding action of rocks swirled around by the current.

pyroxene. A family of silicate minerals that occur mostly in dark, mafic igneous and metamorphic rocks.

quartz. A mineral form of silica. Quartz is one of the most abundant and widely distributed minerals in rocks. It comes in a wide variety of forms, including clear crystals, sand grains, and chert.

quartzite. A metamorphic rock composed of mainly quartz and formed by the metamorphism of sandstone.

radiometric dating. Measure of the age of rocks using radioactive elements in minerals. **Radiocarbon dating** measures age using the decay of carbon-14 in organic material.

residuum. A thin layer of rock debris formed by the weathering in place of a rock surface.

rhyolite. A felsic volcanic rock, the extrusive equivalent of granite. It contains quartz and feldspar in a very fine-grained matrix.

rift. A long, narrow rupture in Earth's crust. A **rift basin** is the trough, or valley, formed by the rift.

sand. Weathered minerals grains, most commonly quartz, between $\frac{1}{16}$ millimeter and 2 millimeters in diameter.

sandstone. A sedimentary rock made primarily of sand.

saprolite. A soft, earthy, clay-rich thoroughly decomposed rock, formed in place by chemical weathering, especially in subtropical to tropical climates.

schist. A metamorphic rock that is strongly foliated due to an abundance of platy minerals.

sedimentary rock. A rock formed from the consolidation of loose sediment.

sequence. Major sedimentary rock units separated by unconformities, usually erosional boundaries.

shale. A deposit of clay, silt, or mud solidified into more or less solid rock.

shear zone. The zone in which deformation occurs when two bodies of rock slide past each other, resulting in crushed and brecciated rock with parallel fractures due to shear strain; commonly mineralized.

siliceous. Said of a rock or plant containing silica.

sill. An igneous intrusion that parallels the planar structure of the surrounding rock.

silt. Weathered mineral grains larger than clay but smaller than sand (between $\frac{1}{256}$ and $\frac{1}{16}$ millimeter in diameter).

siltstone. A sedimentary rock made primarily of silt.

sinkhole. A generally circular, funnel-shaped depression in a karst area, the result of carbonate bedrock dissolving along cracks.

slate. Slightly metamorphosed shale or mudstone that breaks easily along parallel surfaces.

spillway. The overflow channel from body of water, such as a glacial lake.

stagnation moraine. A hummocky area of glacial till deposited when the ice stops moving and melts in place, or stagnates.

striation. A linear scratch on a rock left by a rock embedded in moving glacial ice.

stromatolite. A mound-shaped sedimentary structure formed by trapping and binding of sediment by the growth and metabolic activity of microorganisms, principally blue-green algae (cyanobacteria).

subduction zone. A long, narrow zone where an oceanic plate descends into the mantle below a continental plate or another oceanic plate at a convergent boundary.

syncline. In layered rocks, a folded trough with the youngest rocks in the center.

taconite. A cherty rock with enough iron to be considered low-grade iron ore.

tectonics. A branch of geology dealing with the structures and forces of the outer part of the Earth, including continental plate movements.

terrane. An assemblage of rocks that share a more or less common origin and history, bounded by a major fault zone or suture.

thrust fault. A low-angle reverse fault.

till. Unsorted and unstratified sediment deposited directly from glacial ice. It is likely to contain rock fragments of all sizes.

tombolo. A sand or gravel bar that connects two islands or an island to the mainland.

trench, oceanic. A narrow, elongate depression that develops where the ocean floor begins its descent into a subduction zone at a convergent plate boundary.

trilobite. A three-lobed marine arthropod that lived from Cambrian to Permian time.

tuff. Volcanic ash more or less consolidated into solid rock.

tunnel valley. A shallow valley or trench cut in glacial drift by a stream flowing beneath a glacier.

turbidity current. A gravity-induced flow of one current through, over, or under another, owing to density differences caused by differences in temperature, salinity, or suspended solids. A **turbidite** is the sedimentary bed that forms when sediments settle out of a turbidity current.

ultramafic. An adjective used to describe black to dark green rocks that are more mafic than basalt, consisting mainly of iron- and magnesium-rich minerals such as hypersthene, pyroxene, or olivine. They make up the oceanic crust and mantle.

unconformity. A break or gap in the geologic record where one rock unit is overlain by another that is not next in the stratigraphic succession, due to either erosion or nondeposition.

varves. From the Swedish *varv*, meaning "layer," referring to alternating layers of fine-grained sediment deposited annually in a standing body of glacial meltwater. The lighter, silt-size particles represent the summer layer, and the darker, clay-size particles represent the winter layer.

vein. A deposit of minerals that fills a fracture in rock.

vesicle. A cavity of variable shape in a lava, formed by the entrapment of a gas bubble during solidification of the lava. A rock with vesicles is called **vesicular.**

volcanic arc. A chain of volcanoes that formed above a subduction zone.

weather. To soften, crumble, or discolor because of exposure to atmospheric agents such as air and rain.

Wisconsin glaciation. The last stage of glaciation in Pleistocene time. It began about 75,000 years ago and ended about 10,000 years ago.

zeolite. A hydrous aluminosilicate mineral that often fills cavities in basalt.

ADDITIONAL READINGS

Benson, D. R. 2002. *Stories in Log and Stone: The Legacy of the New Deal in Minnesota State Parks.* St. Paul: Minnesota Department of Natural Resources.

Bray, E. C. 1977. *Billions of Years in Minnesota: The Geological Story of the State.* St. Paul: Science Museum of Minnesota.

Dott, R. H. Jr. and J. W. Attig. 2004. *Roadside Geology of Wisconsin.* Missoula, MT.: Mountain Press Publishing Company.

Green, J.C. 1996. *Geology on Display: Geology and Scenery of Minnesota's North Shore State Parks.* St. Paul: Minnesota Department of Natural Resources.

LaBerge, G. L. 1994. *Geology of the Lake Superior Region.* Oshkosh, WI: Penokean City Press.

Lamppa, M. G. 2007. *Minnesota's Iron Country: Rich Ore, Rich Lives.* Duluth, MN: Lake Superior Port Cities.

Matsch. C. L. 1976. *North America and the Great Ice Age.* New York: McGraw-Hill.

Minnesota Department of Natural Resources. 1999. *A Guide to Minnesota's Scientific and Natural Areas.* St. Paul: Minnesota Department of Natural Resources.

Ojakangas, R. W., and C. L. Matsch. 1982. *Minnesota's Geology.* Minneapolis: University of Minnesota Press.

Sansome, C. J. 1983. *Minnesota Underfoot: A Field Guide to the State's Outstanding Geologic Features.* Bloomington, MN: Voyageur Press.

Sloan, R. E. 2005. *Minnesota Fossils and Fossiliferous Rocks.* Winona, MN: Privately published, 39072 Karen Court, 55987.

Stensaas, M. 2000. *Rock Picker's Guide to Lake Superior's North Shore.* Duluth, MN: Kollath-Stensaas Publishing.

Tester, J. R. 1995. *Minnesota's Natural Heritage: An Ecological Perspective.* Minneapolis: University of Minnesota Press.

Wolter, S. F. 2008. *The Lake Superior Agate.* Minneapolis: Lake Superior Agate.

For additional information

Minnesota Department of Natural Resources. 500 Lafayette Road, St. Paul, MN 55155-4040. Phone: 651-296-6157. Web site: www.dnr.state.mn.us.

Minnesota Geological Survey, 2642 University Avenue West, St. Paul, MN 55114-1057. Phone: 612-627-4780. Web site: www.geo.umn.edu/mgs.

Minnesota Historical Society, 345 West Kellogg Blvd. St. Paul, MN 55102-1906. Phone: 651-259-3000. Web site: www.mnhs.org.

Science Museum of Minnesota, 120 West Kellogg Blvd., St. Paul, MN 55102. Phone: 651-221-9444. Web site: www.smm.org.

REFERENCES CITED

Chandler, V. W. 1991. *Shaded Relief Aeromagnetic Map of Minnesota.* Minnesota Geological Survey State Map Series Map S-18. Scale: 1:500,000.

Chandler, V. W., and R. S. Lively. 2007. *Revised Aeromagnetic Data for Minnesota.* Minnesota Geological Survey.

Clements, J. M. 1903. *The Vermilion Iron-Bearing District of Minnesota.* United States Geological Survey Monograph 45.

Cooper, W. S. 1935. *The History of the Upper Mississippi River in Late Wisconsin and Post-Glacial time.* Minnesota Geological Survey Bulletin 26.

Dott, R. H. Jr., and R. L. Batten. 1981. *Evolution of the Earth.* Third Edition. New York: McGraw-Hill.

Dott, R. H. Jr., and D. R. Prothero. 1994. *Evolution of the Earth.* Fifth Edition. New York: McGraw-Hill.

Farrand, W. R., and C. W. Drexler. 1985. Late Wisconsin and Holocene History of the Lake Superior Basin. In *Quaternary Evolution of the Great Lakes.* Ed. P. F. Karrow and P. E. Calkin. Geological Association of Canada Special Paper 30:33–38.

Goldstein, B. S. 1998. Quaternary Stratigraphy and History of the Wadena Drumlin Region, Central Minnesota. In *Contributions to Quaternary Studies in Minnesota.* Ed. C. J. Patterson and H. E. Wright. Minnesota Geological Survey Report of Investigations 49:61–84.

Grant, J. A. 1972. Minnesota River Valley, Southwestern Minnesota. In *Geology of Minnesota: A Centennial Volume.* Ed. P. K. Sims and G. B. Morey, 177–96. Minnesota Geological Survey.

Green, J. C. 1978. Why Is Lake Superior? *Minnesota Conservation Volunteer* 41:10–19.

———. 1982. *Geologic Map of Minnesota, Two Harbors Sheet.* Minnesota Geological Survey. Scale 1:250,000.

———. 1996. *Geology on Display: Geology and Scenery of Minnesota's North Shore State Parks.* St. Paul: Minnesota Department of Natural Resources.

Hobbs, H. C., and J. E. Goebel. 1982. *Geologic Map of Minnesota Quaternary Geology.* Minnesota Geological Survey State Map Series S-1. Scale 1:500,000.

Jennings, C. E. 2007. Overview of the Quaternary Geological History of the Minnesota River Watershed. In *Native Plant Communities and Rare Species of the Minnesota River Valley Counties.* Minnesota Department of Natural Resources Biological Report Number 89:2.1–2.10.

Jirsa, M. A. 2008. Mesabi Range Geological Society 2008 Fall Field Trip, Gunflint Trail September 20, 2008, Minnesota Geological Survey.

Jirsa, M. A., and T. J. Boerboom. 2003. Geology and Mineralization of Archean Bedrock of the Virginia Horn. In *Contributions to the Geology of the Virginia Horn Area, St. Louis County, Minnesota.* Ed. M. A. Jirsa and G. B. Morey. Minnesota Geological Survey Report of Investigations 53:10–73.

Klinger, F. L. 1956. Geology of the Soudan Mine and Vicinity. In *Geological Society of America Guidebook Series Field Trip Number 1, Precambrian of Northeastern Minnesota.* Ed. G. M. Schwartz, 120–34. Prepared for the Annual Meeting of the Geological Society of America, Minneapolis, Minnesota.

Langseth, M., Ed. 1989. *Sandstone, the Quarry City.* Sandstone, MN: Sandstone History Club.

Lehr, J. D., and H. C. Hobbs. 1992. *Glacial Geology of the Laurentian Divide Area, St. Louis and Lake Counties, Minnesota.* Minnesota Geological Survey Guidebook Series Number 18.

Lively, R. C. 1995. *Caves in Minnesota.* Minnesota at a Glance Series Factsheet. Minnesota Geological Survey.

Marschner, F. J. 1930. *The Original Vegetation of Minnesota.* U.S. Department of Agriculture, Forest Service. Reissued in 1974 and 1988 by the Minnesota Department of Natural Resources.

Matsch, C. L. 1976. *North America and the Great Ice Age.* New York: McGraw-Hill.

Meineke, D. G., R. L. Buchheit, E. H. Dahlberg, G. B. Morey, and L. E. Warren. 1993. *Geologic Map Mesabi Iron Range, Minnesota.* Hibbing, MN: Mesabi Iron Range Geological Society.

Morey, G. B. 1993. *Geologic Map of Minnesota Bedrock Geology.* Minnesota Geological Survey State Map Series S-19. Scale 1:3,000,000.

———. 2003. Paleoproterozoic Animikie Group, Related Rocks and Associated Iron-Ore Deposits in the Virginia Horn. In *Contributions to the Geology of the Virginia Horn Area, St. Louis County, Minnesota.* Ed. M. A. Jirsa and G. B. Morey. Minnesota Geological Survey Report of Investigations 53:79–106.

Morey, G. B., and E. H. Dahlberg. 1995. *Geology of Minnesota: A Guide for Teachers.* St. Paul: Minnesota Department of Natural Resources.

Mossler, J. H. 2001. Bedrock Geology, Plate 2. In *Geologic Atlas of Wabasha County, Minnesota.* Minnesota Geological Survey County Atlas Series C-14, Pt. A, scale 1:100,000.

———. 2008. *Paleozoic Stratigraphic Nomenclature for Minnesota.* Minnesota Geological Survey Report of Investigations 65.

Ojakangas, R. W. 1991. *Theory and Problems of Introductory Geology. Schaum's Outline Series.* New York: McGraw-Hill.

———. 1994. *Sedimentology and Provenance of the Early Proterozoic Michigamme Formation and Goodrich Quartzite, Northern Michigan—Regional Stratigraphic Implications and Suggested Correlations.* U.S. Geological Survey Bulletin 1904-R.

Ojakangas, R. W., and C. L. Matsch. 1982. *Minnesota's Geology.* Minneapolis: University of Minnesota Press.

Ojakangas, R. W., D. G. Meineke, and W. H. Listerud. 1977. *Geology, sulfide mineralization and geochemistry of the Birchdale–Indus area, Koochiching County, northwestern Minnesota.* Minnesota Geological Survey Report of Investigations 17.

Patterson, C. J., B. L. Lusardi, D. R. Setterholm, and A. R. Knaeble. 1995. Quaternary Stratigraphy, Plate 2. In *Regional Hydrogeologic Assessment: Quaternary Geology of Southwestern Minnesota.* Project Manager D. R. Setterholm. Minnesota Geological Survey Regional Hydrogeologic Assessment Series Number A-2, Part A.

Runkel, A. C. 1996. *The Geology of Whitewater State Park.* Minnesota Geological Survey Educational Series 9.

Schwartz, G. M., and G. A. Thiel. 1963. *Minnesota's Rocks and Waters: A Geological Story.* Rev. ed. Minneapolis. University of Minnesota Press.

Sims, P. K., and G. B. Morey. 1966. *Geologic Sketch of the Tower-Soudan State Park.* Minnesota Geological Survey Educational Series Number 3.

Sloan, R. E. 1967. A Teacher's Guide for Geologic Field Investigations in Southeastern Minnesota. In *A Teacher's Guide for Geologic Field Investigations in Minnesota.* Ed. W. C. Phinney, 1–19. Minnesota Department of Education and Minnesota Geological Survey.

Sloan, R. E., and G. S. Austin. 1966. *Geologic Map of Minnesota, St. Paul Sheet.* Minnesota Geological Survey. Scale 1:250.000.

Southwick, D. L., M. Jouseau, G. N. Meyer, J. H. Mossler, and T. E. Wahl. 2000. *Aggregate Resource Inventory of the Seven-County Metropolitan Area, Minnesota.* Minnesota Geological Survey Information Circular 46.

Tape, C. H., C. A. Cowan, and A. C. Runkel. 2003. Tidal Bundle Sequences in the Jordan Sandstone (Upper Cambrian) Southeastern Minnesota, U.S.A.: Evidence for Tides Along Inboard Shorelines of the Sauk Epicontinental Sea. *Journal of Sedimentary Research* 73:354–66.

Webers, G. F. 1972. Paleoecology of the Cambrian and Ordovician Strata of Minnesota. In *Geology of Minnesota: A Centennial Volume.* Ed. P. K. Sims and G. B. Morey, 474–84. Minnesota Geological Survey.

Winter, T. C. 1961. A Pollen Analysis of Kirchner Marsh, Dakota County, Minnesota. MS Thesis, University of Minnesota, Minneapolis.

Wright, H. E. Jr. 1972a. Quaternary History of Minnesota. In *Geology of Minnesota: A Centennial Volume*. Ed. P. K. Sims and G. B. Morey, 515–47. Minnesota Geological Survey.

————. 1972b. Physiography of Minnesota. In *Geology of Minnesota: A Centennial Volume*. Ed. P. K. Sims and B. Morey, 561–80. Minnesota Geological Survey.

Wright, H. E. Jr., and P. H. Glaser. 1983. Postglacial Peatlands of the Lake Agassiz Plain, Northern Minnesota. In *Glacial Lake Agassiz*. Ed. J. T. Teller and L. Clayton, 275–89. Geological Association of Canada Special Paper 26.

Wright, H. E., C. L. Matsch, and E. J. Cushing. 1973. Superior and Des Moines Lobes. In *The Wisconsinan Stage*. Ed. R. F. Black, R. P. Goldthwait, and H. B. Willman. Geological Society of America Memoir 136:153–85.

Zumberge, J. H. 1952. *The Lakes of Minnesota: Their Origin and Classification*. Minnesota Geological Survey Bulletin 35.

INDEX

Page numbers in italics refer to photographs.

ABOUT THE AUTHOR

Richard W. Ojakangas is a native northern Minnesotan who discovered geology late in his undergraduate career at the University of Minnesota Duluth (UMD) and earned his BA in 1955. He then served two years on active duty with the U.S. Air Force in England. He earned his MA in 1960 at the University of Missouri-Columbia, spent a year in Finland as a Fulbright Scholar, and earned his Ph.D. in 1964 at Stanford University. He specializes in the study of the origins of sedimentary rocks and the mineral deposits that they contain. He joined the faculty at UMD, retiring in 2002 after thirty-eight years of teaching and research. Although concentrating his research on the Precambrian rocks of the Lake Superior region and spending many summers with the Minnesota Geological Survey and the U.S. Geological Survey, he has also done research in Antarctica, South Africa, Finland, Russia, Australia, India, Canada, Puerto Rico, Missouri, California, and Utah. He still has various ongoing research projects. He is the author of many articles, geological maps, field guides, and books, including *Minnesota's Geology* with coauthor Charles Matsch. He continues to teach for UMD's University for Seniors and gives lectures on cruise ships. He and his food-writer wife Beatrice (Peaches) have three children and eight grandchildren and live in the country near Duluth.

We encourage you to patronize your local bookstore. Most stores will order any title they do not stock. You may also order directly from Mountain Press, using the order form provided below or by calling our toll-free, 24-hour number and using your VISA, MasterCard, Discover or American Express.

Some geology titles of interest:

_____ROADSIDE GEOLOGY OF ALASKA	18.00
_____ROADSIDE GEOLOGY OF ARIZONA	18.00
_____ROADSIDE GEOLOGY OF NORTHERN and CENTRAL CALIFORNIA	20.00
_____ROADSIDE GEOLOGY OF COLORADO, 2nd Edition	20.00
_____ROADSIDE GEOLOGY OF CONNECTICUT and RHODE ISLAND	26.00
_____ROADSIDE GEOLOGY OF FLORIDA	26.00
_____ROADSIDE GEOLOGY OF HAWAII	20.00
_____ROADSIDE GEOLOGY OF IDAHO	20.00
_____ROADSIDE GEOLOGY OF INDIANA	18.00
_____ROADSIDE GEOLOGY OF LOUISIANA	20.00
_____ROADSIDE GEOLOGY OF MAINE	18.00
_____ROADSIDE GEOLOGY OF MASSACHUSETTS	20.00
_____ROADSIDE GEOLOGY OF MONTANA	20.00
_____ROADSIDE GEOLOGY OF NEBRASKA	18.00
_____ROADSIDE GEOLOGY OF NEW MEXICO	18.00
_____ROADSIDE GEOLOGY OF NEW YORK	20.00
_____ROADSIDE GEOLOGY OF OHIO	24.00
_____ROADSIDE GEOLOGY OF OREGON	16.00
_____ROADSIDE GEOLOGY OF PENNSYLVANIA	20.00
_____ROADSIDE GEOLOGY OF SOUTH DAKOTA	20.00
_____ROADSIDE GEOLOGY OF TEXAS	20.00
_____ROADSIDE GEOLOGY OF UTAH	20.00
_____ROADSIDE GEOLOGY OF VERMONT & NEW HAMPSHIRE	14.00
_____ROADSIDE GEOLOGY OF VIRGINIA	16.00
_____ROADSIDE GEOLOGY OF WASHINGTON	18.00
_____ROADSIDE GEOLOGY OF WISCONSIN	20.00
_____ROADSIDE GEOLOGY OF WYOMING	18.00
_____ROADSIDE GEOLOGY OF THE YELLOWSTONE COUNTRY	12.00
_____GEOLOGY UNDERFOOT IN NORTHERN ARIZONA	18.00
_____GEOLOGY UNDERFOOT IN SOUTHERN CALIFORNIA	14.00
_____GEOLOGY UNDERFOOT IN DEATH VALLEY AND OWENS VALLEY	16.00
_____GEOLOGY UNDERFOOT IN ILLINOIS	20.00
_____GEOLOGY UNDERFOOT IN CENTRAL NEVADA	16.00
_____GEOLOGY UNDERFOOT IN SOUTHERN UTAH	18.00

Please include $3.50 for 1-4 books, $5.00 for 5 or more books to cover shipping and handling.

Send the books marked above. I enclose $_____

Name_____

Address _____

City/State/Zip _____

☐ Payment enclosed (check or money order in U.S. funds)

Bill my: ☐ VISA   ☐ MasterCard ☐ Discover ☐ American Express

Card No. _____ Expiration Date:_____

Security No._____Signature _____

MOUNTAIN PRESS PUBLISHING COMPANY
P.O. Box 2399 • Missoula, MT 59806 • Order Toll-Free 1-800-234-5308
E-mail: info@mtnpress.com • Web: www.mountain-press.com